AUTHORS DIGEST

THE WORLD'S GREAT STORIES IN BRIEF, PREPARED BY A STAFF OF LITERARY EXPERTS, WITH THE ASSISTANCE OF MANY LIVING NOVELISTS

ROSSITER JOHNSON, PH.D., LL.D.
EDITOR-IN-CHIEF

ISSUED UNDER THE AUSPICES OF THE
AUTHORS PRESS

CONTENTS

roy, since his antagonist was Frederic, Lieutenant d'Ahlefeld, son of the Chancellor.

Ordener now left the castle, swam the fjord, and returned to the Spladgest. He heard voices within, knocked loudly and shouted, saw a dark figure climb out of a hole in the roof and vanish, and then was admitted by Spiagudry, the keeper, whose face was pallid and whose bloody hands tremblingly held a lamp.

About an hour after our opening scene, night fell and the Spladgest was closed, when the keeper found in the room where the corpses lay a short, stout man, with reddish beard and ferocious eyes, clad in blood-stained skins, armed with broad-sword, dagger, and a stone ax; his hands in foxskin gloves. Spiagudry called him "Master" and begged to know his will. The little man fiercely hugged the corpse of Gill Stadt, chanted a wild hymn of praise of the dead youth, and denounced the soldier preferred to Gill by the drowned girl—whose body he kicked. He exulted that he had already slain one of that cursed regiment (pointing to Captain Dispolsen) and vowed he would kill them all, so as to get the right one. Then, pulling off his gloves he seized Gill's head with his big hands, armed with long nails like a beast's claws, and compelled the trembling keeper to help, while he cut off the crown from the head, to make a cup of the skull, from which to drink the blood of his enemies, the human race. He gave Spiagudry an iron casket found on Dispolsen's body, which must contain gold, for the keeper to give to the Widow Stadt.

At this point Ordener's knocks and shouts sent the wild man through the roof, and the trembling Spiagudry admitted the cavalier.

General de Knud, Governor of Trondhjem, was interrupted one morning by the Countess d'Ahlefeld, wife of the Chancellor, who came to inquire after his pupil, young Guldenlew. Learning that he had gone to Munkholm, she demanded his object. The General said that he had given him a pass to the prisons, and sent him to make acquaintance with old Schumacker, which might be useful to him as a future ruler. The Countess, whose daughter Ordener was to marry, was troubled because the prisoner had a daughter, and added that Schumacker was reported to be inciting the miners to revolt. The General assured her that Ordener would do nothing dishonorable toward the prisoner's daughter, and declared the rumor of conspiracy certainly unfounded, as regarded Schumacker. Here she was called away.

When Ordener got into the Spladgest, he saw Gill's gory head, and accused the keeper of the outrage, but Spiagudry said it had been done by the one who had murdered Dispolsen. By threats Ordener compelled the old man to reveal the name: it was Hans of Iceland. The keeper denied knowledge of any iron casket on the Captain's body; but under fears of being himself hanged for outrage upon the dead, he agreed to guide Ordener to the wild man.

The next morning Ordener again sought Munkholm. He told the Count that Dispolsen had been killed by Hans of Iceland, while nothing was known of the iron casket containing the precious papers, but that he should pursue the outlaw and get the casket. Ethel privately begged him not to risk his life, her only comfort, but when he said her father's life depended on it she tearfully acquiesced. Before going on his perilous errand he told his guardian, General de Knud, of the plot against Schumacker, and the viler one against his daughter, on the part of the D'Ahlefelds, and received the Governor's assurance that he would protect them.

Up a stony road climbing the hills north of Trondhjem walked Ordener and old Spiagudry. A great thunderstorm coming on, they took shelter in the Cursed Tower, where dwelt the hangman of the province and his hideous wife. They were soon joined by two other storm-driven travelers—a black-gowned Lutheran minister and a short, stout man in a hermit's gown, his face concealed in his hood and his hands hidden by flowing sleeves. Spiagudry shivered as he heard the hermit's voice. Presently came Nychol Orugix himself, the hangman, a colossal man, in red serge, who welcomed them all, and they supped together.

Orugix was savage about a chaplain named Munder, who had petitioned the Governor to pardon twelve criminals in honor of the great wedding, depriving him of his fees and of the bodies, which he sold for dissection. The minister quietly spoke:

"My son, I am Athanasius Munder," and the hangman was angered, till Ordener said:

"Orugix, here are thirteen crowns to pay for the pardon of these criminals, and, Sir Chaplain, your men shall be pardoned, even if the great marriage never takes place."

"Young stranger," replied the priest, "you can do nothing in the matter; but God hears and will reward you."

The storm had ceased, and now appeared a group of bowmen in search of Spiagudry for profanation of the dead. The hermit, learning that they were of the Munkholm regiment, offered to lead them to Spiagudry's hiding-place, and took them off through the forest. Ordener and his companions pursued their way, but were overtaken by the prison chaplain, who gratefully gave Ordener a parchment pass, received from an executed miner, who said it would protect him in the mountains.

The next day it was made known that the bodies of five soldiers of the Munkholm regiment had been brought to the Spladgest, found in the ravine below the cliffs. Their bodies were covered with deep scratches, as from the claws of a beast, which also were noticed on the body of the old Hermit of Lynrass, brought in the day before, stripped of its clothing, as well as on the body of the officer found on the Urchtal Sands.

Twenty-four years earlier the village of Moctree had rejoiced over the marriage of sweet Lucy Pebryhn and handsome Carroll Stadt. Their families had opposed this, until Carroll had rescued Lucy from a brigand who had carried her off to his den; while all were gay at the wedding, Lucy was depressed, although she gazed tenderly upon her husband. At night they remained in their abode, but the next morning Carroll had vanished, and he never returned.

Before the end of the year the Widow Stadt gave birth to a boy, who was named Gill, whose fierce infancy foretold a ferocious manhood. Sometimes a little wild man entered her lonely hut, and then would be heard a woman's shrieks and tiger-like roars. The man would carry off young Gill for months, and then bring him back. At twenty-three the youth loved Guth Stersen, and entered the mines to earn money. His mother never heard from him until one night a little monk came, told of her son's death in the mine, laughed at her misery, related his avenging on the Munkholm regiment the infidelity of Guth Stersen for a soldier, and, learning that the widow never had received the iron casket he had sent, rushed out, growling.

On Kelvel strand, under a great crag, was a broad meadow, and there one night met three men—Kennybol, the mountaineer; Jonas and Norbith, miners, awaiting a Mr. Hacket, who soon arrived. He came, he said, from Count Schumacker and told them that he had secured the giant, Hans of Iceland, as their commander. He showed how Count Schumacker's pity for them had led him to aid them, and their banners and shouts must proclaim his name. They agreed, fixed time and place for action, and parted.

Meanwhile, Ordener and Spiagudry pushed on through the forests and over the mountains. On their way to Walderhog Cave, the special haunt of the wild man, Spiagudry mentioned that Munkholm could be seen from the manor-house of Vermund, an ancient ruin on the peak of Oelmoe cliff, above Lake Sparbo. The lover compelled his guide to show the ascent, and reaching the great court, climbed to the top of the tower, losing himself in reverie while gazing at the shadowy bulk of Munkholm twelve miles away. Spiagudry built a fire, seated himself, and soon bethought him of the iron casket. As he was about to break it open with a stone, he looked up and saw on the other side of the fire a short man in a dress of blood-stained skins, with a stone ax. The little man charged him with theft of the casket and treachery in guiding an enemy to his retreat. Then, strapping the casket about Spiagudry's neck, he bore the old man from the tower, while a shriek rang out, mingled with a horrible burst of laughter. At the sound Ordener turned, and saw that the court was empty; but as he hurriedly descended he heard a dull splash, as if something had been thrown into the lake, and all was silent.

General de Knud sat at his desk, and wondered at the reports of the miners' revolt, of which it was rumored that the much-dreaded Hans of Iceland had taken command. He had already ordered Frederic d'Ahlefeld's company away from Munkholm, and he would further protect the Schumackers if the old man were innocent of the revolt. Just then he received a royal order to go to Bergen, Chancellor d'Ahlefeld being his substitute. He suspected intrigue, but must obey. He sought Schumacker, but could not interrogate the old man, whose bearing and conversation were beyond suspicion.

One morning about this time, Count d'Ahlefeld and his secretary, Musdaemen, sought the wild Arbarmin, capping a lofty peak to find Hans of Iceland. Before they arrived the little man had killed a wolf, which was attracted by a groaning form lying at the man's feet and by the scent of a warm drink that the man took from a skull-shaped cup. A great white bear, seeing his master's peril, had joined the fray, but was kicked off by Hans, who strangled the wolf with his hands and then chopped off an arm from the human body dying on the ground and threw it to the bear, which disappeared through a door opening out over the precipice.

Giving no name, a stranger entered, announcing himself as a friend, and offered the Icelander command of the miners' revolt. Hans refused with scorn, and sneeringly naming the Chancellor, said he already knew about it, and about him, too. He spared the Chancellor, he said, because the tiger does not prey on the hyena. As to Captain Dispolsen with his iron casket, about whom the Chancellor inquired, he had been slain only because he belonged to that vile Munkholm regiment—"like this other wretch," he added, dragging the Count to the mangled corpse. It was D'Ahlefeld's son, Frederic, and the grief-stricken cries of the Count brought Musdaemen and four swordsmen, who attacked Hans. But, whirling his stone ax, he shouted for his white bear and sprang on the animal's back, and they disappeared through the open door above the precipice.

When Ordener found Spiagudry gone from the court, he dropped by the fire and slept till morning; then he set off through the mountains. Toward night he descended to the coast, and in a fisherman's cottage found a welcome, and in the morning a guide to the dreaded Walderhog Cave. He found the Icelander in a circular rock-hewn hall, in the center of which was a stone altar. Ordener boldly demanded the iron casket from the body of Dispolsen; Hans jeered him and sprang upon the altar, whirling his stone ax. Ordener's swift sword-thrusts and the ax made dazzling play, until the ax caught in Ordener's mantle, which was wrapped around his left arm, when the little monster leaped over Ordener's head, and then at him like a wildcat, with teeth and claws and ferocious growls. Seizing his blade by the middle, Ordener drove it into the back of the brigand, who leaped away, and hurled a granite boulder, which the youth escaped. A second shattered his sword, and then a roar outside startled Hans, and he rushed from the cave to aid his white bear, which was at bay against seven hunters. The hunters, paralyzed by fear, fell victims to the two monsters—all but one, who fled, while Ordener disappeared in the forest.

At night he threw himself down to sleep, when he heard voices, and saw figures vanishing into the earth. He plunged after them into a hole where there was a ladder, and at the bottom he found a group of leaders of the miners' revolt, who would have promptly killed him as a spy but that they found on him the dead miner's parchment pass. Mr. Hacket now entered with a giant, whom he introduced as their commander, Hans of Iceland.

On an impulse, hearing Schumacker's name invoked, Ordener joined the revolt, and as it was now morning the leaders sallied out to their forces, who were already moving; and, reënforced by others as they went, they poured down the mountain and along the valleys.

The Chancellor and his secretary, Musdaemen, had well arranged to crush the revolt they had aroused; for, as the peasants marched through a narrow defile they were attacked on all sides by murderous musketry fire and, although fighting desperately, they were frightfully slaughtered. A short man dressed in skins suddenly appeared and, wielding a stone ax, smote rebel and soldier alike, but when he could struck down soldiers of the Munkholm regiment. He disarmed and stunned the false Hans of Iceland, who was captured by a musketeer. The battle was over; the little man had vanished. The three leaders and Ordener were captured and taken to Trondhjem.

General de Knud's departure having left Schumacker and his daughter to the D'Ahlefelds, the Countess, anxious about young Guldenlew's relations there, visited Munkholm. She met Ethel in the garden, and skilfully learned of the girl's affection for him whom she called "my Ordener," although she knew no other name for him. The Countess, turning pale with rage, cried: "Wretched girl! You love Ordener Guldenlew, the betrothed of Ulrica d'Ahlefeld, son of your father's deadly foe, the Viceroy of Norway," and left Ethel fainting upon the ground.

When Ethel next saw her father the old man told her that before his death he wished to leave her to the care of Ordener, who seemed to be the only person in the world that he could trust. But Ethel, in tears, told him that Ordener was the son of Guldenlew, the Viceroy. The old man's surprise and rage knew no bounds. He saw only treachery in Ordener's professed kindness and commanded Ethel to hate and despise him. While they talked a messenger summoned them away.

Separated from her father, Ethel was conducted to an interior grated window, before which sat a veiled woman. Ethel sat beside her, and they looked into the gloom of a large courtroom, where sat at one end seven judges, Chancellor d'Ahlefeld presiding, his private secretary in attendance. Before them was a prisoner's bench, and behind that a mob of onlookers. Six prisoners were arraigned, the first being the venerable Schumacker, the others the false Hans of Iceland, the three rebel leaders, and a young man not easily recognized. The evidence against Schumacker consisted only of banners borne by the rebels with his name, and their admissions that Hacket credited the revolt to the old prisoner. Their own confessions convicted the three leaders, and the false Hans, who privately believed that Hacket would get him off. The sixth prisoner, being called, announced his name, Ordener Guldenlew, Baron of Thorwick, Knight of the Dannenbrog, and said that he alone was guilty, having fomented the revolt himself. He denied any connection with Schumacker, and insisted that the old man knew nothing of it.

After several hours' private consultation the judges returned. The verdict found Schumacker not guilty. The three leaders were found guilty, but, having been misled, they were only to be imprisoned for life and to pay a large fine; Hans of Klipstadue guilty, to be hanged; and Ordener Guldenlew guilty, to be stripped of his titles and beheaded, his body burned, his ashes scattered, and his head exposed on a stake. A shriek rang through the courtroom, and at the sound Ordener's calm and radiant face turned pale. He believed that Schumacker was guilty of the revolt, but rejoiced that he had saved the father to protect the daughter.

Ordener sat, chained, in a dungeon. The door-bolts creaked, and he rose, calmly expectant of the executioner, but saw instead a slender white figure, and Ethel fell into his fettered embrace. After some interchange of loving converse, Ethel, sobbing with grief, said she brought the offer of pardon if he would marry Ulrica d'Ahlefeld; and, despite her own sacrifice, she urged him to accept; but, wounded and distressed, he indignantly refused.

He now noticed a tall figure standing near the door—Munder, the chaplain, who had accompanied Ethel. Recalling their meeting in the Vygla tower, Ordener said:

"When I am dead, go to my father, the Viceroy, and tell him my last request was that he should pardon your twelve *protégês;* so shall my promise be fulfilled."

"This man cannot be guilty," thought the priest, and he was about to withdraw with Ethel, when she spoke:

"Sir, I cannot go until you unite Ethel Schumacker to her husband, Ordener Guldenlew." Turning to her lover, she added: "If you were still free and powerful, my Ordener, I could not link my fatal destiny with your life; but I may be your companion in death."

The ceremony was performed before they parted, to meet in eternity.

The court remained in session until its sentence should be carried out. Question arising as to who claimed the thousand crowns for capturing Hans of Iceland, a Munkholm soldier said, "It is I." But a voice denied it, and a short man wrapped in sealskin advanced, declaring that he had felled the giant and was entitled to the reward. The court decided for the soldier, who had brought the captive. Then the short man denied that the giant was Hans of Iceland, and, approaching the Munkholm soldier, cried to the other:

"Mountaineer of Kiolen, they say that Hans of Iceland drinks human blood. If you be he, drink! Here it is," and he stabbed the soldier to the heart. Then, rushing at the mountaineer, with another dagger-blow he laid him upon the soldier's body, and shouted:

"Ha! judges, where is Hans of Iceland now?" and, flinging off his sealskin cloak, he showed his hideousness. Then dropping his dagger, he allowed himself to be chained, saying that he had had his glut of blood, and now they might drink his.

The judges condemned him to be hanged, and he was taken to a dungeon in the quarters of the Munkholm regiment; hearing which he growled with pleasure.

Before dawn of that same day the body of Spiagudry, found in the lake, had been brought to the Spladgest, and the new keeper, afraid of some sorcery in the iron casket bound about the neck of the corpse, took it to the Bishop of Trondhjem.

The fatal morning had come. In the courtroom Ordener stood, to be degraded from his titles and his knighthood before execution, when the Bishop rushed in, breaking upon the ceremony hardly begun.

"Forbear!" he cried. "The prisoner is innocent!"

The contents of the iron casket were then read: a certificate from Cumbysulsum, the astrologer, offering the genuineness of a document confided to him by Musdaemen, private secretary to the Chancellor, consisting of a note to the noble Count d'Ahlefeld, upon how to rid himself of Schumacker, setting forth the details of the abominable scheme this story has narrated; D'Ahlefeld, secretly gleeful that this entrapped Musdaemen, while not involving himself, had the secretary forthwith arraigned, and, as the chaplain brought word from the dying giant that Musdaemen was Hacket, and had bribed him to personate Hans of Iceland, the wretched man was sentenced to death, while Ordener was released.

That night Hans of Iceland sold his body to the hangman for two ducats, which he paid his jailer for straw to lie on and some live coals to warm himself; while Orugix went to another cell, and there officially hanged Musdaemen, although he discovered him to be his own brother. Toward morning a fire broke out in the cell of Hans of Iceland, which destroyed the barracks and thirty soldiers of the Munkholm regiment, as well as the monster himself.

Ordener soon returned to Munkholm with General de Knud. The Governor brought Schumacker the King's pardon and restoration of his titles, removing the last objection the old man now had to the marriage of his daughter with Ordener, Baron of Thorwick; and from their happy union sprang the race of the famous Counts of Danneskiold.

THE MAN WHO LAUGHS (1869)

This book was begun and ended in Brussels, but most of it was written in the island of Guernsey. Of it Hugo himself says in his preface: "The true title of this book should be 'Aristocracy'"; this was because he intended it as an arraignment of the nobility for their selfishness, vice, and crimes.

DURING the months of December, 1689, and January, 1690, a strong north wind blew continuously over the mainland of Europe, and especially over England. One bitterly cold day in January, 1690, a little vessel, the *Matutina*, was anchored close to the rocks on the coast of Portland Bay. Notwithstanding the threatening weather, the vessel was preparing to sail. A plank extended to the shore, and dark forms were passing to and fro, among them a child of ten: his feet were bare, and he was carrying luggage too heavy for him. When the vessel was about to sail the child rushed on board, but a man from the shore stepped up behind him and pushed him back. The gangplank was then lifted, the boat started, and the child was left on the shore, alone and in the darkness of night.

He gazed after the ship, for his life thus far had been spent with these men. He had no money, no food, was but scantily clad, and was a mile from any habitation. He climbed up on the table-land and looked around. Through the shadows of the night he saw behind him the sea; in front the land; above the sky. No stars were visible, for a blinding mist hid the zenith. A deep silence reigned, far-reaching as infinity; hushed as the tomb.

The ground was white with snow. The child now walked down the hill, hoping to find some trace of a human dwelling. The night was very dark, but he saw something resembling a tree, and heard a sound. He approached, and found that the sound proceeded from a chain, and then he saw a gibbet on which hung the corpse of a man, swinging in the icy wind.

The dead thing had been stripped. His marrow was no longer in his bones; his entrails were no longer in his body; his voice was no longer in his throat. He had had blood, which had been drunk; skin, which had been eaten; flesh, which had been stolen. This specter was a sign. Placed there by man, he awaited God. The corpse was coated with pitch, and the body was wrapped in coarse canvas. The teeth grinned. The boy took the corpse for a ghost. Petrified with fear, he stood there staring at it. The storm increased, the chain shrieked, and the corpse danced violently in the gale. A flock of ravens now appeared, and the child heard them croak, and saw them settle down on the corpse and begin to eat. A great roar came from below: it was the sea. The boy trembled, shut his eyes tight, and made his way down the cliff, leaping from rock to rock, not knowing where he was going.

This same evening a greater tragedy took place at sea. The *Matutina* lost her bearings in the hurricane, struck a rock, sprang a leak, and sank, with all on board. At the last moment the doctor on the ship wrote something on a piece of parchment; this he read to the men. When he had finished he said to them: "Kneel! Let us throw our crimes into the sea, they weigh us down; it is they that are sinking the ship. Let us cease to think of safety; let us think only of our salvation. Our last crime. Oh, wretched beings, it is that which is overwhelming us! He who sins against a child sins against God. Remember that we just now did our best to send that child on high, and he is, perhaps, at this very moment in the world above, a soul accusing us before a Judge whose eye is on us."

Then the doctor signed the document and bade the others do likewise. When everyone had signed, he took a flask, covered with wickerwork, in which was plaited the name of one of their comrades—Hardquanonne—who was then in jail, and putting the parchment into the flask, he flung it into the sea; the wickerwork covering caused it to float.

The storm had been equally severe on land. The child had wandered about for four hours; he was cold, hungry, and discouraged. Looking down, he saw footprints in the snow and he followed them. Suddenly these marks ceased, and there was a mound of snow. From beneath this mound he heard a cry, so he brushed away the snow and discovered a woman clothed in rags lying there dead. On her breast was a babe about six months old; it was the babe that had cried. The child took the forsaken little creature in his arms, wrapped it in his only dry garment, and carried it along with him.

In the distance he saw roofs, dwellings, shelter! This town was Weymouth. He knocked at many doors, but no one heard him. Just as he was about giving up, he heard a growl; he went toward the sound, and there, at the corner of a wall, he saw a cart. From the top rose a funnel, and from the funnel came smoke. There was a light within, and a man came to the window.

"What do you want?" said he.

"I'm hungry."

"Go away."

But the next moment the man opened the door of the cart and said: "Come in."

The boy ascended three steps, entered the van, and saw that there was fire in the stove and something was cooking in a saucepan. The reflection of the firelight on the ceiling enabled the spectator to read: "Ursus, Philosopher."

Ursus was a man between fifty and sixty years of age. He was melancholy, loved to talk to himself, and was a great ventriloquist; also a doctor, and very successful in prescribing medicines made of herbs. He traveled from place to place in the van, which was drawn by his faithful friend Homo, the wolf, and gained his livelihood by performing wherever there was a chance of getting a few pennies.

When Ursus saw how wet the child was, he gave him dry clothes and told him to sit down and eat his supper. On the chest had been placed the bundle, and suddenly this bundle began to cry.

"So it is your bundle that wails! Vale of Jehoshaphat! Who ever heard of a screeching parcel?" said Ursus.

He took the babe on his knee and fed it with milk; then he questioned the child as to how he had found the infant. He told the boy to go to sleep while he went out to see whether the mother of the child were really dead. When he returned it was dawn and the boy was awake.

"What are you laughing at?" said Ursus.

"I'm not laughing," replied the boy.

Ursus gazed at him, and then said: "You are frightful to behold. Do not laugh any more."

"I'm not laughing," said the child.

Ursus shuddered: "You *are* laughing, I say. Who did that to you?"

"I don't know what you mean," said the boy. "I have always been as I am."

Then Ursus took up the babe, and when he saw that she gazed fixedly at the sun he cried: "She is blind."

The boy who had taken refuge with Ursus was named Gwynplaine. He had a mouth that opened from ear to ear, huge ears, two slits for eyes, a shapeless nose, and a weird face, which no one could look upon without laughing. When he was two years old, science had enlarged the mouth, cut away the lips, laid bare the gums, distended the ears, displaced the eyelids and cheeks, enlarged the zygomatic muscle, pressed the scars and cicatrices to a level, and turned back the skin over the lesions while the face was thus distorted. Hence the mask he wore.

Gwynplaine became a mountebank. As soon as he exhibited himself on the platform of the van everyone began to laugh. The operation performed on him must have been frightful. His joints had been dislocated and trained to move the wrong way. His hair, woolly and rough, had been dyed ocher color.

When the year 1705 had come, fifteen years had elapsed since the boy had entered the van that night, and he had grown to manhood. The babe found on the breast of the dead woman was now a frail girl of sixteen. All these years they had lived with Ursus, wandered about with him, and performed at the shows. They called the girl "Dea." Though she was blind, her eyes were wide open and shone with a lustrous glow.

The two young people were perfectly happy; they loved each other. Only one woman on earth saw Gwynplaine, and she was the blind girl. With her mind's eye she gazed out of the depths of the abyss to the glad light of his goodness in the zenith. The crowd knew his face; to Dea he was the savior who had gathered her up in his arms and borne her out of the tomb. Where the multitude saw the monster, Dea saw the archangel. This was because Dea, being blind, could see the soul. Gwynplaine saw a white cloud of beauty descend upon him in the form of a woman; a radiant vision endowed with a heart; he was loved. Out of their hell they had created a heaven. Such is thy power, O love!

By this time the show had prospered; another van had been bought, which was painted green and was called the "Green Box." A large placard in front bore the following inscription:

"Do not fail to see Gwynplaine, who was deserted at the age of ten, on the night of the 29th of January, 1690, by villainous comprachicos, on the coast of Portland. The little boy has grown up and is now known as the Laughing Man."

Hitherto the performances had taken place in villages, or small towns, but a comedy, written by Ursus and called *Chaos Vanquished*, had met with such success that he took the show to London. The van was now placed in the courtyard of Tadcaster Inn, in Southwark, which was united to London by a bridge. The show became very popular. Lord David Dirry-Moir, who came disguised as a sailor, and assumed the name Tom-Jim-Jack, was especially enthusiastic. The "Green Box" excited the jealousy of the owners of neighboring shows, and even the clergy thought so much mirth was leading the people astray. One day a wapentake (bailiff) arrested Ursus, but he was able to convince the magistrate that he was innocent.

During the performance that night, the box, which had been fitted up for the aristocracy, and which had been empty, was occupied by a handsome lady, beautifully attired in Indian muslin embroidered in gold. She wore a large diamond brooch fastened to her corsage, and precious stones were strewn all over her gown.

Gwynplaine never had seen such a dazzling creature. She sat there without moving, and gazed at him, while everyone else was laughing. Behind her stood her page, a boy magnificently attired.

When the show was over a carriage with plumed footmen, carrying torches, was seen driving away from the inn. On the carriage was a golden coronet with eight strawberry leaves, and the lady inside was the Duchess. Tom-Jim-Jack had stepped into the carriage with her.

The Duchess did not return, but her radiance had disturbed Gwynplaine's mind. He was unable to sleep for several nights, but at last he conquered this feeling, for at heart he still loved Dea.

One night when Gwynplaine was out walking, with his hands behind his back, someone slipped a letter into them; it was the page of the Duchess, and he said: "At this hour to-morrow, be at the corner of London Bridge; I will be there to conduct you where you are expected."

The page vanished, and Gwynplaine took the letter to the inn, where he opened it close to the lamp, and read: "You are hideous; I am beautiful. You are a player; I am a Duchess. I am the highest; you are the lowest; nevertheless I love you! Come!"

Should he go? "Yes," said the flesh; "No," said the soul. He felt flattered; he could not sleep. In the height of his agony, and while his eyes were still closed, he heard a wonderful voice asking, "Are you asleep, Gwynplaine?" and he opened his eyes with a start. Dea was standing in the doorway, and the vision of the Duchess suddenly faded from his mind. The blind girl had dispelled the darkness within him. In a moment he became again the noble and good Gwynplaine, the innocent man. There was no vision for him now but the heaven where Dea was, and he threw the note into the fire.

Dea often sat silent, absorbed in that kind of ecstasy peculiar to the blind which seems at times to give them a song to listen to in their hearts, and by some ideal music to make up to them for the vision which they lack. Blindness is a cavern through which celestial harmonies are ever flashing.

As Gwynplaine raised his eyes he saw a man standing behind him. He was a wapentake, and as he touched Gwynplaine with his wand he said:

"Let this man, and no other, follow me."

Gwynplaine silently followed the constable to the jail, which was an old place of torture.

Gwynplaine trembled. "Gentlemen," said he, "whither are you taking me?"

There was no answer. Now he was surrounded by several officers and he traversed with them a long, dark passage. When they reached the end, the wapentake struck his wand against the wall. A sheet of metal then rose in the wall after the manner of a mouse-trap, and through the opening there was a glimmer of light by which Gwynplaine could see a flight of narrow stone steps, at the bottom of which was a dungeon lighted by a lamp suspended from the ceiling. Under the lamp was a pale and terrible form extended on the ground. A head was seen, the eyes of which were shut; also a body, the chest of which was a shapeless mass. The limbs of the man were drawn to four posts by four chains. He was being quartered. He had the look of a livid corpse. This was the torture-chamber. Gwynplaine was petrified with fear. He descended the steps, and saw two men standing by the specter, while in a chair near by sat the sheriff of the County of Surrey, who was trying to make the prisoner confess something. He enumerated all the tortures that had been inflicted on the criminal, and dwelt on those he was about to suffer should he suppress the truth.

The doctor bent over the man, and ascertaining that he could still see and hear, the sheriff continued: "Open your eyes, and see whether you recognize this man!"

The prisoner opened his eyes, looked at Gwynplaine, and quivered. Then he cried: "It is he! It is he!" and he laughed a horrible laugh, and closed his eyes again.

Gwynplaine was greatly frightened. "It is not true!" he said. "It was not I! I do not know this man! What do you want of me? I demand my liberty! You have before you a poor mountebank."

"I have before me," said the sheriff, "Lord Fermain Clancharlie, Baron Clancharlie and Hunkerville, Marquis of Corleone in Sicily, and Peer of England! My lord, will you be seated?"

Then the sheriff read to him a document containing the account of his past until he was left destitute on the coast of Portland. It declared that he was the son of Lord Clancharlie; that he was born in Switzerland, and had been sold to comprachicos when two years of age, after the death of his parents:

and that by the desire of his gracious Majesty, James II, he was mutilated and left alone on the coast of Portland to perish.[1]

It further declared that Hardquanonne had mutilated him, making him a laughing mask; and that he was called Gwynplaine. The writer told that he, in company with others, had tried to escape, that a storm had come up, and that the vessel was sinking as he wrote these lines.

"Oh, yes, I remember the doctor," said Gwynplaine, "and also a Provençal who used to drink out of a flat bottle on which a name was woven in red."

"Behold it," said the sheriff. "It was in this bottle that the men about to perish placed their confession. It was cast up by the sea."

In the wickerwork could be distinctly seen the word "Hardquanonne."

The prisoner uttered a scream and fell back dead. He was Hardquanonne.

"Ah," said Gwynplaine, "awake me!" and he stood up pale as death.

"I came, indeed, to wake you," said a voice which had not been heard before. It was Barkilphedro, and he told Gwynplaine that he had opened the flask washed up by the sea. "It means," said he, "that you have on your brow the coronet of a peer, and that you are about to wed the Duchess Josiana, daughter of a king."

Barkilphedro had tried to crush Lady Josiana, and he had succeeded. He had gone to the show, seen the "Laughing Man," and read the sign nailed against the wall of Tadcaster Inn, which declared that Gwynplaine had been deserted at the age of ten, on January 29th, 1690, on the coast of Portland.

When Gwynplaine came to himself he was sitting in an armchair in the middle of a sumptuous apartment. No one was there with him but Barkilphedro.

Gwynplaine, only half awake, cried: "Where am I?"

[1] Lord Clancharlie had espoused the cause of Cromwell, and after the restoration he retired to Switzerland, where he married Ann Bradshaw, who died in giving birth to a boy. No further details being obtainable, as James II said, he gave the titles to Lord Clancharlie's natural son, who was called Lord David Dirry-Moir, provided he were to marry Duchess Josiana, probably the natural daughter of James II.

"You are in your own house," said Barkilphedro, who immediately showed him a casket containing two thousand guineas.

"These shall be for my father, Ursus," he said.

"I shall take them to him," said Barkilphedro. "You cannot leave this place without my permission; I have the keys. If you do not accept the peerage, it will be given to your natural brother." Then he left.

Gwynplaine now walked up and down, recalling the thrilling events of the past few days, and trying to find a way out. There seemed to be no exit. His heart was calling "Dea! Dea! Dea! Where are you? Dea! What strange words that man said to me: 'That which you have left behind is no longer yours.' Dea! Ursus! I will go to you at once."

In wandering through the rooms he came to a marble bathroom where perfumed water was flowing slowly. Opposite the door was a diaphanous portière through which he could plainly see a woman clad in drapery so thin that she might almost be said to be naked. She appeared to be asleep. The room was dimly lighted. Perhaps the light was more modest than the woman. Gwynplaine recognized her: she was the Duchess. Suddenly she sprang from the couch and stood there nude. Then she threw a silken robe round her and entered the bathroom, and when she saw Gwynplaine she flung herself upon his neck, and told him how she loved him.

"Madame!" stammered Gwynplaine.

"Silence!" said she; "I will be your mistress joyfully. Do you wish to see a madwoman? Look at me! O monster, I love you!"

Then she kissed him.

At this moment a letter came from the Queen, telling Lady Josiana that Gwynplaine was Lord Clancharlie, and that he was to be her husband.

"Be it so," she said, as she calmly pointed her forefinger to the door. "Begone! As you are to be my husband, begone! I hate you!"

Then she left the room.

The next day Gwynplaine took his seat in the House of Lords. But when it came his turn to approve of a bill being passed to increase the pension for his Royal Highness, the Prince, he arose and objected. The other peers laughed, and Gwynplaine continued:

"You say I am a monster! No, I am the people. This laugh which is on my face a king placed there. This laugh expresses the devastation of mankind."

At midnight Gwynplaine had made his escape and went at once to Southwark, for he longed to see Dea, Ursus, and Homo, and to take up his old life again.

He found the inn closed, the Green Box gone. In Gwynplaine's absence the wapentake had arrested Ursus and ordered him to leave England the following day. Ursus replied that he was willing to go, but that he could not leave his comrade, Gwynplaine, behind.

"Gwynplaine is dead," said a voice. It was Barkilphedro who spoke. Then he slipped ten guineas into Ursus's hand and whispered: "Here are ten guineas, sent you by one who wishes you well." The remainder of the two thousand guineas he kept for himself.

Gwynplaine, who, of course, knew nothing of this, was greatly troubled. He retraced his steps and leaned against the wall overlooking the Thames. He thought of plunging into the river, and so he took off his hat, and wrote in his note-book: "I depart. Let my brother David take my place, and may he be happy." Then he signed his name, Fermain Clancharlie, Peer of England, put the book in his hat, and was glancing at the sky, with his hands clasped behind his back, preparatory to taking the fatal leap, when he felt a tongue licking his hands. It was Homo.

Gwynplaine uttered a cry, and followed the wolf, which led him to a vessel at anchor. He at once recognized the old van belonging to Ursus. On the deck he also saw a mattress, on which someone was lying. Ursus was bending over it. "She is asleep. Do not wake her. It is a fever. Keep quiet!" Then he continued: "We are off! Good-by, London! horrible London!"

Suddenly a voice was heard, a voice that sounded far away, the voice of Dea.

"He did well to go," the voice said. "This world was not

worthy of him. But I must go with him. Father, I am not ill. I was asleep, father. I shall soon be happy. Father, do not mourn for me. Gwynplaine is no longer here. Now I am blind indeed. I never knew what night was before. Night is absence. The soul flies away like a bird. I know where to find it. Father, it is up there. Later you will join us, and Homo, too. Now that Gwynplaine is no more, I die. I am going to him. It is easy to die. When I go to what you call the stars we shall marry, and never part again, and we shall love, love, love, for that is what God is."

Gwynplaine heard these last words.

Dea then became delirious, and Gwynplaine took her in his arms. When she came to herself she cried: "Is it you, Gwynplaine?"

"Yes, it is I!" he exclaimed. "I am alive! I am yours! Tell me how all this happened. Where is the Green Box? Why are you on this ship? It is infamous! I will avenge you, Dea! I am a peer of England."

Suddenly Dea arose, placed her hand to her heart, and fell.

"Alas!" said Ursus, "you have killed her."

She heaved a sigh and murmured: "I am dying."

"Die! You die! No! It shall not be!"

"Come to me as soon as you can," said Dea. "I shall be very unhappy without you, even in heaven. Oh, I cannot breathe!—Light! light! I see!" Then she fell back on the mattress, dead.

Gwynplaine went to the edge of the boat, gazed into the heavens and, as if led by a heavenly vision, called out: "I come! I understand the sign you are making to me."

His eyes were fixed on a point in the sky. One step more, the void was before him. He fell, and calmly and silently he disappeared.

Ursus had lost consciousness. When he came to, Gwynplaine could not be found, and Homo was at the edge of the boat, looking down into the water.

NINETY-THREE (1874)

This title means the year 1793. The story is of the French Revolution and the series of ferocious wars in the northern provinces, Vendée and Brittany, where the peasants rose in support of their Catholic faith and of their hereditary nobles against the Commune of Paris. This story is like the *Toilers of the Sea*, in that it has contributed one famous incident to the miscellaneous reading of the whole world. This part of the story, which is rarely omitted from any system of selected readings, is the description of the breaking loose of a carronade from its fastenings on the British sloop of war *Claymore*.

ON the 28th of April, 1793, the Commune of Paris gave this order to the volunteers under Santerre, who were in Brittany, to stamp out the rebellion of the peasants: "No mercy, no quarter." At the end of May, of the twelve thousand Parisian troops two thirds were dead.

Three hundred of these men were cautiously scouring the terrible woods of La Saudraie. The number of murders committed there made one's hair stand on end. Suddenly a soldier heard something like a whisper in the thicket. It seemed to another that he had just seen a movement among the leaves. Signs were made from man to man, and instantly a circle of muskets was aiming into the thicket.

In that moment the vivandière who had come to the front ventured to peer through the branches, and her cry interrupted the sergeant just as he was about to give the order "Fire!" She rushed headlong in. A woman was sitting on the moss, with an infant at her breast, and in her lap the blonde heads of two sleeping children. The woman looked up, stupefied, petrified. She was young, thin, ragged, and her bare feet were bleeding. Bewildered, as in a dream, this human flotsam tossed in the tempest of war answered questions. Her village had been burned; her husband had been shot; she was carrying her children away, whither she did not know. "I am surrounded with gunshots," she stammered. "I don't know what it all means. They have killed my husband, I only understand that."

The sergeant straightened himself up. "Let us adopt these three children!" he said. "Behold the children of the battalion of Bonnet-Rouge!"

At almost the very hour when this thing happened in La Saudraie, a man-of-war was sailing in the cover of a welcome fog through the dangerous passages between the Channel Islands. She was the *Claymore*, of thirty guns. Though she was British, her officers and crew were French—picked men loyal to the King. At one of the islands this ship had taken on board a tall old man, straight and sturdy, with a stern face, full of years and strength, with white locks on his brow and fire in his eye. He wore the threadbare costume of a Breton peasant; but the officers of the vessel addressed him as "General" and "Prince."

The sea grew more tempestuous hourly as the ship ran on, and they drew near La Courbière. Suddenly a wild cry was heard within the ship, and the gunners swarmed in panic from the gundeck. One of the carronades had broken loose. It was the fault of the gun-captain, who had neglected his duty. A heavy sea had struck, the carronade had broken its mooring, and its first terrible dart had killed four men of the battery. Sliding back, and then shot out again as the ship rolled, it cut in two another, and unshipped a gun on the starboard. The men had no recourse but to flee from this inanimate enemy, more terrible than the most terrible intelligent foe. It moved hither and yon on the gundeck, like a drop of water running over glass. It shattered four other guns, and smashed two holes in the side of the ship, and its four wheels passed back and forth over the dead men. Its convulsive blows cracked the mizzen-mast and cut into the mainmast. The battery was being reduced to nothing, and the corvette was beginning to leak.

Suddenly a man sprang down with an iron bar. It was the gun-captain. In the semidarkness an unprecedented battle began—a gladiator of flesh attacking a beast of brass. The carronade was like a gigantic insect of metal, having the will of a demon. It ran at the man. He writhed away from it like a snake. The blow fell against the side of the ship. An end of broken chain hanging to the cannon whirled desperately like an iron lash in a brazen hand. Suddenly the cannon made a quick dash at the gunner. He sprang out of the way, and the monster smashed a carronade on the port side. Then it was hurled back to the starboard side again, at the man, and three carronades gave way.

As if blinded, it turned from the gunner and rolled from stern to bow, making another breach. The next instant it slid backward at the man, swift as a falling ax, and he was driven against the side of the ship. The crew cried out in terror. At that moment the peasant darted down the ladder. He leaped like one leaping at the throat of death and threw a huge bundle between the wheels of the carronade. It stumbled. The gunner plunged his bar between the spokes of a wheel and it stopped.

The man had conquered. But the cannon had conquered as well. Twenty of the thirty guns lay useless, the ship had five holes in her side, a gale had begun to blow, and the vessel was far out of her course.

On the deck of the half-wrecked corvette the gunner was brought before the man in the peasant's dress. He took a cross of St. Louis and pinned it on the gunner's jacket. The marines presented arms, and the sailors cried "Hurrah!"

"Now," said the peasant, "have this man shot."

A few minutes afterward a shot sounded in the bows, and a body fell into the sea. The Captain of the corvette said to his lieutenant: "La Vendée has found a head."

In the east appeared a whiteness, which was dawn. In the west another whiteness, which was the setting moon. Against these two bright strips were outlined black figures, straight and motionless. Those in the west were rocks. Those in the east were the cruisers of the French Republic. The Captain laughed: "Shipwreck on one side, battle on the other. Both sides have thrown double fives."

The corvette cast six anchors, and her remaining carronades were put on the side toward the enemy. Then the Captain said to the man in peasant's dress:

"Sir, we are cramped in our tomb. We must die. But you must live, for without you the monarchy is lost. I will give you a man and a boat. It will not be impossible for a small craft to escape."

The stern old man made a solemn sign of acquiescence, and a few minutes later he was being rowed through the passages between the rocks. Hardly had they gained the reefs when the corvette suddenly stood out like a black skeleton against a fearful crimson light. The squadron of the Republic had opened fire from three hundred guns.

Long after the battle had sunk below the horizon of the peasant, there came a prolonged roar that shook the air. The corvette had been blown up.

The next day, in a thicket on the Breton coast, a thousand men, armed with guns, scythes, poles, bayonets, and swords, were kneeling before the man who had escaped from the sea.

A young man stepped forth. "Marquis," said he, "there are seven thousand of us in these woods. To-morrow there will be fifteen thousand. This morning we attacked yonder farm, where the Paris battalion of Bonnet-Rouge were encamped. We have captured them all. What shall we do with the wounded and the prisoners?"

"Shoot them."

"There are two women."

"Shoot them. And burn the farm and the hamlet for giving shelter to the enemy."

A month later four men were in the back room of a house in Paris. One of these was Robespierre. The second was Danton. The third was Marat. The fourth was a man obscure, humble; but he belonged to the Evêché. His name was Cimourdain. He had been a priest, had ceased to believe, but at soul was still a priest, with endless pity for the wretched and endless hatred for monarchy.

To this man Robespierre was saying:

"The Vendée has a chief. She is going to be tremendous. He is the Marquis de Lantenac, who calls himself Prince of Brittany."

"I know him," said Cimourdain. "I was a priest at his castle."

"He is frightful," said Robespierre. "He burns villages, massacres the prisoners, shoots women. Citizen Cimourdain, this man is the greatest danger now to the Republic. One Vendée is more dangerous to France than ten Germanys. He must be taken and guillotined. You will be commissioned by the Committee of Public Welfare with full power."

"I accept," said Cimourdain.

"You will be sent as delegate to the commandant of the column that is acting against Lantenac. He is a young man, and is showing admirable bravery and intelligence. For two weeks he has held the old Marquis in check."

"But he has one fault!" interrupted Marat. "Clemency! A crime! What would you do with a Republican general who gave a Royalist general his liberty?"

"I should have him guillotined within twenty-four hours," answered Cimourdain.

"Here are the papers," said Robespierre. "Citizen Cimourdain, the commandant over whom you will have full power is a former Viscount. His name is Gauvain."

Cimourdain's face grew pale as death.

This avenger, who loved mankind, reserved nothing from that love excepting only one human being—a pupil whom he had taught and formed, of whose mind he had become the father, whom he had come to love ineffably, pouring out on him all the affection that another man might have lavished on a woman. And that pupil was Gauvain—and Gauvain was the nephew and heir of the Marquis de Lantenac, the scourge of Brittany!

When Cimourdain reached Brittany he found evidences everywhere of the added fierceness that this relationship gave to the war in La Vendée. Placards signed by the Marquis promised his nephew a speedy death if captured. Placards signed by Gauvain responded in kind. As if to add lust to lust, placards of the Republic flaunted another decree of death to all who might connive at helping Royalist prisoners to escape.

When Cimourdain came into the terrible forest country he learned that the Marquis had struck at the town of Dol because it would give him a fastness on the coast where the English could land forces to help him; and Gauvain had hastened with an inferior force to rout him out.

The peasants encamped carelessly in the market-place, and Lantenac rode off with his officers to investigate the points for a coast battery to cover an English landing. Before messengers could bring him back, Gauvain burst on the town, surrounded it, and drove the peasants off in wild panic.

When all was over, Gauvain approached a wounded peasant and said: "You are my prisoner. You are a brave fellow. Come, you are wounded." And he held out his hand to him.

The peasant fired, and swept at him with a sword, and Gauvain would have been killed instantly but for a man on horseback, who hurled himself between the two. The horse received the bullet, the man the saber stroke, and both fell. Gauvain looked at the man. The blood was pouring from the saber gash on his face and formed a red mask. A surgeon brought water and sponged it off.

"Cimourdain!" cried Gauvain. "Cimourdain! It is you! This is the second time you have saved my life!"

Cimourdain, not severely wounded, was soon in the column, marching with saber and pistols, which no one ever saw him use. He faced the shots, and gave none in return. Yet throughout Vendée he was known as "the cruel," for he lost no opportunity to proclaim that mercy to an enemy of the Republic was treason to the Revolution.

July passed, August came; a blast of heroism and cruelty blew over France. In La Vendée the war was now an immense skirmish in the wood, and "No mercy! No prisoners!" was the cry of both parties. At last Lantenac was cut off from his forces and driven to seek refuge in the great tower of La Tourgue.

One evening bivouac fires twinkled in the plain far below, and La Tourgue was besieged. A figure appeared on the top of the tower and called to the men below.

"I speak to you in the name of Monseigneur the Marquis de Lantenac, Prince of Brittany, seigneur of the seven forests," cried the man. "We have in our hands three prisoners, three children. These children were adopted by one of your battalions and they are yours. We offer to give up these children to you if you will let us go free. If you refuse, listen attentively. In the building on the bridge we have placed six barrels of tar. The middle story is full of papers. The upper is full of straw. The iron door is closed. I have made an opening under the door and through this passes a slow match leading to the tar. The other end is in the tower here. If you refuse to let us out, the three children will be placed in the middle story. If you attack by the bridge, you will be the ones to set fire to the building. If you attack by the tower, we shall be the ones. In any case the children will perish. Now choose."

A voice from below cried out: "To-morrow at this hour, if you do not surrender, we shall attack."

In the tower were nineteen men. Four thousand men besieged them.

Gauvain scoured the country in vain for a ladder. The peasants had destroyed every one, as they had destroyed every wagon. At last he despatched a mounted man post haste to the nearest garrison at Javene, with orders to send a ladder with a mounted escort.

Early in the morning of the next day a woman was limping across the plains toward La Tourgue. Anyone near her would have heard her say repeatedly: "La Tourgue." This was the mother whom the battalion of Bonnet-Rouge had found in the wood.

When the peasants under De Lantenac had destroyed the battalion in the farm she was one of the two women whom they had shot. They left her for dead; but a beggar succored her, and at last her wounds healed and she went forth to seek her children.

As she walked, a wagon drawn by five horses harnessed with chains overtook her. On it was a heap that looked like a pile of long joists, in the middle of which was something strange and shapeless. It was covered with a black cloth that looked like a shroud. Twenty armed men rode with it. Some peasants who stood aside to let it pass muttered: "The guillotine!"

An hour later the thickets through which runs the Javene highway were full of peasants lying in wait for the guillotine. Suddenly they heard the noise of wheels and horses. A long wagon appeared, and a hundred guns were fired at once. When the smoke disappeared five men lay dead. The peasants ran to the wagon.

"Hold!" said the leader. "We have made a mistake. It is not the guillotine, but a ladder."

The guillotine was two leagues away, having taken another road.

The mother in the wood took the right path, then the wrong one.

Suddenly she emerged from the wood. Before her lay a plain. A mighty voice shook the air, and she looked in its direction and saw a tall tower. That same mighty voice, the first cannon-shot in the attack on La Tourgue, awoke three little children who were lying in a half-naked, loving, beautiful group on the floor of the old library.

Gauvain had waited till the last moment, and watched the roads with his glass. After a long search he exclaimed: "At last! The escape ladder at last. Now we can begin, for we have the means of saving the children." He had seen a wagon a mile away on the plain.

Turning round, he saw the sergeant and ten men of the battalion of Bonnet-Rouge. These were the only men who had escaped the massacre of the peasants. The sergeant saluted, twisted his moustaches and said: "Our children are there, Commander, our three children. Commander, we who are all that is left of our battalion wish to save the children or to be killed. Let us lead the attacking party."

Gauvain held out his hand and said: "Come!" He gave the word.

The place of attack was horrible. When the Marquis was first penned there the besiegers made a breach in the lower part of the tower—a fracture that was barely large enough to permit a few men to enter at a time, and into this deadly hole it was necessary to crawl under fire.

Whoever entered there was suddenly deaf and blind—deafened by the explosions of firearms, blinded by the darkness and the smoke. The wounded were stamped to death by the struggling who remained upright. Blood began to flow from the tower through the breach. It formed a dismal pool in the grass outside. The dead were heaped on the ground. Ten besiegers were falling to one besieged. But it could not last long. The besieged decreased one by one.

At last seven were left. The Marquis saw the opportunity to retreat to the second line of defense, the upper story of the tower. Swiftly the survivors sprang clear of the hand-to-hand conflict and rushed up the spiral staircase; and here they stood in ominous, cold, calm despair. To retreat through the iron door into the châtelet was useless. It would be only to exchange one trap for another. They had only four shots left, and the sound of the besiegers' creeping feet was heard stealing cautiously up the stairs.

"It is all over," said the Marquis. "Let us pray."

At that moment a hole opened in the wall. A stone turned on a pivot, and a man's face looked in. The Marquis recognized an old serf.

"Quick!" said the latter. "This passage leads to the ravine."

"One of us must stay behind to hold the enemy back," said L'Imanus, a fanatic peasant. "Let me stay. You will need fifteen minutes to escape."

One after another the rest entered the opening and disappeared. L'Imanus took two pistols in each hand and waited. Soon he saw an eye peering round an angle. He fired. He fired the second pistol at random at a rushing crowd, and then fell back. Seizing the other two pistols, he looked down. He saw a head, fired, and the soldier fell. At the same instant a sword entered his bowels. The wound was frightful. He ground his teeth, dragged himself to the slow-match leading under the iron door and lighted it. The flame ran along and passed under the door. Then this man who was now about to die smiled and murmured: "They will remember me. In these little ones I avenge our little one, the King in the Temple."

When the besiegers at last dared to enter they found only this one ghastly dead man. The opening that had been left, because the long-unused stone had jammed, told the story.

While they stood looking round, astounded, bitterly disappointed, a great cry rang out below them. The mother, standing before the tower, had seen the building on the bridge break out in flame.

"The ladder! The ladder!" cried Gauvain.

"Commander," said his lieutenant, "the wagon did not bring the ladder. It brought the guillotine."

"Burst open the iron door!" cried a hundred voices.

"It cannot be done!"

The fire wreathed the first story. A whole army stood in despair. Ax after ax broke on the iron door. Sappers came with iron bars, but they broke like glass. The flames licked up to the second story where the children were.

Suddenly a white head appeared in the opening through which the Marquis had escaped. It was the Marquis returned.

He had a large key. Without saying a word, he walked to the iron door, opened it, a gulf of flame roared out, and he went in. Shaken by his foot, the floor fell in behind him, and he disappeared in the red glare.

The soldiers ran out of the tower into the ravine. They looked up in despair. The sergeant madly buried his nails in the stone of the bridge and tried to climb, but fell back raging.

Heavy cracking was heard above the snapping of the fire. A window in the library fell outward. Little voices were heard calling "Mamma! Mamma!" The soldiers clenched their fists. They sobbed. They cursed. They were in paroxysms of agony. The Marquis appeared at the window. He had a huge ladder, which had been stored in the library, and with the agility of an athlete he tilted it and let it down.

Men swarmed up, and he passed the three children to them amid the cheers of the old grenadiers. Then slowly, deliberately, haughtily, he stepped through the window and, without turning round, straight, erect, with his back to the fire, he descended.

The soldiers retired before him, and when he reached the ground a hand was laid on his collar.

"I arrest you," said Cimourdain.

The Marquis had really descended into the tomb. They led him into a crypt dungeon under La Tourgue.

"We shall convene a court-martial," said Cimourdain to Gauvain. "You will not take part in it. It will be to-morrow. The day after, the guillotine. La Vendée is dead."

Gauvain drew the hood of his cloak over his head and walked away.

Two o'clock struck. Gauvain went slowly toward the tower. A sentry saluted. He pointed to the door of the dungeon. "Open!" said he. Gauvain entered. The door closed behind him. He threw his cloak over the shoulders of the prisoner, pulled the hood over his face and cried: "Lieutenant, open the door!" The door opened, and Gauvain pushed the amazed Marquis out.

Early the next day a table was brought into the hall in front of the dungeon. On a chair facing the door sat Cimourdain, presiding over the court-martial. A captain of Gauvain's command sat on one side. On the other sat the sergeant of the Bonnet-Rouge. The door was flung open. Gauvain stepped out. Cimourdain turned white and cried: "Where is the prisoner?"

"I have helped him to escape," said Gauvain.

Cimourdain steadied his voice and said:

"Seat this man."

He no longer addressed the prisoner familiarly. Coldly, formally, he propounded the questions that were necessary to draw forth the story. Then he turned to the Captain. "What do you vote?"

The Captain dropped his gaze and said: "I vote death."

"Speak, Sergeant," said Cimourdain.

The sergeant rose and cried: "I would have done what my commander has done!"

"Acquittal," said Cimourdain. "Write, clerk."

Cimourdain rose, took off his hat, and in a solemn voice said: "Accused Gauvain, in the name of the Republic, the court-martial, by a majority of two to one—"

He stopped. There was a moment of suspense. All held their breath. Cimourdain continued: "Condemns you to death!"

When the sun rose again it shone on a wall of soldiers enclosing the red scaffold. Near it stood a platform on which was the table of the tribunal draped in tricolor. Under the flags sat Cimourdain, motionless, with folded arms.

Then came the muffled roll of drums covered with crape. The ranks opened. A platoon of grenadiers appeared. Behind them walked Gauvain, unbound, his brown hair floating in the wind, his heroic eye full of a solemn joy. The sun shone on him in his beauty; and that terrible thing, the sob of an army, sounded through the silence. A shout arose: "Mercy! Mercy!"

Some fell on their knees. A grenadier cried: "Will you take a substitute? Take me!" Again came the frantic cry: "Mercy! Mercy!" But an inexorable voice responded, "Enforce the law!" and the executioner approached with a rope.

"Wait," said Gauvain. He waved a farewell to Cimourdain and then allowed himself to be bound. "Long live the Republic!" he cried.

They laid him on the plank, and a hideous sound was heard. At the same instant another sound was heard. A pistol-shot responded to the blow of the ax, and as Gauvain's head rolled into the basket Cimourdain sent a bullet through his own heart. The blood poured from his mouth; he fell dead; and these two souls, tragic sisters, departed together, the darkness of one mingling with the light of the other.

JEAN INGELOW

(England, 1820–1897)

OFF THE SKELLIGS (1872)

Though Jean Ingelow's poems appeared as early as 1850, it was not till twenty years later that *Off the Skelligs*, her first long story, was published. The Great Skellig and the Lesser Skellig are rocky islands ten miles off the southwest coast of Ireland, forming the extreme point of British land. The Great Skellig rises nearly a thousand feet high. During a storm the waves rise to two hundred feet over its ledges, and the spray reaches four hundred feet higher. The Lesser Skellig is one of the breeding-places of the gannet, and at certain seasons millions of these birds hover about the rock.

MY early home was in a quiet country town of England, and my only companions were my brother, a precocious boy two years older than I, and a baby sister. We were left almost entirely to the care of a nurse, as my mother was never very well and when able to be about was always writing. The nurse told me she wrote mathematics. My brother was very fond of teaching me, and before I could speak I could hand him my lettered blocks as he called for them. Our chief play was reciting scenes from Shakespeare, until a severe illness came to my brother and the doctor said he must not be allowed to use his brain. After that we continued our games surreptitiously but all studying was denied us.

In the absence of my father and mother, our nurse often left us with her father, the sexton of the church, and we played among the pews with great glee, often acting the scenes of the paintings on the walls; but the curate told us how wicked this play was, and we were obliged to give it up. We then began going into the tower and up to the big bells. Once we found a strange man there, who must have been an escaped convict.

He bound us to secrecy, and for two weeks my brother and I ran to the bake-shop for him and provided him with food. We did not know this was wrong, and we felt very bad when we found he had gone and our adventure was over.

Soon after my parents returned my father went to Australia and my mother took us to a small cottage in the country. Here she did even more writing than before, and the nurse told us that was her means of obtaining money to take care of us. Tom and I never were dressed like other children, and our education was entirely neglected. The nurse and a neighbor called our mother's attention to the fact that we were queer little children, and she allowed them to cut our hair and get such clothes for us as other children wore. She then engaged a tutor for us; but we so overwhelmed him by offering him instruction in a new language we had made, and then proceeding to "do some Shakespeare" for him, that he left immediately. The next applicant was more successful, and won Tom and me at once. He taught me to sew and to play with dolls as well as to do many school tasks. I used to wander over the fields with him, and sometimes we met a beautiful lady. One day I heard her tell him that she could not love him, and his coming to her part of the country was of no use. I felt very sorry for him and cried all that night. The next day he left, and then my mother tried for a short time to teach us.

In the following two years we had a succession of tutors and my mother continued to write. My father had met with some success, but could not yet pay the debts contracted in England. Therefore my mother and sister went out to Australia, and Tom and I were sent to her uncle, who always lived on board his yacht, the *Curlew*. Uncle Rollin was very kind to us and made us comfortable on board his beautiful boat. I never had seen anything so clean and shiny; but on our first sea trip I was very sick, and as soon as I came on deck my uncle told me I was to be sent to a school for young ladies. I was very unhappy there, but I tried to learn and I worked particularly hard on my music, which I knew my uncle most wanted. I never liked Mrs. Bell, who kept the school, and, knowing that all the letters I sent or received were read by her, I soon lost all freedom in communicating with my family.

I remained at the school until I was fully grown up, and at last, in spite of Mrs. Bell's presence, I managed to ask Uncle Rollin to take me away with him. Mrs. Bell was horrified, but my uncle had really come for that purpose, though he was too shy to come out in the face of so much protest. He took me with him, and I was rid of the school at last.

My mother had died, and my father never had the means to send for us, so our home continued to be with Uncle Rollin. He did not like my protestations and thanks, but he provided most generously for me and wished me always to be handsomely dressed.

I found Tom much changed. He was kind to me, but now he was more of the elder brother and less of the comrade.

My first voyage, on joining them, was to the Great Skellig, and I was much interested in studying about it, but a fog came on as soon as we approached. I was awakened in the night by hearing ropes and chains drawn on deck, and learned that a burning vessel had been sighted. My uncle had boats lowered and put off with Tom in command to seek the passengers who might be drifting near the wreck. No one was found except a drunken sailor clinging to the bowsprit. He was brought on board, but could give no satisfactory account except that the vessel was from America and fire had caught in the cargo of cotton. We put into port next morning and left him. One boatload of sailors had come in, but no passengers, and my uncle then turned about to look carefully for any survivors. We had nearly given up hope when about midnight Tom and I, who were walking on deck, saw a light apparently bearing down on us. The lookout man sang out, "Light ahead!" and soon all was confusion. I became entangled in one of the ropes and fell, and when I recovered from the giddiness I heard such stamping I knew the boat must have come alongside and that her occupants were on board. What I saw was a motley crowd, two or three men and a good many limping women, wet and disheveled. Then followed a man with two children. He was badly burned and could not speak, so I led him into my cabin and brought food at once. I bandaged the poor fellow's arm and bound up his blistered hands and left him to sleep in the empty berth.

The other passengers were suffering only from exposure and want of food, and when they had had a night's rest and we had fitted them out with clothes they were able to go on shore.

As the man in my cabin grew better he asked me to read to him from a Greek Testament. I became suspicious that he was not the common sailor I had taken him to be, and soon learned that he was an Englishman and a scholar. There had been very few first-class passengers, and he had interested himself in the steerage passengers, who seemed most unfortunate. The mother of the little children had died on the voyage, and he had promised her to place the two little girls with their grandmother in Chartres. My uncle liked the man very much and insisted that, as he was sailing to France, Mr. Brandon (for that was his name) and his two charges should remain with us. At Southampton we stopped, and Tom and Mr. Brandon went in search of English relatives of the children. When they returned, the aunt, a most uncompromising spinster, came with them and persisted in going with us to see the children safe in the hands of the French grandmother. She was greatly shocked to find that the children were not dressed in black, and made herself generally disliked.

Uncle Rollin did not accompany us to Chartres, but remained on board the yacht at Havre. After leaving the children we went about the town and visited the cathedral. I did not like the hideous black Virgin, nor the dirty flowers. When Mr. Brandon whispered, "Well, what do you think of it?" I replied: "Think—I cannot think. There is such solemn, awful splendor, and such trash and rubbish."

We returned to my uncle the next day and were soon in Southampton again, where the maiden aunt and Mr. Brandon left us. Though Mr. Brandon had given me a very pretty ring as a souvenir, he left the yacht without bidding me good-by, and I was deeply hurt. I was angry with Tom, for I was sure he was to blame. He reproached me with showing an unladylike interest in my patient; but I could see nothing out of the way in this, for Mr. Brandon was an unusual man. Uncle Rollin had taken to him from the first, Tom liked to hear him talk, and why should I not feel the same?

Later Mr. Brandon came again on board and brought his

stepfather, Mr. Mortimer, a delightful gentleman about eighty years old. We spent that winter cruising about the West Indies, and when we returned we received a cordial invitation from old Mr. Mortimer to visit his home. Uncle Rollin declined, but Tom and I were delighted at the prospect of again being in a house.

Mr. Brandon met us at the station with his two stepsisters and his stepbrother, Valentine, a remarkably fine young fellow. Valentine was then home from school on account of a bad cough, and I was soon spending my mornings helping him with his Greek. He manifested much sentiment toward me.

Though there was time for pleasant rambles and our evenings were always gay, Mr. Brandon was very busy. The property was entirely his, and had increased very much during his boyhood when Mr. Mortimer was his guardian, and besides having the care of the estate he was a great philanthropist, making speeches at county meetings and helping persons to emigrate to Australia. Knowing how occupied he was, I was much surprised when one morning he and Tom came down equipped for a trip to Southampton. It was evident that this journey, which the family supposed to be undertaken to please Tom, was really done at Mr. Brandon's pleasure. I was much vexed, as it now seemed that Mr. Brandon had been flirting with me and I felt he had done wrong to drag Tom away.

Valentine expressed himself as much pleased that his brother, Giles, had gone, and now he might have me to himself. He tried hard to make me accept a ring and construed it into an acceptance when I gave it to his sister, as I could not have given away what was not my own. It appeared that under these conditions he was to win a camera from his brother. It was in vain for me to protest, and the camera was ordered that very morning. From that time forth we spent several hours each day taking pictures.

One day when we were sitting on the lawn and Valentine as usual was making love to me, Mr. Brandon came upon us. As he shook hands with me I exclaimed:

"Oh, Mr. Brandon, you are come home! Where is Tom?"

"I left him behind with the Captain," he answered cheerfully. "We have been cruising about, and they put me ashore yesterday."

I had already remained nearly the whole month for which we had been invited, and now I was left with no directions how to act. My uncle had put to sea, and who could tell when he would be in port again?

The Greek lessons, the photography, and Valentine's protestations went on, and other guests arrived. At length the expected letter came from Uncle Rollin. He and Tom were going to Iceland and, having put me on an allowance of a hundred and eighty pounds, they left me to live and act as I chose.

This news was most unexpected, and I confess it was a great blow. Mr. Mortimer kindly asked me to remain two weeks longer, while I made my plans for the future. Valentine now began in earnest to insist upon our engagement, but I laughed at him as a mere boy. Mr. Brandon appeared more reserved and hardly spoke to me, yet I felt that he was still my best friend. One day he chanced upon me in the wood and sat down by me. He told me how in his youth he had often met here a beautiful girl who afterward died and left him to go on his way alone. At first I could not see why he was telling me of this first love, but as he went on I felt that he was warning me to my face that I loved him and must try to overcome my love. All my pride was roused to revolt; I refused to hear another word, and left him in anger.

As my plans were now complete, I went to London accompanied by Anne Moulton, an able woman whom I had engaged as a maid with the promise of allowing her leisure for charitable work. As my allowance was not large, I did some tutoring and thus earned the money to study wood-engraving. I went with Anne to a clergyman, and he assigned us a district in which to work. My effort was a failure, as the poverty and distress were too great for me to cope with, but Anne was in her element. I allowed her the time and gave her what money I could spare. I cannot chronicle this good woman's deeds. She nursed the sick, taught several young girls to work with their needles, and induced the men to lay up money.

All this work was done before we had been in London six

weeks, and then I received my first letter from my uncle. I gave up any hope of returning to him, and gathered that he was uneasy about Tom, who was not conducting himself so as to please him.

Valentine was the only one that continued to take notice of me, sending flowers and writing constantly. He wrote that he was spitting blood and the doctor would not let him go to Cambridge. I believe the knowledge of his illness and the loss of his cherished wish made me feel more affectionately toward the poor boy.

During the holidays Mr. Brandon and Valentine came to see us. Mr. Brandon took a great interest in our poor people and began to set on foot plans for taking some of them out to the colonies, where he expected to go himself in a few weeks. Valentine's health was still poor, and he wished me to consider going to New Zealand with him. Mr. Brandon was very reserved toward me, but evidently looked upon me as a good wife for his brother, who, he thought, should be both guided and amused. I did not think that I could ever accept Valentine, and I told him so almost every day, but he was quite imperturbable. I was offended that Mr. Brandon could think I was in love with him in June and ready to marry his boy brother in December. However, I promised to consider this matter for a year. On the whole, the visit was very pleasant, and I missed them both when they were suddenly called away by Mr. Mortimer's illness.

In the year that followed Anne was a great comfort to me. She was my friend as well as my maid. My uncle wrote a second letter and sent me ten pounds, which we promptly used in our work. I hired the cellar of each house in my district and let out little cupboards in them at a penny a week to encourage the people to have a larder and to be more frugal. I also took a wash-room, where for a few pence each woman could come and do her washing. Anne also kept a hiring-room, where she let out pails and scrub-brushes, and after a certain number of hirings the utensil became the woman's property. We did the same with clothing, and thus, with very little help from me, Anne was fast reclaiming her people from barbarity.

In the spring I received a letter from uncle's stewardess,

telling of my brother's marriage to a barmaid and of my uncle's great displeasure. Tom came on board whenever he chose, but his wife stayed in Southampton.

In August Anne and I, having shipped off about forty persons to Mr. Brandon's colony, went to the seashore. Valentine was there and though, out of respect to his father, who had died in the year, he had waited beyond our prescribed time, he again pressed his suit. He was a strong-looking fellow, but always subject to a cough, and an immediate change of climate now seemed desirable. I did not think we really cared enough for each other, but I did not like to be left alone, so I consented and we were both very happy. Mr. Brandon entered heartily into our plans. We were to go among our colonists in New Zealand, and the time was set for the last of January. Anne Moulton was to sail before our wedding with three young women we wished to befriend and the two little girls from Chartres. Their grandmother was dead, and Mr. Brandon had asked us to have them with us. Of course I agreed gladly.

Anne and I returned to London and were busy with our preparations till a week before the wedding, which was to take place in the family home. Valentine was in Derbyshire, but would be home in time to meet me. At the station I parted with Anne, who was to sail in two days and prepare our new home for our coming six weeks later.

When I arrived at my destination no one was there to meet me. I had written to Valentine the hour, but at the house I learned he had not yet returned. All were busy with preparations for the coming event, and the beautiful trousseau sent me by my uncle took all my attention, but when two days went by and Valentine did not come, we knew not what to make of it. Word came that he was ill. Then we learned that he had set out, but he did not arrive, and at last his brother went for him. He returned on the eve of the wedding-day, bringing me a letter from Valentine. The boy had fallen madly in love with Lucy Nelson, a girl he had known for several months. He had had a bad attack of influenza while visiting at the girl's home. Feeling he could not face me, he had gone to London, where Mr. Brandon had at last found him alone and miserable. I do not know how I ever lived through that night or the days that followed. Of course the wedding was postponed indefinitely. Messengers were despatched in every direction, but I heard carriages come and turn away with guests who had been too far away to be reached.

After several days I became stronger and was eager to get about. I sent Valentine a letter of forgiveness, which brought an affectionate response from the poor boy, who thanked me for his release and continued to regard me as the dearest of sisters. I saw Mr. Brandon was alarmed about his health, so I asked him to be gentle with his brother and allow him to come to us.

Mr. Brandon grew ever more tender of me, and his sympathy was my strong support. One day he told me of a sad attachment of his own following the only other one of his boyhood. When he had finished, and I told him how sorry I was, he said I was that woman. He loved me, and went to my uncle for his consent; but when he had found his young brother so in love with me he could not stand in his way, and had given up. His one protest, made that memorable day in the wood, I had misunderstood. He also told me of that sudden trip he took with Tom to Southampton. The wretched girl who later became my brother's wife had followed him there, and Mr. Brandon had persuaded Tom to go back to Uncle Rollin, trying to induce the girl to leave him alone. She was bought off for a short time, but more they could not do.

When Valentine came he soon saw our attachment and was silly enough to show some jealousy. We never had really cared for each other, and I was quite unmoved by his presence. He seemed still the good-natured boy without regard for consequences. Affairs did not go at all smoothly between him and Miss Nelson, as her mother did not approve of his conduct toward me; and I therefore wrote to her and tried my best to remove the difficulties. At last Valentine said that if I would marry someone else that would remove all objections. Mr. Brandon told me this in trying to gain my consent; but I was not sure of myself, and I went to the Isle of Wight to spend some time with the curate and his wife, who used to talk with me in the church where Tom and I played as children.

Mr. Brandon came to see me, and we talked much of Valen-

wrote another letter to the Nelsons, and told
of my engagement to Mr. Brandon, but it did no
elson insisted that they should wait two years,
Valentine's illness and his scanty means. This
ne, who refused to wait, and the engagement was

letters from Anne Moulton telling us that on the
she had met an excellent man, a missionary, and had
him, so I felt relieved of all responsibility concerning
I knew the colonists would fare well in her hands.
ecided on an early day for our marriage, but I could
e, even when we stood before the clergyman, that my
could be regularly accomplished, and indeed it was
the ring had been forgotten. The clergyman's wife
ain to supply the deficiency. Her finger had grown
let her own ring slide off. At last the sexton ran out
ed with a good-natured woman, who loaned hers for
, and later some were sent into the vestry for our
When one was chosen and paid for, then I knew
rs. Brandon.

WASHINGTON IRVIN

(United States, 1783–1859)

RIP VAN WINKLE (1819)

This legend of the Catskills appeared in *The Sketch Book,* a
papers published in 1819, and in England in 1820. The Englis
brought out by the famous publisher, John Murray, through the
Sir Walter Scott, who greatly admired Irving. These writings,
declared in the "Advertisement to the First American Edition,"
fluctuations of his own thoughts and feelings; sometimes trea
before him, sometimes of others purely imaginary, and sometin
back with his recollections to his native country. The modest
expressed, "to have a secure and cherished, though humble, cor
opinions and kind feelings of his countrymen," has been more

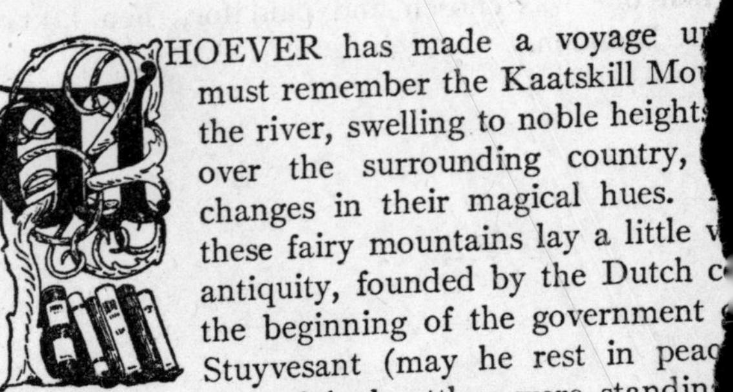

HOEVER has made a voyage u
must remember the Kaatskill Mo
the river, swelling to noble height
over the surrounding country,
changes in their magical hues.
these fairy mountains lay a little v
antiquity, founded by the Dutch c
the beginning of the government
Stuyvesant (may he rest in peac
the houses of the original settlers were standin
years, built of small yellow bricks brought from
ing latticed windows and gable fronts, surmount
cocks.

In that village lived, years ago, when the c
province of Great Britain, a simple, good-nat
Rip Van Winkle—moreover, a kind neigh
husband. He was a great favorite wit
village, and the children, whose const
shout with joy whenever he approa
Rip's composition was an insuperab

profitable labor. He would fish all day, carry a fowling-piece for hours, and was ready to attend to anybody's business but his own. But to do family duties at home, or to keep his farm in order, that he found impossible. His children were as ragged and wild as if they belonged to nobody, and his son Rip promised to inherit the habits, with the old clothes, of his father.

Rip's sole domestic adherent was his dog Wolf, which was as much henpecked as his master, for Dame Van Winkle considered him the cause of his master's going so often astray. The good wife's temper never mellowed. A sharp tongue is the only tool that grows keener from constant use. Poor Rip would hie for sanctuary to the bench before a small inn, designated by a rubicund portrait of his Majesty, George the Third, where Derrick Van Bummel, the schoolmaster, and Nicholas Vedder, the village patriarch and landlord of the inn, with other cronies, smoked and told endless sleepy stories about nothing. But even from this stronghold Rip's wife would rout her husband. His only escape then was to stroll off into the woods, gun in hand, with Wolf, his brother sufferer, trotting along at his side.

In a long ramble of this kind, one fine autumn day, Rip had scrambled to one of the highest peaks of the Kaatskill Mountains, pursuing his favorite sport of squirrel-shooting. At last, panting and fatigued, he threw himself, late in the afternoon, on a green knoll that commanded a lordly view of the country below. For some time he lay musing over this scene, until evening advanced. He then saw it would be dark long before he could reach home, and heaved a heavy sigh as he thought of his wife's greeting.

As he began to descend, he heard a voice calling from a distance: "Rip Van Winkle! Rip Van Winkle!" He paused and then, thinking it a delusion, walked on, when he heard the same cry ringing through the still evening air. Wolf bristled up his back, growled, and skulked closer to his master's side, looking fearfully down into the glen. As Rip turned his gaze in the same direction, he saw a strange figure slowly toiling up the rocks, bending under the weight of something on his back.

Rip good-naturedly went to assist him, and was surprised at the stranger's appearance. He was a short, square-built fellow, with thick, bushy hair, and a grizzled beard. He wore the old Dutch dress—a cloth jerkin strapped around the waist, and several pairs of breeches decorated with rows of buttons down the sides. He bore on his shoulders a stout keg that appeared to be full of liquor. Rip assisted him to clamber up the dry bed of a torrent with it, toward a deep ravine between lofty rocks, from which issued long peals, like distant thunder. Continuing in silence, the two passed through the cleft between the rocks and arrived at a hollow like a small amphitheater, surrounded with perpendicular precipices.

Here, on a level spot in the center, were odd-looking persons, dressed in outlandish fashion, playing at ninepins. They had long knives in their belts, and had beards of various shapes and colors. One appeared to be the commander. This stout old gentleman wore a laced doublet, with a broad belt and a hanger, a high-crowned hat and feather, red stockings, and high-heeled shoes with roses in them. The whole group reminded Rip of an old Flemish painting in Dominie Van Schaick's parlor, which had been brought from Holland at the time of the settlement.

What seemed particularly odd to Rip was, that these folks, who were evidently amusing themselves, maintained the gravest faces, the most mysterious silence. Nothing interrupted the stillness but the noise of the balls, which when they were rolled, echoed along the mountains like rumbling peals of thunder.

They stared at Rip and his companion with such strange, uncouth, lack-luster countenances, that his knees smote together. Liquor was drawn from the keg they had brought, and his companion made signs to Rip to serve the flagons, which he did with fear and trembling. The others quaffed the liquor in silence and returned to their game.

Rip's awe subsided by degrees, and finally, when no eye was on him, he tasted the beverage, which had the flavor of excellent Hollands. He was usually thirsty, and was soon tempted to repeat the draught. He repeated his visits to the flagon so often that at length his senses were overpowered, his eyes swam in his head, his head gradually declined, and he fell into a deep sleep.

On waking, he found himself on the green knoll where he had first seen the old man of the glen. It was a bright, sunny morning. The birds were hopping and twittering among the bushes, and the eagle was wheeling aloft and breasting the pure mountain breeze. "Surely," thought Rip, "I have not slept here all night." He recalled the strange man with the keg of liquor, the ravine, the wild retreat among the rocks, the wobegone party at ninepins, the flagon. "Oh, that wicked flagon!" thought Rip. "What excuse shall I make to Dame Van Winkle?"

He looked around for his gun, but in place of the clean, well-oiled fowling-piece, he found an old firelock gun lying by him, the barrel incrusted with rust, the lock falling off, and the stock worm-eaten. They had dosed him with liquor, then, and stolen his gun. Wolf had disappeared, and did not return when called and whistled for.

He decided to look up the scene of the last night's gambol and try to recover his gun. As he rose to walk, he was stiff in the joints.

"Mountain beds don't agree with me," said Rip, "and if this frolic lays me up with rheumatism, I shall have a blessed time with Dame Van Winkle!"

He found the gully, but a mountain stream now foamed through it. When he had scrambled to the point where the ravine had opened to the amphitheater, there was no trace of any opening. He felt famished, and he grieved to give up his dog and his gun. But he could not starve up there! So he shook his head and turned his steps homeward, full of trouble.

When he approached the village, he met several persons, but none whom he knew, which caused him great wonder. They dressed also in a fashion unusual to his eyes, and stared at him, invariably stroking their chins as they did so. Rip involuntarily made the same gesture himself at last, when, to his astonishment, he found his beard had grown a foot long!

He had now entered the village. It was larger and more populous, but much altered. Rows of new dwellings, but none of the old haunts so familiar to him! Strange names—strange faces—everything was strange. He began to wonder whether he and the world around him were not bewitched. Surely this was his native village, which he had left the day before. There stood the Kaatskill Mountains, there ran the silver Hudson, every hill and dale as it had always been. "That flagon last night has addled my poor head sadly!" he thought.

When, with difficulty, he found his old house, it was in decay — roof fallen in, windows shattered, door off the hinges. He entered—it was empty, forlorn, abandoned. He hurried forth, and ran to the village inn. That, too, was gone. A large wooden building stood in its place, with "The Union Hotel, by Jonathan Doolittle," painted over the door. Instead of the great tree, there was a tall, naked pole, with something like a red nightcap on it, and a flag fluttering from it, a singular assemblage of stars and stripes. There was the old sign, but strangely metamorphosed. The red coat of King George was now buff and blue; the hand held a sword instead of a scepter; the head wore a cocked hat; and underneath appeared, in large characters, the legend: *General Washington.*

But none of his old associates was there. Instead of any familiar acquaintance, there was a lean, bilious fellow haranguing in a Babylonish jargon to the bewildered Rip about rights of citizens—election—members of Congress—Bunker Hill—heroes of 'Seventy-six, and the like.

Rip excited much attention. Somebody asked him whether he was Federal or Democrat. A fussy man in a three-cornered hat planted himself in front of him and demanded austerely: "What brings you to an election with a gun on your shoulder and a mob at your heels? Do you mean to incite a riot?"

"Alas, gentlemen!" said Rip, somewhat dismayed, "I am a poor, quiet man, a native of the place, and a loyal subject of the King, God bless him!"

A general shout broke from the crowd: "A Tory! A spy! A refugee! Hustle him!" The important man quieted them, and asked Rip who were some of his friends. Rip inquired for Nicholas Vedder.

"Why, he's dead and gone these eighteen years!" piped an old man.

"Where's Brom Dutcher?"

"Oh, he joined the army in the beginning of the war. Some say he was killed at the storming of Stony Point; others, that he was drowned in the squall at the foot of Anthony's Nose. He never came back."

"Where's Van Bummel?"

"He went to the war, too, but was a militia general, and now he's in Congress."

Rip's heart sank at such changes, such lapses of time, and things which he could not understand: War — Congress — Stony Point! He had not courage to ask for more friends, but cried out in despair:

"Does nobody here know Rip Van Winkle?"

"Oh, Rip Van Winkle!" exclaimed two or three. "To be sure. That's Rip Van Winkle yonder, leaning against that tree."

Rip looked, and beheld an exact counterpart of himself as he went up the mountain, apparently as lazy and certainly as ragged. This confounded the poor fellow entirely. The man in the cocked hat demanded who he was, and his name.

"God knows!" he said, at his wits' end. "I'm not myself—I'm somebody else—that's me yonder—no, somebody else in my shoes. I was myself last night, but I fell asleep on the mountain, and they've changed my gun, and everything's changed, and I'm changed, and I can't tell what's my name or who I am!"

The bystanders began to tap their brows, wink, and nod to one another.

A fresh, comely young woman, with a chubby child, pressed forward to see the gray-bearded man.

"Hush, Rip," she said to the baby; "the old man won't hurt you, you little fool!"

The name, the woman's air and her voice, awakened recollection in Rip's mind.

"What is your name, my good woman?" he asked.

"Judith Gardenier."

"And your father's name?"

"Ah, poor man! His name was Rip Van Winkle. It's twenty years since he went away from home with his dog, and never has been heard of since. His dog came home without him. But whether he shot himself, or was carried away by the Indians, nobody can tell. I was only a little girl then."

Rip had but one more question to ask; but he put it with a faltering voice: "Where's your mother?"

She had died only a short time before. She broke a blood-vessel in a fit of passion over a New England pedler. There was a drop of comfort in this intelligence! The honest man could contain himself no longer, and he caught his daughter and her child in his arms.

"I am your father!" he cried. "Young Rip Van Winkle once, old Rip Van Winkle now! Does nobody know poor Rip Van Winkle?"

An old woman, tottering forward, put her hand to her brow, and peered into his face. "Sure enough, it's Rip Van Winkle. It is himself! Welcome home again, old neighbor! Why, where have you been these twenty long years?"

Rip's story was soon told. The twenty years had been to him as one night. This tale was received with much incredulity. The man with the cocked hat screwed down the corner of his mouth, and shook his head and many others followed suit. The oldest inhabitant of the village, Peter Vanderdonk, descendant of the historian of that name, was called in. He recollected Rip at once, and said something that corroborated his story: that Henry Hudson, the discoverer of the river, was said to keep a vigil every twenty years and to revisit the shores of the Kaatskill with the crew of the *Half Moon*. Vanderdonk's father had once seen the weird crew playing ninepins in the hollow of the mountains.

Rip's daughter took him home with her to live. Her husband was one of the urchins that used to clamber on his back. Rip took up his old walks and habits, with some of his old cronies who were still in the neighborhood. He frequented the bench in front of the inn, and told his story to every arrival that wished to hear it. He could go in and out with no dread of Dame Van Winkle's tyranny.

Some think Rip went out of his head, and that his story was what survived of his flightiness. The old Dutch inhabitants, however, almost universally gave it full credit. Even to this day, they never hear a thunder-storm of a summer afternoon in the Kaatskill that they do not say, "Hendrick Hudson and his crew are at their game of ninepins"; and it is the common wish of all henpecked husbands in the neighborhood, when life hangs heavy on their hands, that they might have a quieting draught out of Rip Van Winkle's flagon.

THE LEGEND OF SLEEPY HOLLOW (1819)

In a preface to *Rip Van Winkle,* Irving said he had found the source and material of his sketches of early Colonial events among the papers of one Diedrich Knickerbocker, an old gentleman of New York, who was a sedulous investigator into the history and manners of the Dutch settlers in the Province, and who published a history of the Dutch governors. Irving sought to give still more reality to this fictitious person by decrying the literary quality of the good Dutchman, while admitting his "scrupulous accuracy" and "unquestionable authority"; and avowed that "his memory is dear among those whose good opinion is well worth having." Certain biscuit-makers of the period established a claim to immortality for Diedrich by imprinting his likeness on their New Year's cakes.

IN the bosom of one of those spacious coves with which the Tappan Zee indents the eastern shore of the Hudson lies a rural port generally and properly known as Tarry Town, a name bestowed upon it by the good housewives of the adjacent country because their husbands were prone to linger about the village. There is a little valley, a lap of land among the high hills, which is one of the quietest places in the whole world. A small brook glides through it, with just murmur enough to lull to repose, and the whistle of a quail or the tapping of a woodpecker is the only sound to break its uniform tranquillity.

If ever I should wish for a retreat whither I might steal from the world and dream quietly away the remnant of a troubled life, I know of none more promising than this little valley, which has long been known as Sleepy Hollow. The place has a witching power that causes one to walk in a continued reverie, subject to visions. The neighborhood abounds with local tales, haunted spots, and twilight superstitions.

The dominant spirit haunting this enchanted region is a headless apparition on horseback. Some said it was the ghost of a Hessian trooper whose head had been carried away by a cannon-ball in some battle of the Revolution. This horseman's haunts are not confined to the valley, but extend to adjacent roads. Certain local histories allege that the trooper's body was buried in the churchyard not far away, and that his ghost rides forth to the battle-field in quest of his head. The rush with which he hurries along the Hollow is due to his wish to get back to the churchyard before daybreak. He is known as "The Headless Horseman of Sleepy Hollow."

In this by-place of nature, in a remote period of American history, to wit, thirty years ago, abode a worthy wight named Ichabod Crane, who "tarried," as he expressed it, in Sleepy Hollow, to instruct the children of the vicinity. He was born in Connecticut, a state that sends forth yearly legions of frontier woodmen and country schoolmasters. The cognomen of Ichabod was not inapplicable to his person. He was tall, lank, with narrow shoulders, long arms and legs, hands that dangled out of his sleeves, feet like shovels, and a loosely hung frame. His head was small, flat at the top, with huge ears, large green, glassy eyes, and a long snipe nose, so that it looked like a weather-cock perched on his slender neck. To see him striding along a hilltop on a windy day, his clothes bagging and fluttering about him, one might have thought him some scarecrow eloped from a cornfield.

His schoolhouse was a low building of one large room, constructed of logs, the windows partly glazed, partly patched with leaves of copy-books. It was ingeniously fastened in vacant hours by a withe twisted in the handle of the door, and stakes set against the window-shutters; so that, though a thief might get in with perfect ease, he would find some embarrassment in getting out—an idea possibly borrowed by the architect, Yost Van Houten, from an eelpot. The schoolhouse stood in a lonely but pleasant spot, with a brook running close by, and a formidable birch-tree growing near at hand. The murmur of the pupils conning over their lessons could be heard in a drowsy summer day, interrupted at times by the master's menace or command, or the appalling sound of the birch that urged the loiterer along the flowery path of knowledge. The golden maxim, "Spare the rod and spoil the child," was borne in mind. Ichabod Crane's pupils certainly were not spoiled. A double portion fell to the little, tough, wrong-headed, broad-skirted

Dutch urchins, who grew sullen and dogged beneath the chastisement so well meant.

The revenue from the school was small, and but for the custom in those parts of lodging and boarding the pedagogue by the parents of his pupils, Ichabod would not have earned his daily bread; for he was a huge feeder. To lighten the burden of his benefactors, he would help them by sundry small services. He also instructed the young folks in psalmody. Thus, by hook and by crook, he got on tolerably enough.

As the schoolmaster is of some importance in the female circle of a rural neighborhood, Ichabod was happy in the smiles of the country damsels, quite surpassing the bashful country bumpkins by his superior elegance and address.

He was an odd mixture of small shrewdness and simple credulity. He would con old Cotton Mather's *History of New England Witchcraft* after school was over, until dusk; and then, as he firmly believed it all, he was fluttered by countless fears on his walk home. It was a fearful pleasure for him to listen to the old Dutch wives telling of ghosts and haunted fields, and especially the galloping Hessian of the Hollow, as the headless horseman was called. The daylight routed these evils, however, and Ichabod would have passed a pleasant life had not his path been crossed by a being that causes more perplexity to mortal man than ghosts, goblins, or the whole race of witches put together—a woman.

One of his musical pupils was Katrina Van Tassel, the only child of a substantial Dutch farmer. She was a blooming lass of eighteen, plump as a peach, and was famed not only as a beauty, but also for her vast expectations from old Baltus Van Tassel. No wonder this tempting morsel found favor in Ichabod's eyes, especially as his mouth watered at the sumptuous winter fare beneath the high-ridged but lowly sloping roof of the Van Tassel farmhouse. He could picture every roasting pig running about with a pudding in its belly and an apple in its mouth; the pigeons put to bed in a pie and snugly tucked in under a coverlid of crust; the daintily trussed-up turkey, a gizzard under its wing, and peradventure a necklace of savory sausages!

Is it any wonder that Ichabod's only study was to gain the affections of the peerless Katrina? But there were more difficulties than beset a knight-errant of yore; for she was a country coquette, full of caprices, and beset by a host of rustic suitors, who kept an angry eye upon one another. The most formidable of them was Brom Van Brunt, a burly, roystering blade, the hero of the country round for feats of strength and hardihood. He was broad-shouldered and double-jointed, with short, curly black hair and a bluff, not unpleasant countenance. He was a Tartar for skill in horsemanship, and with three or four boon companions would startle old dames from sleep, as they clattered by at night, with whoop and halloo, like Don Cossacks. This rantipole hero had singled out the buxom Katrina as the object of his uncouth gallantries, and his advances were signals for rival candidates to withdraw.

Such was the formidable rival with whom Ichabod Crane had to contend. A stouter or wiser man than he would have retired; but he had pliability and perseverance. To take the field openly against his rival would have been madness. So he made his advances in a quiet, gently insinuating manner. Ichabod's obstinately pacific system in his wooing of Katrina, while extremely provoking to "Brom Bones," as Abraham Van Brunt was called, left the latter no appeal to open warfare, but reduced him to boorish practical jokes on the Dominie, and to ridiculing him to Katrina. Matters went on in this way for some time without any material effect on the relative attitudes of the swains.

One fine autumn day Ichabod received an invitation to a quilting-frolic that evening at Mynheer Van Tassel's. He spent an extra half-hour in brushing and furbishing up his best suit of rusty black, and borrowed a farmer's steed to give him more the air of a true cavalier. His courser was a broken-down plow-horse, which nevertheless had a lurking devil of viciousness in him. Ichabod rode with short stirrups, which brought his knees up to the pommel of the saddle; his sharp elbows stuck out like grasshoppers', and the motion of his arms was not unlike the flapping of a pair of wings, while his coat-skirts fluttered out almost to the horse's tail.

When he arrived at Herr Van Tassel's, he found assembled the pride and flower of the adjacent country. Old farmers, in homespun coats and breeches; their brisk, withered little dames in crimped caps, long-waisted gowns, and homespun petticoats; while the buxom lasses were almost as antiquated as their mothers, and the young swains wore short-skirted coats with rows of stupendous brass buttons, and their hair queued. Brom Bones, the hero of the scene, had come on his mettlesome steed, Daredevil.

Ichabod Crane did ample justice to the lavish banquet of the Dutch country tea-table with its heaped-up platters of various and indescribable cakes; the doughty doughnut, the tender olykock, and the crisp and crumbling cruller; sweet cakes and short cakes; ginger cakes and honey cakes; apple pies, pumpkin pies; sliced ham and smoked beef; delectable dishes of preserved plums, and peaches, and pears, and quinces; broiled shad and roasted chicken; bowls of milk and cream, all mingled higgledy-piggledy, about as I have enumerated them, with the motherly teapot sending up its clouds of vapor from the midst. Ichabod's spirits rose with eating as some men's rise with drink. One day he might be lord of this unimaginable luxury and splendor.

He prided himself on his dancing, as well as on his vocal powers. Not a limb, not a fiber about him was idle. To have seen him clattering round the room to the squeak of the old gray-headed negro's fiddle, you would have thought it was St. Vitus himself. The lady of his heart was his partner, smiling graciously to his amorous oglings, while Brom Bones in a corner brooded with love and jealousy.

After the dance, Ichabod was attracted to the eager folks, drawling out long stories about the war. The neighborhood abounded in chronicle and great men. It was also rich in legendary treasures in the way of ghosts and apparitions. In most of our villages there is no encouragement for ghosts, for they hardly have time to finish their first nap, and to turn in their graves, before their surviving friends have traveled away from the neighborhood, and when they turn out at night to walk their rounds, they have no acquaintance left to call upon. This is, perhaps, the reason that we so seldom hear of ghosts except in our long-established Dutch communities.

Many of the tales turned on the specter of Sleepy Hollow, the headless horseman. The sequestered church, near a dell through which a wild brook rushed headlong, was the place where he was most frequently met. Once he had encountered old Browner, a heretical disbeliever in ghosts; had made him get up behind him, and when they reached the bridge, he turned into a skeleton, threw old Browner into the brook, and sprang over the tree-tops with a clap of thunder. These tales, told in a drowsy undertone in the glimmering light, sank deep into the mind of Ichabod.

When the guests departed, Ichabod lingered behind for a word with the heiress. What passed in that interview I will not pretend to say, for in fact I do not know. Ichabod sallied forth quite soon, with a desolate, chap-fallen air. Was Katrina's encouragement of the poor pedagogue all a mere sham to secure her conquest of his rival? O these women! these women! Suffice it to say that Ichabod stole forth with the air of one who has been sacking a hen-roost, rather than a fair lady's heart. Heavy-hearted, he set out on his midnight ride homeward along the sides of the lofty hills that rise above Tarry Town. Far below, the Tappan Zee spread its dusky waste of waters. In the dead hush of midnight he could hear the bark of a watch-dog across the Hudson, and again, the crowing of some awakened cock. He never had felt so lonely and dismal. The night grew darker, the stars sank deeper in the sky, and driving clouds obscured them. He was approaching the scene of many of the ghost stories. A gnarled, fantastic tulip-tree, near which Major André was captured, towered like a giant above everything about.

As Ichabod approached it he began to whistle. He thought he heard another whistle, but it was only the wind sharply driven through the dry branches. He saw something white hanging on the tree, and he stopped whistling. But it was where lightning had struck the tree and bared the white wood. Suddenly he heard a groan, his teeth chattered and his knees smote against the sides of the saddle; but it was only the rubbing of two boughs.

Ahead of him, a brook ran across the road, and a narrow bridge of logs crossed it. The thick oaks and wild grapevines threw a cavernous gloom over the place. It was the identical spot where André had been captured. This has ever since been considered a haunted stream, and fearful are the feelings of the schoolboy that has to cross it after dark.

Ichabod's heart began to thump. He gave his horse a half score of kicks in the ribs, but he only ran against a fence at one side. He kicked the horse on the opposite ribs, and then plied it with both whip and heels. Old Gunpowder dashed forward, but halted so abruptly that his rider nearly went over his head. Just at this moment a splashy tramp by the side of the bridge caught Ichabod's sensitive ear. In the dark shadow of the grove, on the margin of the brook, he beheld something huge, misshapen, black, and towering. It stirred not, but seemed gathered up, like some gigantic monster ready to spring upon the traveler.

The hair of the affrighted pedagogue rose upon his head with terror. What was to be done? To turn and fly was now too late; and besides, what chance of escaping ghost or goblin, which could ride upon the wings of the wind? Summoning up a show of courage, he stammered, "Who are you?" but received no reply. He repeated his demand in a more agitated voice. Still no answer. Once more he cudgeled the sides of the inflexible Gunpowder, and, shutting his eyes, broke forth into an involuntary psalm tune. Just then the shadowy object began to move, and, with a scramble and a bound, stood in the middle of the road. The unknown, so far as the dismal darkness permitted it to be conjectured, was a horseman of large dimensions, on a powerful black horse. He made no offer of molestation or sociability, but kept aloof on the side of the road, jogging along on Gunpowder's blind side.

Having no relish for this midnight silent companion, Ichabod spurred his horse, hoping to leave him. The strange rider quickened his pace so as to keep by his side. Ichabod then pulled up, so as to lag behind. His companion did the same. His heart sank; he tried to resume his psalm tune, but his tongue clove to the roof of his mouth, and he could not utter a stave. There was something mysterious and appalling in the dogged silence of this pertinacious companion, but it was soon fearfully accounted for. On mounting a rising ground, which brought the figure of his fellow-traveler against the sky, gigantic in height, and muffled in a cloak, Ichabod was stricken with horror to see that he was headless. But what was more appalling, he observed the head which the horseman should have carried on his shoulders, resting on the pommel of his saddle. His terror rose to desperation, and he rained kicks and blows on Gunpowder, hoping to give his companion the slip by a quick flight, but the specter started on the full jump with him. Away they dashed, through thick and thin, stones flying and sparks flashing at every bound. Ichabod's flimsy garments fluttered in the air as he stretched his long, lank body away over his horse's head, in the eagerness of his flight.

They had now reached the road that turns off to Sleepy Hollow, but Gunpowder, who seemed possessed of a demon, instead of taking it, plunged downhill to the left. This road leads through a sandy hollow, shaded by trees, for about a quarter of a mile, when it crosses the bridge famous in goblin story, and beyond stands the whitewashed church. Just as he got half way through the hollow, Ichabod felt his saddle-girths give way, and he escaped slipping off when his saddle fell to the ground only by clasping old Gunpowder round the neck. He heard his borrowed saddle crunch under the steed of his pursuer, and he had much ado to keep from following it himself, for he was an unskilled rider. He slipped on this side, then on that, and sometimes jolted on the high ridge of his horse's backbone with a violence that he feared would verily cleave him asunder.

An opening in the trees cheered him with the hope that the church bridge was at hand, and Ichabod remembered that in some of the legends the ghostly specter had disappeared at that spot. "If I can but reach that," he thought, "I am saved." He heard the black steed panting and blowing behind him; but a fierce kick in the ribs sent Gunpowder convulsively upon the bridge, and in a moment he had gained the opposite side. Ichabod cast a look back to see whether the pursuing goblin should vanish, according to rule, in a flash of fire and brimstone. Just then he saw the goblin rising in his stirrups, and in the very act of hurling his head at him. Ichabod tried to dodge the horrible missile—but too late. It encountered his cranium with a tremendous crash, and he tumbled headlong into the dust, while Gunpowder, the black steed, and the goblin rider passed by like a whirlwind.

The next morning the old horse was found without his saddle, and with the bridle under his feet, soberly munching the grass at his master's gate. As Ichabod did not appear throughout the morning, they looked for him. They found at the bridge heavy tracks of horses, and beyond it, on the bank of the brook where the water ran deep and black, was discovered the hat of the unfortunate Ichabod, and close beside it a shattered pumpkin.

The brook was searched, but the schoolmaster's body was not discovered. He had received his quarter's allowance but a day or two before, and must have had it with him when he disappeared. It grew to be a conviction with the village gossips that the Headless Horseman had carried Ichabod away.

An old farmer, who visited New York several years after this, brought back word that Ichabod Crane was still alive; that he had left the neighborhood partly through fear of the goblin and Hans Van Ripper, and partly through mortification at his dismissal by the heiress; that he had gone to a distant part of the country, turned politician, electioneered, and finally had been made a justice of the Ton Pound Court. Brom Bones, who after his rival's disappearance, led the blooming Katrina to the altar, looked very knowing when the story of Ichabod was told, and always burst into a hearty laugh at mention of the pumpkin.

The old country wives, however, maintain to this day that Ichabod was spirited away by supernatural means, and the old bridge is more than ever an object of superstitious awe. The schoolhouse fell into decay, and was said to be haunted by the ghost of the unfortunate pedagogue; and the plowboy, loitering homeward on a still summer evening, has often fancied his voice at a distance, chanting a melancholy psalm tune among the tranquil solitudes of Sleepy Hollow.

WILLIAM WYMARK JACOBS

(England, 1863)

AT SUNWICH PORT (1902)

This author, who in his broad way is perhaps the funniest writer of English of his generation, at the beginning peddled his manuscripts here and there without avail. None of his stories had been printed, and the English editorial mind did not think their humor would appeal to the English people. At last he sent one of his stories to a brother humorist who was also an editor, Jerome Klapka Jerome. The recognition of their uncommon merit and dry humor was instantaneous; Jerome wrote to Jacobs for more of the same kind, and he received more in abundance. *At Sunwich Port* is Mr. Jacobs's first novel.

CAPTAIN NUGENT, of the quaint little seaport town of Sunwich, was in anything but a pleasant mood. He and his steward, Sam Wilks, were on their return from the inquiry into the collision of his ship *Conqueror* with the German bark *Hans Muller*. The result of the finding was that his certificate had been suspended for six months, while his first officer had been commended. To make it worse, it was probable that this same first officer, Mr. Hardy, would receive command of the ship, and that Captain Nugent would be in the bosom of his family for a longer period than they would have chosen had the choice been left to them.

The Captain was not a man of agreeable ways, and his son Jack, aged thirteen, felt that his own conduct would have to be more exemplary than he deemed pleasant, while Miss Nugent, aged nine, although of an independent disposition and not greatly in awe of her gruff father, did not relish the idea of his being six months away from his native element. A sea-captain at home has many opportunities of exercising authority, and Captain Nugent's ways were more dictatorial than fatherly.

One there was who was sincerely sorry for the Captain's

disgrace, his faithful steward, Samson Wilks. Wilks insisted upon resigning his place on the *Conqueror*, and, in spite of the Captain's rebuffs, he made himself handy about the house until the hateful old sea-dog got tired of cursing him and allowed him to act as a sort of man-of-all-work.

It is possible that Jem Hardy, who was about Jack Nugent's age, could have borne his father's elevation and the equally sudden lowering of the pride of Captain Nugent without undue crowing; but it did not please young Kate Nugent to rest tamely, and next day, when she was out with her brother and met Jem, she so skilfully stirred up rancor on the part of both boys that Jack finally decided that he would have to punish Jem. They chose a place alongside the church, removed their coats, rolled up their sleeves, and there—Jem got the better of it. This unexpected outcome of the fight caused Miss Nugent to pitch into Jem herself, and he chased her down the street and was almost on her when he ran into the irascible Captain Nugent.

Feeling that this attack on his daughter by the son of his former mate and present "usurper" was adding insult to injury, the Captain waited on Captain Hardy, preferred charges against Jem, and insisted that Hardy punish his quarrelsome son.

"I sha'n't do it," said Hardy, and intimated that he had something better to do than to interfere in children's quarrels, pointedly saying that *he* hadn't spare time.

Captain Nugent then furiously told him he would take the law into his own hands, and was as furiously answered that if he dared lay a finger on the boy Sunwich folk would have the rare pleasure of seeing two middle-aged ship-masters at fisticuffs, and they parted with mutual expressions of ill-will.

Jem and little Miss Nugent did not become friendly as the weeks went on, mainly because friendliness to her father's "enemy" did not chime in with the high-spirited child's desires. With sincere pleasure she watched the household effects of the Hardys being moved away in a van, Captain Hardy having given up housekeeping and sent his son to live with an aunt.

It was some months before Captain Nugent obtained command of a steamer sailing between London and Chinese ports, and during that time he and his son Jack fostered feelings of mutual dislike and distrust, and at the age of seventeen the boy's schooling was brought to an end by his father and he was placed in a bank, where, however, he failed to give satisfaction. Then his father, having learned that he would not care to go to sea, immediately obtained a berth for him on a bark bound for Melbourne, a place that was distasteful to the boy every waking hour and a good part of the night.

In fact, so displeased was Jack that he deserted the ship at Melbourne, and his further doings remained a sealed book to the Nugent family for years.

About the time that Miss Nugent reached the age of twenty her father retired from the sea, having received a windfall from an almost forgotten uncle. Captain Nugent found not only that his daughter was pretty and spirited, but that she was regarded as attractive by the young men of Sunwich, and he felt that he should have his hands full in keeping her as a prop for his declining years.

Not long after the Captain's retirement from active life—that is, active sea-life—he kept things lively for himself and his family on land—Jem Hardy returned to Sunwich. This news was conveyed to Captain Nugent by his sister, Mrs. Kingdom, but it was not received with any manifestations of approval on the part of the irritable gentleman. Her innocent comment on the young man as having been much improved by his residence in London called forth the command from the dictatorial sea-dog that his name be forgotten from that time forth.

When Jem Hardy returned to Sunwich it was to become the partner in business of Adolphus Swann, the ship-broker. The thing that struck him very early in his new residence in Sunwich was the fact that Kate Nugent was wondrously pretty and attractive.

Swann, his partner, was an elderly man with a jovial disposition, who early divined in which quarter lay the wind, and indulged in much innocent amusement at the expense of the decidedly peppery Jem. But if he got amusement out of the fact of Jem's heart-condition, he was also willing to help him, and with that intent he told him that Kate was very fond of her father's old steward Sam, and went to call on him every Friday. If Jem happened in on Sam, and Kate was there, or came there later, why—

Friday evening consequently found Jem in Wilks's little parlor, talking over "old times" with the astonished old man, who remembered Jem as an enemy rather than as a friend.

Miss Kate came in while the two were talking; but it cannot be said that there was anything in her frigid manner to encourage the young man. She gave him several hints that his room was better than his company; but he, being of a daring disposition, did not leave until he felt like it. Not only that—he made up his mind to call "on Sam" when the mood seized him, and to trust to the law of chances to bring about a meeting between himself and the fascinating Kate.

One day when Captain Nugent was out walking he met a tattered young man who bore a remarkable resemblance to his son Jack, from whom he had heard nothing in years. The Captain was not what is called soft-hearted, and there was no thought of stopping at the butcher's to order veal when he realized that the prodigal had returned. In fact, his reception of Jack was such as to make that young man feel that fatherly affection was a rare attribute. Jack was philosophical enough to realize that repining would not help him, and he went on his way jauntily, not knowing that his father watched him until he was out of sight.

"Well, he didn't whine," said the Captain. "He's got a bit of pride left."

Driven to make a harbor somewhere, Jack Nugent took lodgings with one Kybird, a dealer in second-hand goods, not overscrupulous as to the previous ownership of the things that fell into his greedy hands. Mr. Kybird had a blowsily pretty daughter, who had been receiving attention from Mr. Teddy Silk, a clerk at Swann and Hardy's.

Jack, having lost his pride, together with his other worldly possessions, was not above "making up" to Amelia, and as he was rather better favored than the somewhat pessimistic Mr. Silk, Miss Kybird smiled on his attentions. In this she was aided and abetted by her parents, who knew that when Jack was twenty-five he would fall heir to a matter of "five 'undred pounds."

Jack made no more attempts to seek for a home in his father's house, but obtained humble work at the harbor. He found that few of his old friends would speak to him, but there was one old enemy who came to him with outstretched hand, Jem Hardy. Whether Jem was moved entirely by generous motives is doubtful. Jack was Kate's brother, and she and Jack had always been friendly. A friend at court is never more desirable than when one is courting.

It is not to be supposed that Mr. Silk would long brook a rival, and so it came about that one evening Amelia was called upon by him to take her choice.

"Me or 'im—which is it to be?"

Put to the test, Miss Amelia was not long in making up her mind, and that night when Jack retired he realized the grim fact that the girl with whom he had been fooling was engaged to him—and she the daughter of a second-hand-clothes man.

"I wonder what the governor'll say?" said he.

What his father said was not polite. Indeed, Captain Nugent was seldom polite. What Jem said to Jack made the latter demand an apology. He purposed to stand by the girl of his "choice," and he soon made Jem understand his attitude.

Jem, who had hoped to bring about a reconciliation between Jack and his family, with a view to bettering his own affair, was not pleased at the engagement, and in an interview with Jack made bold to tell him why. Jack was astonished to hear that his sister Kate, who had always been so "nasty" to Jem, had now inspired him with the tender passion, and, not without malicious pleasure, he told him that Kate was off to London for a three-months' visit next day. However, he told him he'd do what he could for him.

Time failed to soften Captain Nugent's ideas respecting Jack's engagement, and he forbade all reference to the ne'er-do-weel.

One by one, various schemes for preventing his son's projected alliance were dismissed as impracticable, but after several days he hit on a plan that appealed strongly to his tastes. This was, to have Jack "crimped" and placed upon a vessel going to some distant port.

The plan was soon unfolded to Sam, and the old man balked at it. If it had been anyone but Jack, he would not have minded, but he and Jack had always been good friends.

But Captain Nugent was accustomed to obedience, and it was not long before Wilks agreed to secure the services of Nathan Smith, keeper of a sailors' lodging-house, who was a most unscrupulous man. The Captain was to meet his son at Wilks's, ostensibly with a view to becoming reconciled. Drinks would follow, Jack would be "knocked out" and conveyed aboard the *Seabird*, and when he woke up next morning he would find himself a "stowaway" and well out to sea. Smith was to receive five pounds for the successful issue of the plot, and Wilks was to keep his mouth everlastingly shut.

"My son will be one of the first to thank you for getting him out of such a mess as a marriage with that Kybird girl."

The scheme was put into operation that night. After Wilks had seen his master's son drink the drugged ale, he left the house and took his way to a tavern, his feelings not being altogether pleasant.

Upon his return to his house at eleven he was met by Smith, who told him it was "all over." "He went off like a lamb." He also told him that the Captain had taken a little more than was good for him and was sleeping upstairs in Wilks's bed. He warned him not to go near him, as he might be ugly in liquor, and so Wilks made his bed on the floor that night.

At about half-past seven in the morning there was a loud crash upstairs, and Wilks knew that the Captain was awake. A moment later a heavy pair of feet stumbled down the stairs, and the man who had honored the humble Mr. Wilks with his company came into the room.

Wilks was petrified with astonishment and horror when he discovered that it was not the Captain, but Jack himself.

Explanations that did not explain followed, and then came Mrs. Kingdom and Kate, looking for the Captain, who had not returned the night before. Consternation was at its height when Smith appeared with a message from the Captain.

According to Smith, Sam had been instrumental in getting Jack into his house for the purpose of being crimped, but after a drink or two the Captain's heart had softened and he had decided not to send his son away, much as he desired to break up the match between him and "Mr. Kybird's gal," but instead Jack had been put to bed upstairs, being a little the worse for liquor, and the Captain had gone away on a little visit to London.

There was one person who did not think the Captain had gone to London—Mr. Swann. It occurred to that astute man that possibly Nathan Smith, who was known to be a great friend of the Kybirds, might know where the Captain was.

So he paid Smith a visit, and a judicious reference to the police made that gentleman admit that, out of friendship to the Kybirds, he had substituted the Captain for Jack when both were sufficiently fuddled by the drugged ale, and at the present moment the Captain was playing the amusing part of stowaway on his old ship the *Conqueror*, now commanded by Captain Hardy.

When Nugent came to himself on board his old vessel he at first refused to believe the testimony of his wits, but on making his way from cabin to deck he found that he was indeed putting to sea under the command of Captain Hardy. It was a trying situation for a man of the Captain's pride and pugnacity, but to Captain Hardy the situation was mainly ludicrous. Captain Nugent was not forced to work, but he was sent to the forecastle for allowing his temper to get the better of him.

When Jem Hardy heard of the whereabouts of the Captain he went to tell Kate the news, exulting that he should be the bearer of glad tidings, for Miss Nugent believed that her father had come to some harm.

To a man with initiative ways of contriving, interviews with the woman he loves are not slow to suggest themselves, and Jem took advantage of Captain Nugent's enforced sea-voyage to call several times on Kate, who gradually found her attitude toward him changing. That she cared for him she would not have admitted to her innermost self, but she derived some amusement from their verbal encounters.

When the steamship reached Port Elizabeth "stowaway" Nugent left her. Captain Hardy was the first to reach home, and the story he told of Captain Nugent's adventures was a sweet morsel for sailormen and others to roll under their tongues.

A few days later Captain Nugent returned to Sunwich and walked boldly down the main street to his home. It would have been a brave man who had dared ask him how he had enjoyed his little outing. His own family found out that the less said the better for the safety of the roof.

It slipped out by way of Mrs. Kingdom's mouth that Jem Hardy had been at the house during the Captain's absence, and his manner at once became the reverse of phlegmatic.

After the return of the Captain Jem found his house an impregnable fortress. Wilks had offered him his own humble rooms as a rendezvous; but as Miss Nugent merely nodded to Jem when she met him it was not likely that he would need any rendezvous soon.

Jem had enough to keep him busy about this time, for Mr. Swann was taken ill and Jem had to do double work. While the genial Swann was lying in bed he was visited by Nathan Smith, to whom he had rendered a little service, and finding the shady rascal an amusing fellow enough with his breezy accounts of unconventional experiences, he encouraged him to call again.

This he told Jem when the latter came to see him, and the mention of Smith's name suggested to Hardy an audacious idea —an idea that, if successfully carried out, would release Jack from his undesirable engagement, make a friend of Captain Nugent, and perhaps soften the hard heart of Kate.

He outlined his scheme to the genial ship-broker, who smilingly denounced him as a scoundrel for thinking of such a thing, and then readily promised to aid him.

Jem's first move was to seek out Captain Nugent in his garden, where he told the astonished and indignant man that he had a plan that would release his son from his entanglement, and that as a business man he wanted to make something out of it. This served to interest the Captain, who heard him through and finally gave his reluctant consent to Hardy's coming to the house twice a week in "payment" for his services.

Meanwhile Swann appeared to be failing rapidly. It was town talk that he was not long for this world. Gossip was also concerned with the approaching marriage of Jack and Miss Kybird, so Captain Nugent felt that he would better endure the visits of Jem, who might have it in his power to prevent the disgraceful union.

On one occasion Jem managed things so well that he actually

had an interview with Kate in the garden, and, even though there was no chance to say anything of permanent interest, an interview was a precious thing.

From the Nugents he went to have a talk with Wilks, and there it fell out that Mr. Silk was still faithful to Miss Kybird. This, strange to say, was a news item of the greatest interest to Jem. He walked home with a mind more at ease than it had been at any time since his overtures to Mr. Swann. The only scruple that had troubled him had been removed, and in place of it he felt that he was acting the part of the guardian angel of Mr. Edward Silk.

What Jem had been up to will be revealed to the reader when he learns that Mr. Smith went one day from Mr. Swann's bedside to the shop of Mr. Kybird and with little circumlocution told him that he and Dr. Blaikie had that very day witnessed the last will and testament of Mr. Swann, who had left everything—amounting to more than ten thousand pounds—to Mr. Silk.

The upshot of it was that Mr. Smith advised that Amelia marry Silk after all, and at once, before he should hear of his luck, as he might look higher if he knew he was a moneyed man. It probably would be a matter of only a few days when Swann would die, and then—

Kybird gasped at the prospect.

As for Amelia, she didn't know but that she liked Silk best after all—even without the money—and so it was settled, and the delighted Teddy Silk got a special license, and the twain were made one before many hours had passed, although nothing was said to Jack.

It had been Jem's idea that Jack would be summarily dismissed on some pretext by Amelia, that steps would be taken by her family to publish her banns together with those of Mr. Silk, and when nothing of the kind occurred; when Mr. Silk went about his work in his usual quiet and gloomy fashion, and, after a day's leave for the purpose of arranging the affairs of a sick aunt in Camberwell, came back only a little less gloomy than before; when Swann's convalescence was nearly at an end, and a letter addressed to Jem made it plain that he was longing to be up and about once more, the young man felt that his carefully laid plans were doomed to failure. This was doubly unfortunate, because he fancied that Captain Nugent was softening toward him.

Matters were brought to a crisis one evening when Mr. Silk discovered Jack hugging Amelia. Then he announced in proud yet angry tones that she was his wife, and Jack, on whom the news fell like a benison, took his speedy departure, assuring the Kybirds that his heart was broken, and assuring himself that he was the luckiest man alive.

The next day, as Smith and Mr. Kybird were talking it all over, the boarding-house keeper started as if he had seen an apparition. Coming down the street, well rested and completely restored to health, was Mr. Swann, he who had left his fortune to Mr. Silk. He stopped and chatted with Smith, and in the presence of Kybird, whose face was a study, he said:

"By the way, I hope you never spoke of that little matter at my house the other day. One has fancies when one is ill. Of course I burned the document five minutes after you had gone."

That same day Mr. Swann raised Mr. Silk's wages and Jem had an interview with Captain Nugent, and told the whole story of the plot to the unmoved countenance of Kate's father, who, after all was said and done, reminded him that the visits were by agreement to cease when the marriage took place, and bade him good-day.

"One word more," said the Captain in conclusion. "If ever you try to come bothering me with your talk again, I'll forbid you the house."

"Forbid me the house!" repeated the astonished Hardy—then as the Captain's meaning dawned on him he stepped forward impulsively and, seizing his hand, began to stammer out incoherent thanks.

"You'd better clear out before I alter my mind," said Captain Nugent, roughly. "I've had more than enough of you. Try the garden, if you like."

And in the garden he found Kate.

There he told her what he had done, and was roundly scolded for his Machiavellian tricks, and there he said to her that he would do anything to please her.

"Would you promise never to try to see me or speak to me again if I asked you?"

"No," said Hardy, promptly.

And then the tide of battle turned and he carried everything before him. And when Kate went in to supper her father was on one side of her and Jem was on the other.

HELEN HUNT JACKSON

(United States, 1831–1885)

RAMONA (1884)

Much of Mrs. Jackson's literary work was devoted to pleading in one form or another for better treatment of the North American Indians. She wrote out of personal knowledge of their habits, characters, and sorrows, for she lived long in the Southwest and studied her subjects at first hand. *Ramona* was announced at the time of its publication simply as "a story"; and it does not read like a novel with a purpose, but the purpose was undoubtedly in the author's mind when the tale was conceived, and it shows itself clearly to the reader without detracting in the least from its purely romantic interest. The scene is in southern California, and the time an indefinitely fixed period covering a few years subsequent to the war with Mexico in the early 'fifties.

FELIPE MORENO was nominally the head of the vast estate that bore his name, but after his father's death the real ruling power was the Señora, his mother. She made her will known in such a subtle way that Felipe did not realize it; but it was true, nevertheless, that down to the smallest detail the property was managed according to her ideas. Time had been, before the hated Americans conquered the country, when she could ride with her husband from their ranch-house forty miles to the coast and never once set foot on land that was not their own. Since the war a considerable portion of this land had been claimed and taken by Americans; but what was left was still a vast tract whereon cattle and sheep grazed by thousands, requiring the attention of Mexican employees numbered by the score, and on special occasions scores of Indians also. Yet the Señora felt herself poor, and bitter was the pride with which she resisted all tendencies to the introduction of new, that is American, ways. To her last day she was sternly loyal to three things: Mexico, the Church, and her conception of family dignity.

Aside from the servants and Felipe, there was one other in the household, Ramona, a beautiful girl of nineteen years, as devout as the Señora herself, as industrious, and far more lovable. Indeed, Ramona was as warmly loved by all on the estate as the Señora was respected, which is saying the utmost, for nobody dared dream of opposing the known will of Felipe's mother. Ramona's place in the household was that of an equal, so far as appearances went, but to the Señora there was a difference that the girl herself had come to perceive vaguely in late years. She was not of the Moreno blood, was not even indirectly related to the family.

A Scottish sea-captain had paid such eager court to a sister of Señora Moreno that she consented to marry him. His name was Phail. He returned from his first voyage after the betrothal with a box full of valuable gems as a present for his bride, and found that in his absence she had married one Señor Ortegna. Phail plunged headlong into dissipation, abandoned seafaring, and at last consorted with Indians. One day, years after the jilting, he suddenly appeared before the childless and sorrowful Señora Ortegna with a girl baby in his arms. He told his former sweetheart that the child was his and the mother an Indian woman, and he begged the Señora to take the little one and bring her up as her own. She consented, and Phail then gave her the box of jewels, the only items of his once large fortune that he had not squandered. A year later he died. The girl's mother never was seen or heard of.

Señora Ortegna called the child Ramona, and cared for her tenderly four or five years. Then, seeing her own end near, she summoned her sister, Señora Moreno, and confided the child to her. She accepted the trust as one of sacred obligation, and executed its provisions literally, but she could not comprehend that it was any part of her duty to love the girl. Ramona therefore grew up with all the advantages that wealth on a ranch could provide, but without so much as a semblance of a mother's love. She knew there was a mystery about her life, but the Señora never permitted her to learn that she had Indian blood.

Felipe, who was a few years older, had always been her playmate, and when they matured he came to know that he loved her deeply; but he had sufficient wisdom to perceive that Ramona looked him in the eyes in a way that no maiden could who loved him other than as a brother. He took this much to heart, but admitted the fact manfully, and when the time came that put his latent renunciation to active test, he was not found wanting. That time was the occasion of the summer sheep-shearing, when a band of Temecula Indians came to the ranch, as they always did, to do the work. Their captain was Alessandro Assis, son of their chief, both men of education so far as the Franciscan missionaries could educate them, both with the interests of their people deeply at heart. Alessandro saw Ramona for the first time since she had grown to womanhood, and one glance was enough to set his heart on fire. He loved, but without so much as a dream of hope, for he supposed her purely Mexican, and he knew well how impassable was the gulf between the races.

The shearing was unlucky for the Señora, but fortunate for the development of love between Alessandro and Ramona. The work was hardly begun when Felipe met with a serious accident, which confined him to his bed for many weeks. He was delirious at first, and kept calling for Alessandro. Somebody was sensible enough to guess that the sick man wanted to hear the Indian sing, or play the violin, for Alessandro was famous thereabout as a musician. Alessandro was summoned, and under the spell of his music Felipe sank to his first refreshing sleep. After that nothing would do but Alessandro must remain, after the other Indians departed, to minister to the invalid. He was glad to stay, for his duty brought him into daily, ay, hourly contact with Ramona; and he had not been long about the place when an aged servant in his gossiping let out the fact that Ramona had Indian blood, the servant immediately falling into great fright at his indiscretion and adjuring Alessandro not to mention it, much less let the Señora know that the secret had been betrayed.

Alessandro kept the secret willingly, for then he hoped. Felipe, watching from his sick bed, could not fail to perceive the Indian's passion for his sister—for so he always regarded Ramona—and he saw, too, plentiful evidence that she was attracted by Alessandro as she never had been by any other man. Revolving these things, and dwelling on their significance, the sick man said to himself, "Why not?" and then shuddered as he thought of his mother. Ramona was by adoption first an Ortegna, and second, a Moreno. Her physical inheritance had been of the white father, for her eyes were blue, and she looked no more an Indian than did Felipe himself. What other inheritance there might be was a matter to which Señora Moreno never dreamed of paying attention, though she was destined to find it out in full measure; the one point with her was, that the girl was of the family, and marriage with an Indian was unthinkable. Such Felipe knew would be her attitude, and therefore he shuddered and tried to bring himself to the task of speaking to his mother and forewarning her of the situation, hoping thus to forestall her opposition and reason her into acquiescence with a union that seemed to the son natural and desirable; for he liked Alessandro, and respected both his character and his ability.

Often Felipe said, "To-morrow I will speak to her, for then I shall feel stronger"; but each to-morrow ended as did yesterday, save that he grew stronger steadily. Señora Moreno came upon Ramona and Alessandro in the willows at the foot of the garden just after he had declared his love, and Ramona had confessed her own. The Señora was shocked and furious. Even then she did not comprehend the true situation. She believed that here was an intrigue which she would not have tolerated in the meanest of her servants. Ramona essayed to speak, but the Señora would not listen.

"Go to your room, shameful creature," she said. "As for you," to Alessandro, "you will be answerable to your master."

Alessandro looked to Ramona for orders, and she bade him go. For herself, she went calmly with the Señora, who caught her by the arm with a grasp that hurt and fairly dragged her up the garden path. Felipe saw them, and understood. He took pains secretly to see Alessandro and advise him to absent himself for as long as it would take him to go to Temecula and return, four days. Meantime Felipe thought the storm might blow over. The Señora locked Ramona in her room that night, and on the day following led the girl to her own room. There she began to upbraid her, but Ramona answered with amazing simplicity that she intended to marry the Indian. The Señora was aghast

"Are you mad?" she cried; "I will never permit it."

"I never have disobeyed you," said Ramona, anxiously but quietly, "but this is different from all other things; you are not my mother. I have promised to marry Alessandro."

"You cannot marry without my permission," the Señora retorted icily. "I forbid you ever to speak of it again."

Ramona sprang to her feet, crossed the room with a swiftness that startled the elder woman, and, standing close in front of her, she said:

"You may forbid as much as you please. The whole world cannot keep me from marrying Alessandro. I love him, I have promised, and I shall keep my word."

Here spoke the inheritance of the darker blood, but Señora Moreno knew it not, and if she had she would not have known, or, knowing, would have disregarded its significance. She still sought to deal with the girl as she would deal with a product of pure Spanish civilization. She threatened to shut Ramona in a convent, and the girl, who had been the embodiment of obedience, simply declared that she would run away, that Alessandro would free her. The Señora angrily cried that she would have the servants set the dogs on Alessandro, and Ramona told her she dared not, for Alessandro was Felipe's friend. Bewildered at the unfamiliar sensation of opposition, Señora Moreno at last pulled the statue of a saint from its place against the wall and revealed a secret door, which she unlocked. From the chamber within she dragged the box of jewels and a great number of costly garments.

"These are all yours," she said, "if you marry worthily," and she read Señora Ortegna's letter of instructions as to the care of Ramona. It declared that if the girl married unworthily, the jewels and fabrics were to be given to the Church.

Ramona listened eagerly. "It doesn't say who my mother was," she said.

Señora Moreno was fairly stupefied. She must believe that the gems attracted the girl, and that she was feigning a lack of interest.

"Your mother doesn't matter," she sneered; "she was only an Indian."

Ramona's blood leaped. Then she was of Alessandro's people! She exulted in the thought.

"Who was my father?" she asked, and the Señora, staggered by the evident failure of her devices, answered mechanically: "His name was Phail."

Ramona then took an old handkerchief in which priceless pearls had been wrapped, letting the pearls scatter among the other gems.

"I will keep the handkerchief in memory of my father," she said. "You may give the gems to the Church."

In the simplicity of her soul, Ramona gave to the words "marry unworthily" the same interpretation that Señora Moreno had put on them, namely, marry against the Señora's will.

Then followed a painful scene between Felipe and his mother. He loved her ardently, but he burned with indignation against her cruelty. For once he openly rebelled, and the mother was nearly prostrated at this second and graver defiance of her authority; but with her marvelous subtlety she suggested reason after reason for withholding consent to the marriage, until Felipe was confused. He was conscious that he was somehow not defending his sister as he ought, but he saw not how to give her the complete support he wished. And the upshot was a kind of drawn battle. The Señora took no steps to force Ramona into a convent; she took, instead, the attitude that the matter was out of her hands, although Felipe pointed out that this was in effect forcing Ramona to run away.

Alessandro was gone much longer than the four days, and when he came again it was in secret that he might gratify his eyes with one more look at his beloved. The Americans had taken possession of Temecula, scattered the people, seized or destroyed their property, and killed those who resisted. The chief was dead, and Alessandro, his successor, was a chief without a people, or habitation, or means to support life. He did not mean that Ramona should see him, but she felt his presence and went forth as if drawn by a magnet to find him. He told her the tragic story, his blood rising hot with racial wrath at thought of what he had seen and suffered.

"I am of your people," said Ramona; "you must take me with you wherever you go."

Then Alessandro's love was manifested in all its grandeur. With his sweetheart clinging to him, her breath warm on his face, he resisted her appeal. He argued that the life she must endure with him, a wanderer, would be impossible for one brought up as she had been; that he could not provide her with food, to say nothing of the comforts to which she was accustomed; every argument that wisdom could discover this Indian lover uttered; but the end was victory for Ramona's insistence. She did not argue. She trusted in God that food would be supplied, and she asked whether the wives of the dispossessed Temecula men had deserted their husbands. Of course they had not, and Ramona would not desert him who was her husband in the sacredness of love and plighted word. She bade him wait for her while she returned to the house to get such necessities as they could carry with them on Alessandro's pony, his splendid horse having been taken by the Americans toward paying the costs of the "litigation" by which they had acquired the right to Temecula lands. While she was gone he crept to the corral and whispered "Baba," the name of Ramona's horse. The animal, which knew Alessandro almost as well as he knew his mistress, came joyfully, and, passing the stables, the Indian found and took her saddle. Ramona returned with two nets filled with clothing and food, and they traveled all that night and rested during the day following in a cañon.

Alessandro feared pursuit. Baba was Ramona's property, but the taking of the horse might readily be construed as theft, and the punishment for horse-stealing was death. More than that, distrust of all whites was now the leading motive of Alessandro's life. So they journeyed ever by night, and confused their trail, and took ways known only to Indians. They passed through devastated Temecula, where Alessandro's horse, which had escaped its tether, came to them. After that their journey was rapid, for both horses were of the best. They were married by the priest at the San Diego mission, and pushed on without unnecessary pause to the Indian village of San Pasquale, where Alessandro had a friend.

The San Pasquale people welcomed the newcomers, and the chief told Alessandro of a hundred sheep and a small herd of cattle there that belonged to him. Alessandro's father had sent them up early in the summer, when pasturage at Temecula began to be scant. Thus this little property had escaped the

Americans, and Ramona felt piously and joyfully justified in her trust in God; for here was food, and what the white man would call capital to begin life on.

They lived in San Pasquale for three years. Alessandro built an adobe house, managed his herds skilfully, so that their increase was abundant, and cultivated broad fields of grain. He was prosperous, and Ramona was happy. A daughter was born, whom father and mother loved with all the tenderness of which human nature is capable, whether enfolded in a red skin or a white. Alessandro, too, was as happy as possible, the limitation implied in this phrase being his constant dread of the time when the Americans would lay hold of San Pasquale as they had taken Temecula. He brooded much on this, and when at last they began to appear, he was so disheartened that he almost lost the power of initiative. Why should he not? Of what use was it to till the fields when the conquerors were at hand? But he aroused himself and continued to work, hoping for one more harvest, until he found the white man's stakes driven into his own ground. He tore up and burned the stakes, and when the new "owner" protested, Alessandro offered to sell him his house and the standing wheat. The white man laughed.

"I can take them without paying," he said.

Alessandro calmly denied this.

"Who will prevent me?" asked the American.

"I will," Alessandro replied without heat. "I will burn my house and set fire to the wheat."

The American paid him two hundred dollars in gold. Alessandro packed his household goods on his wagon, Ramona and the baby perched themselves on the load, and they journeyed to the Saboba village at the base of San Jacinto mountain. On the way they were caught in a blinding snowstorm and would have perished but for aid given to them by a white family traveling from Tennessee to the Pacific. Jed Hyers, ignorant and shiftless, his wife, known wherever she went as "Aunt 'Ri," and their grown-up, consumptive son—these were the Samaritans that took the freezing Indians into the shepherd's hut where they themselves had found shelter, and cared for them. They became warm friends. Hyers was fond of hunting, Alessandro knew the country thereabout, and they roamed the mountains together for months. Meantime the Indians lived in a vacant house in the Saboba village, and when at last the Tennesseans went to San Bernardino, Alessandro betook himself again to agriculture. He wished to build himself a better house, but Ramona advised to the contrary. She, too, had begun to feel the uselessness of an Indian's striving to accumulate property.

The burden of the wrongs of his people became heavier and heavier for Alessandro, and some time after the departure of the Hyers family tragedy came to increase the load. The baby wasted slowly away. It seemed she had never fully recovered from the exposure of the snow-storm. Alessandro rode thirty miles to San Bernardino to beg the agency doctor to visit the little one; but the doctor only laughed at his impudence, for Alessandro was not an agency Indian. Alessandro offered to pay gold, and the doctor laughed again. The idea of an Indian beggar having money! He had enough to do where he was, and would not ride sixty miles for anybody. But he gave Alessandro some medicine for the child, which made the baby's condition worse. Well, then, said Alessandro and Ramona, if we must be agency Indians to get help for the little one, so be it; we will take her to San Bernardino. They set forth, and the baby died on the way.

About this time the Americans began to reach out for the lands of the Sabobas. Alessandro would not wait for them. He knew of a little valley high among the mountains, which was all but unapproachable. The secret and difficult way to it was known only to himself. There they could be safe, for there was water the year round, and plenty of arable soil for the needs of one family. It was so inconvenient of approach that the Americans, even if they should find the place, would not care for it. He took Ramona there, but he did not take his splendid horses, for they would not be suited to the roughness of the life there. He let the son of Jed Hyers have the use of the horses, and contented himself with an ordinary pony.

Life was peaceful in the secluded valley, and there another daughter was born; but while both welcomed the child, and both felt safe from the encroaching whites, there was one terrible shadow upon Ramona: Alessandro was gradually losing his mind. The sorrows of his race, the sense of helplessness, had undermined his reason. He had more and more frequent periods of harmless insanity, during which his memory left him. This was known to all the Indians and the white settlers throughout the San Jacinto country, but it did not save Alessandro when, in a fit of madness, he left his pony in a white man's corral and took away one of the settler's horses. He did not come to his senses until he reached his cabin on the plateau, and meantime the settler had pursued him, being close enough behind to find the difficult trail. The settler shouted when he arrived in sight of the cabin. Alessandro went out, saying, "It was a mistake; I will explain," when the settler shot him dead.

When Ramona disappeared from the Moreno ranch she was indeed pursued, but not in hostility. Felipe, against his mother's will, tried to find her and induce her to return. He inferred that she had gone with Alessandro, but he could find no trace of them. White men had not seen or heard of them, and every Indian he met lied to him. Not an Indian in the country could have been persuaded that Felipe did not wish to punish Alessandro for stealing the horse Baba. Felipe inquired at all the missions, hoping to learn of the marriage. At San Diego he saw the marriage register; but Alessandro was a common name, and Ramona had declared herself by the Indian name her husband gave her, and her father's name, which the priest not only spelled "Fayeel," but blotted so that half of it was illegible. Felipe gained no clue there. At length he gave up and returned to the ranch, where matters ran on listlessly until his mother's death. She had put off telling him about the box of gems until, in her last moments, she had strength only to reveal the secret closet.

After her burial Felipe opened the closet, drew forth the box, saw the fortune it contained, and read Señora Ortegna's letter of instructions. With horror he interpreted "marry unworthily" in a fashion contrary to the meaning made by his mother. He felt that her pride in the honor of her family was sadly belied by this deliberate robbery of Ramona; for to Felipe the marriage with Alessandro was eminently worthy. This discovery and the feelings it aroused caused him to resume his search. He traveled wherever there were Indians, finding no trace, for he still was met by deceit; but directed his course to San Jacinto after many weeks, simply because there was an Indian village that he had not visited. His way took him through San Bernardino, where he chanced to see Baba and Alessandro's horse harnessed to a delivery-wagon that young Hyers was driving. This gave him the clue, and he found it on the same day when the Hyers people were made frantic by the news that Alessandro had been murdered.

Aunt 'Ri went with Felipe to the mountain. They found Ramona in delirium, cared for as best they knew by some poor Cahuila Indians whose village lay nearest to the plateau where had been her home. Alessandro's murderer had surrendered, and there had been a form of trial. As no one came forward to testify against him, his story that he had shot in self-defense was accepted, and he was released. Then, fearing the vengeance of Indians, he fled the country.

Ramona was nursed back to life and strength by Aunt 'Ri, and spent her convalescence with the Hyers in San Bernardino. This was a matter of many months, during all of which Felipe remained near her. Her sisterly affection for him was as before. His love steadily grew to be that of a man rather than a brother, but Felipe gave himself no hope, and never offended Ramona with manifestations of any but a brother's affection. This endured for a long time after she returned to the Moreno ranch. She became perfectly well again, and lived down her sorrows in love for her daughter. The time came when Felipe, like the Indians, felt that life was hopeless and intolerable under American law. It was all strange to him, and he could not be secure in his property. Hesitatingly he suggested to Ramona that he would like to sell his estate and spend the rest of his life in Mexico. This was the one thing she desired. The estate found a ready purchaser at a price that assured Felipe independence, and Ramona was provided for by the gems, which, after Felipe's explanations, she felt she had the right to regard as her own. They arranged, therefore, to go to Mexico City.

On the night of embarkation Felipe's love overpowered his reason, and before he could check himself he had made it known. Ramona was not shocked; she told him calmly that one part of her was dead; but, she reasoned, if being his wife would make Felipe happy, it was her duty to consent. They were married after their arrival in Mexico; and sons and daughters came to them; but the most beautiful, and, it was said, the best beloved by both, was the step-daughter of the Señor, Ramona the younger, whose father was Alessandro the Indian.

GEORGE PAYNE RAINSFORD JAMES

(England, 1801–1860)

HENRY MASTERTON (1832)

When Mr. James was young, Washington Irving encouraged him to write a biography of Edward the Black Prince, and four years later Sir Walter Scott had good words for his *Richelieu*. He ventured into the field of historical romance at a favorable moment, both he and Dumas reaping profit from the popularity that Scott had conferred upon that class of literary work. He was prolific in his writings; which in their several kinds amounted to more than seventy.

WAS born at Masterton House, Devonshire. My father, Lord Masterton, held a place of trust in the court of Charles I, and was somewhat akin to that monarch in character. Between Lord Langleigh and him, with naught but honor and unswerving integrity in common, there was a strong friendship. Opposition to some measures of Charles led to the banishment of these two men from favor; and my father retired to his Devonshire place just as my mother died after bringing me into the world. Soon afterward, Lord Langleigh was sentenced to death for treason, and his wife died from the shock. The evening before his execution he entrusted his infant Emily to my father's care, who declared that in due time she should marry his elder son. Lord Langleigh and a young officer escaped from the Tower the night preceding the day set for his execution, and took passage for France in a vessel that was subsequently wrecked and only one person, a fisherman, was known to be rescued.

My earliest remembrance is of my brother Francis, ten years old, I being then five, and little Emily Langleigh, who was three, as residents of my father's Devonshire home. I wept bitterly when Frank told me that Emily was to be his wife, not mine.

Though utterly different in character, my brother and I were thoroughly devoted to each other. He was grave and reserved. Emily was educated in a convent until she was thirteen, when my father brought her home, there to remain until she should be old enough to marry my brother. Unconsciously, there was a rivalry between him and me from the beginning.

Gabriel Jones, my brother's servant, often broke in upon my innocent rambles with Emily. He was a hypocritical villain, wearing a cloak of religious fanaticism. William Fells, my own servant, was honest and by no means a Puritan.

Emily was to marry Frank when she was seventeen, but important events intervened. The contention of Cavaliers and Roundheads fermented about the King. My father had sworn, when dismissed, that he never would lift a hand to assist his ungrateful monarch. One day I met two gentlemen—a General St. Maur, and a thin man in black, Du Tillet—who had an encounter with a quartet of Puritans, among whom was a Walter Dixon.

"Clear the way," said Du Tillet to him. "Thou shalt never see her more."

"Take that!" retorted the man addressed, discharging his pistol.

No harm was done by it, and the other attacked him with his sword and routed him. General St. Maur made very earnest inquiries about my father, and I wondered why.

My brother and I soon took the field with the Cavaliers, each of us commanding a troop of horse, and were to join Lord Goring's force in Kent. On our way we ran across Master Walter Dixon, who promised to help us. After he left us, William Fells told me that Master Gabriel Jones and Dixon had had secret talks frequently, and advised me to watch Jones.

While we were halting at a lovely spot at Pentford-Bourne, a servant came to tell my brother that Lady Eleanor Fleming would fain have Lord Masterton's sons as her guests, and offered her services for the cause, and we accepted her hospitality. Our hostess was the most beautiful woman I had ever seen. She was twenty-eight, tall, exquisitely formed, with enchanting blue eyes, and mobile mouth.

My brother was so smitten by the charms of Lady Eleanor,

who had fallen madly in love with him, that he neglected his obvious duty of hastening forward with his troops to find Lord Goring. As my protests failed to move him to duty, I marched on with my own troops and chanced to lend valuable assistance in an attack from which the King's party was suffering defeat. As a reward, I was promoted to the rank of commander which my brother held, and Lord Goring severely censured his delay.

Even when I returned to Pentford-Bourne, my brother still refused to leave his charmer. Afterward the King's forces were so routed that we were ordered to disband and await other opportunities. Lord Goring gave me a little messenger, John Marston Hall, son of a dead cavalier. They called him "Ball o' Fire," he was so quick and intrepid, and I took him back with me to Lady Eleanor's. To my surprise, the boy not only knew her but had seen her husband, a dark, handsome Sir Andrew Fleming, who had parted from her and crossed the sea. I hoped this would quench Frank's passion and recall him to his betrothed, for it was a surprise to us to learn that Lady Eleanor was married.

I learned that Frank had engaged in a duel with a mysterious man in black, because of which he had to be removed to Masterton House in a litter.

"You will not fail me?" I heard him murmur to Lady Eleanor.

"Never! I swear it by all I hold dear on earth or beyond it," she replied in passionate tones.

The troops were disbanded. When we reached home, Emily Langleigh, lovelier than ever, sought my eyes with hers, while Frank pressed his lips upon the cheek of his affianced. Madness seized me. I rushed to my room and locked myself in, suffering an agony of despair, for I loved her.

A month later Frank stood before the altar in our private chapel, with Emily, pale but resigned, at his side. Her father's cousin, Lady Margaret Langleigh, had been with us for three weeks, and proved a great moral support to the dear girl. Just before the words were spoken that would have made the woman I adored my brother's wife, Ball o' Fire, now my page, ran in to declare that a force of armed men filled the corridors; and as he spoke, a band of twenty musketeers, with General Walter Dixon at their head, rushed in. They arrested my brother as "a malignant, lately in arms." My father resisted, and when called on to surrender he struck the soldier that was advancing to arrest him.

"Fire!" cried Gabriel Jones, and a volley rang through the chapel.

My father staggered, caught at my arm, and without a word fell dead at my feet! There was wild confusion. My brother was a prisoner. I beat my way out, aided by Ball o' Fire, and guiding Emily, who followed silently but swiftly. We escaped through a secret door, though I had to kill the miscreant and traitor, Gabriel Jones, who followed us.

We escaped to a cave on the coast, and Ball o' Fire told me, later, that the invaders had departed, having pillaged Masterton House, and that the Hall was deserted. I returned and placed my poor father's body in the family vault. On the floor of the chapel I discovered a note from Lady Eleanor Fleming to my brother, which showed that the ceremony had been interrupted through her planning, and his safety was provided for.

"Beloved, I am willing to sacrifice all for you," she wrote.

To my amazement, I encountered Lady Margaret Langleigh, who had successfully concealed herself, but on seeing me came forth. I secured all the money I could, and that night, thanks to a sloop which the sage little Ball o' Fire had engaged to remain in the neighborhood, took them all to France. Long before we reached that country I had discovered that my conviction was true: Emily Langleigh had always loved me.

I established them in a convent at Dinan, and determined to return to England to see my brother in London, where they had taken him, and secure Emily's release from him. After leaving them I met a singular Frenchman, Monsieur de Vitray, a gray gentleman of fifty-five, who thought France the apex of perfection.

When my little Ball o' Fire and I returned to England, disguised as traveling agents for French merchants, we soon found Hezekiah Manual, the London representative of the Frenchman for whom we had come, and with him was a man who wished me to carry a letter to France. Someone came at this moment, and we were shut in an adjoining room. Ball o' Fire, with his wonted craftiness, left the door ajar, and thus I heard Walter Dixon claim from Major-General Ireton the estates of Lady Eleanor Fleming. Cromwell's worthy abettor declared to him that they reverted to Sir Andrew Fleming, her husband, who never had drawn his sword against the State.

Ireton recalled us and gave me the letter, to a General St. Maur, admonishing us not to betray his presence in London. I then went to the goldsmith to exchange bills I had carried away from Masterton House, and from him I learned that my brother and Lady Eleanor were in France. I heard of a gentleman having engaged a boat to take him to Calaïs the following morning, and secured a passage with his skipper, only to find myself with Walter Dixon! Finding that I knew so much about him, he confided more to me. Eleanor, daughter of his uncle, Lord Ashkirk, had married Sir Andrew Fleming, a jealous, vindictive man, a Papist. All Dixon wished for was Pentford-Bourne. As I thought, he had arranged the attack on Masterton Hall.

An odd straying from my course toward Paris, after I had landed in France, brought me to the house of M. de Vitray. His guest was a striking Benedictine monk, grave, dark, and fascinating, despite his severe air. That night the monk came to my room and inquired as to my family history. When he asked about my brother's marriage and I told him it had been prevented through Dixon, he burst into an almost insane passion of anger; but he quieted down at last.

"Should you come to Paris and wish to see me, inquire at the Benedictine monastery in Quartier Saint-Jacques, for Dom André," he said, and left me.

When I reached Dinan it was to find the convent in ashes! I learned that no one was lost, and that the secular ladies who had been there were at St. Benedict's convent. And there I learned to my grief that Emily and her cousin had left the convent some time before the fire. Unfortunately, the letter they had left for me was burned. Inquiry drew out the fact that they had departed with a gentleman. They had left in a coach with gray horses, and I, wild with anxiety and fears, followed in pursuit.

[*Note.*—The remainder of this history is compiled by John Woolsanger, A.M., 1675-76.]

Masterton followed traces of his love for some time, until they disappeared. He then hastened to Paris, thinking the Benedictine might aid him. Things were in some confusion there through the struggle between the Fronde and the King's party. Masterton was wounded and was about to be hanged by a crowd of soldiers when he was rescued by M. de Vitray, the kindly Frenchman who thought France the one spot on earth. He had him taken to his residence in Paris, where the Benedictine monk, Dom André, came to console him. The monk told him that his brother was commanding the Marquis de Noirmoutier's cavaliers, and was also taking part in many gay dissipations. This surprised Henry, as it was contrary to his brother's temperament.

Henry recovered under proper care, and one day, when the monk was with him, Dom André said with a sigh:

"At times I feel myself oppressed by a dark cloud, which I hold to be the forerunner of a coming fate. I felt it when you were at my friend's house. I feel it now. I have a conviction that my days are drawing to a close. Death, and something more terrible than death, is at hand. It is in vain to fly from the slow hands of Fate. If not to-day or to-morrow, nor this week, nor the next, still come it will. Well, come when it may, I am prepared for it."

Soon afterward he left. Ball o' Fire, in the mean time, had discovered where Lord Masterton, the brother Henry was seeking, was located. He had seen him riding from the gateway of a house in the Rue des Minimes. He had also seen the Benedictine making inquiries of the concierge at the house. Ball o' Fire had a tantalizing conviction of having seen this monk somewhere, but he could not recall the place or the time. The shrewd little page was convinced that the Benedictine's interest in the case was not disinterested.

Though the next day was raw and cold, Henry Masterton repaired to the house his page had told him of. He found no servant at hand, penetrated to its interior rooms unmolested, and while he stood he thought he heard sounds like moaning.

He entered the room from which they proceeded, and to his horror was met by the maid in tears, while Lady Eleanor Fleming lay doubled up on the floor near a couch, apparently in the agonies of death.

"You come at a terrible moment. I fear she has taken poison. She was left too much alone in her seclusion here, while my Lord was away, and she parted from him not an hour ago, after some reproaches between them."

This idea was correct. Lady Eleanor revived only to declare herself dying, cast off by God and by him for whom she had sacrificed her happiness in this world and in the next. Henry's feeling and consoling words brought her to a more penitent mind, and he hurried out to find a confessor.

Running down the street, he saw a monk and a man with him in fervid talk—Dom André and Walter Dixon. The latter hurried away, exclaiming: "Here is his brother!" Dom André at first declared he was unfit to minister to dying souls.

"My own soul is too black with burning rage over what I have heard but now. But yet," he added, "O God! I will go."

He returned and heard the dying woman's confession, his cowl drawn about his face. He learned that she had accepted the wealthy Sir Andrew Fleming to escape marrying her cousin, Walter Dixon. But while she was still innocent, her husband was madly jealous, and in a fury left her. Then came the young Cavalier, the only one she had ever loved. When she thought of her vindictive husband, "O God! O God! How I did hate him!" she gasped.

"Woman!" groaned Dom André, throwing back his cowl. "O God! O God! How that man did love you!"

She looked upon him in terror. Then, despite her weakness, she rose to her knees, her eyes still upon his face, clasped her hands as in prayer; remained thus a moment, and fell forward as her spirit took its flight.

The monk clasped his forehead with his hands, and stood for a moment, with love, anger, sorrow, and despair mingled in his expression. Then he raised her, composed her dead form upon her couch, closed the eyes that looked imploringly toward him, and printed one long kiss upon the pale lips. Then thrusting his right hand into his breast, he rushed forth groaning: "Now! Now!"

Henry Masterton paced the apartment alone. Why this connection between the Benedictine and Dixon, and his brother? He reflected, however, that the seal of confession, under which Lady Eleanor had so unburdened her innermost soul to Dom André before she passed to her judgment, never had been known to be violated, and that all entrusted to the monk's ear was sure of oblivion.

Suddenly there was a sound of hurrying steps, and Frank Masterton, blood-stained and ruffled, burst in, followed by General Walter Dixon.

"Harry! *You* here?" he exclaimed. "Tell me, and confound this man's statement, is Sir Andrew Fleming in this house of mine? We have already once crossed weapons, and his frock shall not save him now from my sword."

"Frank, you will find here only a dead woman," Henry replied.

"What! Is it—is it Eleanor?" he gasped. "Then that villain has killed her! Let me go, Henry Masterton. Let me go to her at once."

The opposite door opened as he spoke, the tapestry was flung aside, and, with madness and fury, the Benedictine flung himself in. He paused, a deadly concentrated hate flaming in his eyes as they saw Lord Masterton. His hand rose and fell like lightning, and the other, his hands thrown up, fell into his brother's arms, deluging him with blood from the dagger's wound.

"Villain! Atrocious wretch!" cried Walter Dixon, and like lightning thrust the murderer twice through the body with his sword.

Without a word or a groan, Sir Andrew Fleming fell dead upon the floor. The monk was the husband of Lady Eleanor.

Frank Masterton still lived, but refused all assistance, calling "Eleanor!" with great effort. The maid, who had entered, sobbed: "Alas, my lord, I have no lady now!"

Lord Masterton closed his eyes, raised his hand, and let it fall. His eyes opened, his jaw fell—and Henry Masterton was alone, the last of his race.

Walter Dixon had calmly wiped his sword and departed.

The great objects of his life had been attained that morning. His vengeance on a rival had been satisfied, and obstacles to his possession of a coveted estate were removed. He was put under arrest for murder by the French authorities, only to be released again.

Henry went to the good M. de Vitray's hotel and narrated the tragic incidents. That gentleman told him of Sir Andrew Fleming's trip to England at the time of the troubles, accompanied by General St. Maur, who wished to offer his services to his King, and by a Jesuit, Du Tillet, who died soon after they arrived. Sir Andrew then passed under Du Tillet's name. This accounted to Henry for the likeness he had noticed, but could not trace, in Dom André, and the encounter he had witnessed in which Walter Dixon had been engaged. General St. Maur lived, De Vitray told him, at St. Germains, and he said he would arrange for Henry to see him and deliver Ireton's letter. To his mortification, the General wrote very explicitly that he had not any intention of seeing Lord Masterton, and that his friend need not bring him. Henry flushed indignantly, and poor M. de Vitray shrugged his shoulders, remarking: "*C'est un original!*"

Soon afterward, Henry Masterton met General St. Maur at a reception at the Duc de Longueville's. When he learned that Henry was Lord Masterton now, and had received an affront intended for his brother Frank, he invited him warmly to dine with him at his château that day, and deliver Ireton's letter. Arraying himself with some care, the young man presented himself at the appointed hour, and delivered the missive, which was indeed important.

"This letter restores to me my English estates, from which I have so long been banished, and in a way that I think may be accepted with honor unimpaired, though it comes from Ireton," said General St. Maur, as he rose and led his guest to a superb but cheerful dining-room. The dinner was over, when there was a scratching at the door, then a rush, and Lord Masterton's own beautiful spaniel, Rupert, overpowered him with his ecstatic joy at finding him again.

"It is all over," said General St. Maur smiling. "Rupert, you dog, you're a traitor."

Henry's heart leaped wildly, and at the sight of a beautiful young woman advancing toward him, he gasped: "Emily! My beloved! Is it possible?" In a moment he held her locked in his arms.

"Now that it is all out," said General St. Maur, "send for Lady Margaret, and the family will be united."

When Lady Margaret arrived, the General rose. "Emily, my beloved, your hand. Henry Masterton," he continued, smiling, as he placed it in that of the young lord, "I give this to you the first time it has been rightfully given, by the right of her father. Yes, young man, I am William, Lord Langleigh, your father's old friend! You can see that the report that I was drowned is not true. Now it is your place to explain why these ladies have remained unfound by you so long."

"We did not go to Paris at all," said Lady Emily. "And I had no idea my dear papa was alive until he presented himself at the convent in Dinan, where you left us."

The estate that had been restored to General St. Maur was Pentford-Bourne. His own feeling that he should not receive his estates, since those who offered them had no right to dispose of them, appealed to both Emily and Lord Masterton. But there was wealth enough without this estate to provide for luxury and happiness. General St. Maur despatched a messenger to London refusing the estate as restored, but not waiving his just claim upon it.

Two mornings later Ball o' Fire told his master he had seen Walter Dixon prowling about the estate, and soon afterward General St. Maur was called to his gardener's house by illness there. After he departed, forebodings caused Lord Masterton to follow after him, especially as a letter addressed to "Lord Langleigh" had been left at the house. So he excused himself to Emily and hurried after the General. Some cause drew his attention to the neighboring woods, and he espied two men, one of whom was deliberately aiming with a steel cross-bow at General St. Maur, some distance away. Henry could do but one thing—shout Lord Langleigh's name with all his force as he bounded forward.

There was a rustle in the opposite wood, and Ball o' Fire

had flung himself upon the man. The two rolled to the ground together, and shortly the lad emerged covered with blood.

"Walter Dixon struck me once. I have paid him back. He is dead!" he remarked grimly.

King Charles has now been restored twenty years. Lord Langleigh has gone to join the wife he cherished, in heaven, while the Earl of Kinlivingston, in Ireland, once Henry Masterton, lives in quiet joy with his lovely Countess at the restored estate of Pentford-Bourne.

HENRY JAMES

(United States, 1843)

DAISY MILLER (1878)

This delightful story holds an important place in our literary history, since the date of its publication is popularly fixed as the beginning of the international novel. *Daisy Miller* was not, indeed, Mr. James's first venture into this field, but it was his first to receive wide attention. The story is essentially one of manners, in which the author exhibits the crudities, the wilfulness, the social *gaucherie*, but at the same time the essential innocence, of a young American girl against the background of European etiquette and essential corruption. The book is in effect as much an indictment of the latter as it is a satire of the former, though the failure of Mr. James's readers to see this, especially about the time of its publication, gave rise to much protest against the misrepresentation—or what was so regarded—of the young American girl. It was declared that American girls were not like Daisy—at least, not all were. Of course women or girls of refinement and good manners were to be found in America as well as elsewhere. They could not, however, be called American any more than they could be called English or French. What Mr. James showed, in effect, was something typical of America, in that no other country could have produced her. The case rested in Daisy's favor, and all her open-minded critics became her sincere mourners.

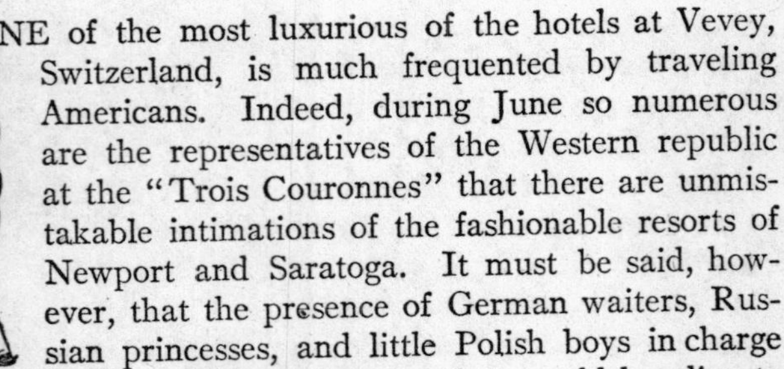

ONE of the most luxurious of the hotels at Vevey, Switzerland, is much frequented by traveling Americans. Indeed, during June so numerous are the representatives of the Western republic at the "Trois Couronnes" that there are unmistakable intimations of the fashionable resorts of Newport and Saratoga. It must be said, however, that the presence of German waiters, Russian princesses, and little Polish boys in charge of their governors provide certain notes that would be alien to the scene in its American counterpart.

One summer morning a young American sat in the garden of the hotel, occupying his mind now with the analogies and now with the differences of the two situations. He was twenty-seven years of age, and had come from Geneva the day before to visit his aunt, who was staying at the hotel. Geneva had been his place of residence for several years. He had acquired his education there; but in addition to these early associations and the influence exerted upon him by the natural fascinations of the place, rumor included an attachment that bound him to a foreign lady—a person older than himself.

On the morning in question he had knocked at his aunt's door and received word that she was indisposed. Headaches were the frequent cause of her seclusions. Winterbourne thereupon repaired to the garden, where he was taking his coffee following breakfast when he was joined by a strange little boy, an urchin of nine or ten. The child looked thin and sickly, and was carrying a long alpenstock which he cast about on all sides, prodding the settees with its iron point or thrusting it into the walk and sending the gravel flying. Pausing in front of Winterbourne, he asked for a lump of sugar. Winterbourne gratified his request, but told the newcomer that he thought sugar not good for little boys. The urchin thought differently, however; and when he had an opportunity he selected three lumps, though he complained that they were "har-r-d" when his poor little teeth failed to crack them. He laid the blame for his imperfect teeth upon "this old Europe," and hastened to establish infantile comparisons between it and America, his own land. Even before these patriotic observations Winterbourne had discovered a fellow-countryman. The boy had to put the question before discovering the same fact concerning his elder companion, but he followed up the reception of it with the remark, "American men are the best."

Shortly thereafter the boy looked up and announced the approach of his sister, with the addition that she was an American girl. He was willing to declare American girls the best, though he demurred at calling his sister the best of American girls, for, as he complained, she "was always blowing at him." Winterbourne of course imputed the fault to him, and at this point in the conversation the young lady herself arrived. She was adorably pretty, and beautifully dressed—that is, expensively; though the quiet taste of the alienated American thought he detected too many frills and flounces. The young lady looked over the parapet, out across the lake, while the boy, whose name was Randolph, hopped about the graveled walk astride his alpenstock. He paid no attention to his sister's words of rather weak remonstrance, and presently called to her attention to the fact that "he"—meaning Winterbourne—was "an American man."

The young lady only replied: "Well, I guess you had better be quiet."

Winterbourne ventured to regard this as in effect an introduction, and, throwing away his cigarette, he arose and pleasantly observed that he had already made the acquaintance of the little boy. Such a meeting with a young girl, he knew, was beyond the strict usage of Geneva, but at Vevey he ventured to admit a little latitude. The young lady made no reply, neither did she retreat from her position; but she kept up a desultory conversation with her brother, wondering where he had obtained "the pole," and questioning whether he intended to take it to Italy.

The mention of Italy led Winterbourne to ask whether she was going there. Glancing again his way, she simply said, "Yes, sir."

In reply to his further question she could not tell whether they were going over the Simplon, and referred the matter to Randolph. He was equally vague, and promptly put the question aside by repeating his preference for America.

During the conversation Winterbourne had time to observe that the young lady, besides being young and pretty, had eyes that were "singularly honest and fresh." Her face "was not at all insipid, but it was not exactly expressive." Winterbourne, who was much addicted to analyzing feminine beauty, decided that there was a certain want of finish. He believed, moreover, that she was probably a coquette. These observations quickened his interests to such an extent that he determined to learn her name if possible. He thereupon turned and asked the boy what his name was. The youth, who had no hesitation about imparting information, quickly told Winterbourne that his name was Randolph C. Miller, and that his sister went by the name of Daisy Miller, but that her real name—the name on her cards—was Annie P. Miller. His father was Ezra B. Miller, and they lived in Schenectady. "He's got a big business," he added. "My father's rich, you bet!"

With that the youth departed with his alpenstock, leaving Winterbourne and Daisy Miller to discuss this prodigy. Daisy declared that he was "smart," and Winterbourne assented. Conversation became easy after this. Daisy, indeed, talked to Winterbourne as if she had known him a long time, gave him details of their journey in Europe, of the hotels they had lived in, and of the dresses and things she had bought in Paris. She also gave an account of her social success at home, particularly in New York, where, in the previous winter, seventeen dinners were given for her, "and three of them were by gentlemen." Winterbourne was "amused, perplexed, and decidedly charmed." He felt that he had lived so long in Geneva that he "had become dishabituated to the American tone." After mature reflection upon the novelties of deportment to which she introduced him, he felt that the formula that applied to her was that of "a pretty American flirt."

The view of Chillon across the lake presently drew their attention, and Miss Miller lamented that she had been unable to visit "that old castle." Randolph had refused to go, she explained, not being interested in old castles; her mother had not dared leave him alone at the hotel, their courier having distinctly refused to undertake his charge. When Winterbourne expressed his interest in the prospect of such an expedition, Miss Miller promptly thought it might be arranged, by leaving her mother and Eugenio with Randolph.

New ideas were crowding upon Winterbourne; but he made out that Eugenio was the name of the courier, and he further perceived that the casual nature of this young lady's reference to him implied that that dignitary occupied an unusual position in the family *ménage.* His perceptions further supplied the conviction that Miss Miller intended to make the little excursion with him alone.

At this point Eugenio himself arrived on the scene, having come to announce luncheon. Miss Miller's new plans were familiarly disclosed to him, and Winterbourne thought he detected what he called impertinence in the tone of the courier's reply. Even to Miss Miller's own apprehension a slightly ironical light seemed to be thrown upon the situation; yet she said to Winterbourne: "You won't back out?"

He hastened to reassure her, and immediately coupled his affirmation with the intimation that he wished to present his aunt.

"Oh, well, we'll go some day," said Miss Miller, ignoring that latter part of his speech. As she went down the gravel walk beside Eugenio, Winterbourne said to himself that she had the *tournure* of a princess.

The promise he had made in behalf of his aunt, Mrs. Costello, was not so easily fulfilled. That lady was exclusive in her acquaintances, and she informed her nephew that she had already observed the Millers, and thought them "very common." She admitted that the girl was pretty and was dressed to perfection. Her taste in such matters was unimpeachable, but—she displayed an intimacy with her mamma's courier. The mother herself was pronounced just as bad. Winterbourne retailed to her the events of the morning, and when he came to the point of the proposed visit to Chillon, and Miss Miller's intention to go there alone with him, Mrs. Costello declined outright the honor of the acquaintance he was pressing upon her. She admitted that she herself was an old woman, but declared that she was not too old, thank Heaven, to be shocked.

This attitude on the part of Mrs. Costello seemed for Winterbourne to throw some light upon the matter of the habits of young ladies in the United States. But he was impatient to see Miss Miller again and was vexed with himself that, by instinct, he should not appreciate her justly.

His next meeting with her took place that evening in the garden. It was ten o'clock, and she was alone. Her mother, she explained, had been walking with her, but had departed to find Randolph and try to induce him to go to bed. Randolph was said to be not amenable to his mother's entreaties, so that parent had gone to ask Eugenio to talk to him. The mother's absence was considerably prolonged; and meanwhile Miss Miller talked to Winterbourne concerning his aunt, Mrs. Costello, declaring that she had heard all about her from the chambermaid. That the lady was regarded as "exclusive" did not trouble Miss Miller in the least; she liked people to be so; she and her mother were exclusive.

"We don't speak to everyone," she said, "or they don't speak to us—I suppose it's about the same thing."

Winterbourne tried to excuse his aunt on the score of her wretched health, but Miss Miller, if she got from him an inkling of the real state of things, successfully concealed it and straightway reassured him with:

"You needn't be afraid. Why should she want to know me?" The train of her thought was revealed a little later by a reflective "Gracious! she *is* exclusive."

Presently Mrs. Miller was seen approaching with a movement that became slow and wavering when she noticed her daughter accompanied by a gentleman. This was attributed by the daughter to timidity in the presence of strangers. Mrs. Miller did not look at Winterbourne when he was presented. "Common," was the mental comment that he passed upon her, yet she also, he thought, had a singularly delicate grace, and, like her daughter, dressed with extreme elegance.

In reply to her daughter's question, Mrs. Miller admitted that she couldn't get Randolph to go to bed. Daisy thought him "real tiresome," whereupon the elder lady said:

"Well, Daisy Miller, I shouldn't think you'd want to talk against your own brother!"

Daisy, however, reiterated her charge that Randolph was tiresome, adding that he wouldn't go to that castle, and next she said: "I'm going there with Mr. Winterbourne."

As Daisy's mamma offered no response, Winterbourne believed that she deeply disapproved. Then followed some desultory conversation upon castles, after which Winterbourne asked Mrs. Miller whether she, too, were not disposed to undertake the journey. He received no immediate reply, but presently, "I guess she had better go alone," she said simply. Daisy thereupon tempted Winterbourne into a proposal of an immediate journey across the lake in the moonlight. This project was debated between them; but Mrs. Miller finally appealed to Eugenio to forbid it. But when the factotum showed himself compliant with the young lady's wish, she herself suddenly changed her mind and declared that she didn't wish any longer to go. All she had wanted was "a little fuss."

Two days later the trip was made, and Daisy comported herself in so natural and charming a way that Winterbourne began to question his earlier verdict that she was "common." Was she so, after all, or was he simply getting used to her commonness? During their conversation Daisy asked whether he did not wish to travel with them and "go round" with them, and also teach Randolph. He pleaded that he had other occupations, and announced the melancholy fact that he was obliged to return to Geneva the following day.

To the first Daisy said, "Oh, bother! I don't believe it." For the second announcement she thought him "horrid." She charged him with a "mysterious charmer" in Geneva who allowed him only three days' absence. By way of compromise he promised her, if she would stop teasing him, that he would go down to Rome in the winter.

When he mentioned the Chillon journey to Mrs. Costello that evening, she sniffed and said:

"And that is the young person whom you wanted me to know?"

Winterbourne paid the promised visit to Rome toward the end of January. His aunt, already on the spot, had informed him by letter that "those people" he had been so devoted to at Vevey had "turned up here, courier and all." The young lady, she said, had become very intimate with some third-rate Italians.

On arriving in Rome, Winterbourne declared his intention of calling on the Millers, but Mrs. Costello remained obdurate. Her report of their doings was coupled with innuendo, and she openly declared them "hopelessly vulgar." Winterbourne refused to believe them "bad," but admitted that they were "very ignorant—very innocent only." The news of her attending Italians, however, checked him from rushing off to see Daisy. Instead, he went to see an American lady whom he had known in Geneva; but before his call was ended a servant announced "Madame Mila!" The first to enter the room was Randolph; then followed his pretty sister; and after a considerable interval Mrs. Miller slowly advanced.

Randolph at once claimed Winterbourne's acquaintance. Daisy with nonchalance chided him for not having called upon her.

"I arrived only yesterday."

"I don't believe that!" the young lady declared.

Mrs. Miller began to occupy herself in keeping Randolph within bounds, though later she was tempted into discussing her dyspepsia, her liver, the bracing climate of Schenectady, and the doctor whom she was forced to leave behind there. Her one esthetic observation was a preference of Zurich to Rome.

Randolph, bursting into the conversation, preferred the City of Richmond to anything, and that, instead of being a city on the map, was explained as the ship they had come over in.

When Daisy gave her attention to Winterbourne she charged him with "meanness" for not remaining at Vevey when she had asked him. She argued this point to no conclusion though, and finally turned from it to ask her hostess, Mrs. Walker, whether she might bring a friend to the party that lady was about to give. Permission to bring any of her friends was accorded to Mrs. Miller; but Mrs. Miller promptly disowned them as her friends, saying she had never spoken to them.

"It's an intimate friend of mine—Mr. Giovanelli," said Daisy, without a tremor.

He was extolled as a great friend—"the handsomest man in the world—except Mr. Winterbourne!" And when it was granted that he might attend the party, Daisy announced that she must depart to join Mr. Giovanelli at the Pincio.

Mrs. Walker looked aghast at this announcement, but her protests against the impropriety of the step were silenced by Daisy's declaring that "if Mr. Winterbourne were as polite as he pretends, he would offer to walk with me!"

Winterbourne's politeness hastened to affirm itself, and the two set forth. When they had passed the gate of the Pincian gardens Miss Miller began to wonder where Mr. Giovanelli might be. Winterbourne had no intention of joining in the search, but the desired gentleman was presently detected by Daisy, leaning against a tree and staring at the women in the carriages.

"Did you ever see anything so cool?" she asked.

The man had a handsome face, but he impressed Winterbourne unfavorably. When he joined the party, Daisy performed an introduction. Winterbourne determined that he ought to remain with Miss Miller, and gave himself to speculation as to who and what Giovanelli might be. A music-master, a penny-a-liner, or a third-rate artist he might easily be, from appearance. From this the American found himself reflecting disagreeably whether a nice American girl would have made a rendezvous with this comparative stranger. Yet Daisy showed no impatience of his own presence, and throughout the walk comported herself with an inscrutable combination of audacity and innocence.

About fifteen minutes later a carriage containing Mrs. Walker drew alongside. She called Winterbourne and with considerable agitation explained she had come to save Daisy—that is, to take her into the carriage and drive about, letting the world see that the girl was not "running absolutely wild." Winterbourne was skeptical of her success.

When the proposal was made to the person most concerned, Daisy politely demurred. Mrs. Walker pressed her, and finally brought it out that what Daisy was doing was highly improper. The young girl seemed mystified, and asked Winterbourne whether he thought that she, to save her reputation, should get into the carriage. Winterbourne, in accordance with the finest gallantry, felt bound to tell her the truth. The truth, accordingly, he declared was on the side of Mrs. Walker.

Daisy, with a violent laugh, said: "I never heard anything so stiff! If this is improper, then I am all improper, and you must give me up. Good-by! I hope you'll have a lovely ride."

And she departed with the triumphant Giovanelli.

Daisy kept her promise about coming to Mrs. Walker's party, though she did not put in an appearance until after eleven o'clock. By way of apology, she sent her mother an hour or more ahead, and when she presented herself before the frigid face of her hostess, explained that she had remained behind "to make Mr. Giovanelli practise some things before he came."

"We had the greatest time at the hotel," she added.

Somehow during the evening Mr. Giovanelli managed to favor the company with half a dozen songs, though Mrs. Walker afterward declared that she had been unable to find out who asked him. Daisy sat and talked with Winterbourne, discussing the incident at the Pincio Gardens. He tried to impress upon the volatile young lady that flirting was not a habit of the country, that there were dangers in carrying on such a thing with Mr. Giovanelli, because he would not understand it. Daisy argued her own side until she finally admitted that neither she nor Mr. Giovanelli was flirting—they were, in fact, too good friends for that.

"Ah," rejoined Winterbourne, "if you are in love with each other, it is another affair."

She got up, blushing at this, and left him, saying that her Italian friend never said such disagreeable things to her.

Mrs. Walker turned her back when Daisy came to take leave of her; and Winterbourne saw her pass out of the door with a pale, grave face.

"She never enters my drawing-room again," Mrs. Walker declared.

From this time Miss Miller was cut off from the society of her compatriots. They talked of her scandalous behavior with Giovanelli, and called the association an "intrigue." Winterbourne defended her to Mrs. Costello, and asserted that the word intrigue was too strong to apply to what she did so openly. Yet he, too, was forced to admit, when he saw Daisy and Giovanelli drive away together from vespers at St. Peter's, that she was going "too far."

Winterbourne went one day to warn Mrs. Miller to be on her guard, but he found her state of mind so unprecedented in the annals of parental vigilance that he gave up the attempt. He frequently found himself balancing his judgment for and against the girl herself. Could her defiance of all social custom come from a consciousness of innocence, or from her being essentially a young person of the reckless class? However he looked at the case, he failed to find her. Meantime she was "carried away" by Mr. Giovanelli.

One day he met her with her customary companion in the ruins of the Palace of the Cæsars, and after some chaffing conversation he tried to impress a warning by telling her she might expect from the other Americans at Rome what Mrs. Walker had already given her — the cold shoulder. Daisy appeared quite serious when she said: "I shouldn't think you'd let people be so unkind!"

When she told him she thought he ought to say something, he replied that he did. He was saying that her mother had told him she believed she was engaged.

"Well, she does," said Daisy, very simply.

Winterbourne began to laugh. "And does Randolph believe it?" he asked.

"I guess Randolph doesn't believe anything," she said.

A little later she affirmed, and almost in the same breath denied, the engagement, and so left Winterbourne.

A week afterward he found himself, on his way home from a beautiful villa on the Carlian Hill, in the neighborhood of the Colosseum. He approached one of the vacant arches, and as he entered noticed an open carriage stationed near by. The rays of a waning moon were veiled in a thin cloud curtain. One half of the gigantic circus was in deep shade, the other was sleeping in the luminous dusk. As he advanced toward the center of the arena, his mind was busy with the lines from Byron's *Manfred*. Suddenly he recalled the warning of doctors against the nocturnal meditation of poets in that historic atmosphere, and he was turning to leave when he heard voices and became aware of two figures seated in the shadow of the great cross in the center of the arena. When he recognized Daisy he found that his horror was mingled with the ultimate conviction that she was a young lady whom a gentleman need no longer be at pains to respect. He checked his first impulse to advance, and was turning away when he heard her say: "Why, it was Mr. Winterbourne! He saw me and he cuts me!"

He turned back again and asked how long they had been there. When he was told they had been there all the evening, he mentioned the terrible Roman fever, and wondered that Giovanelli should countenance such an indiscretion.

"Ah," said the handsome native, "for myself I am not afraid."

"But I speak for this young lady."

"I told the Signorina it was a grave indiscretion; but when was the Signorina ever prudent?"

Daisy was without fears, but Winterbourne advised a speedy return home. On the way out to the carriage she asked whether Winterbourne believed her engaged the other day. That gentleman answered laughingly that it didn't matter what he believed the other day. Being asked whether he believed it now, he replied that it made very little difference whether she were engaged or not. In the gloom he felt the eyes of the girl fixed upon him; but Giovanelli hurried her into the carriage.

"I don't care," said Daisy in a little strange tone, "whether I have Roman fever or not."

Word was passed round a few days later that the little American flirt was alarmingly ill. Winterbourne called often to ask for news, and one day saw Mrs. Miller. Her mother, who at last was showing herself efficient in her care of her daughter, reported that Daisy had spoken of Winterbourne, and wished him to be told that she never was engaged to that handsome Italian.

"I don't know why she wanted you to know; but she said to me three times, 'Mind, you tell Mr. Winterbourne.'"

A week after this the poor girl died.

As Winterbourne stood next Giovanelli near the grave in the little Protestant cemetery, the Italian said, "She was the most beautiful young lady I ever saw, and the most amiable"; and then he added in a moment, "and she was the most innocent. If she had lived, I should have got nothing. She would never have married me, I am sure."

"She would never have married you?"

"For a moment I hoped so. But no. I am sure."

When Winterbourne visited his aunt again at Vevey in the following summer, he said that he had done the young girl an injustice.

"She sent me a message before her death, which I didn't understand at the time; but I have understood it since. She would have appreciated one's esteem."

Winterbourne reflected that he was making a mistake in living too long in foreign parts. Nevertheless he went back to Geneva.

THE PORTRAIT OF A LADY (1881)

This story was begun by the author in 1879 while he was on a visit to Florence, Italy. It entered upon a serial publication in *The Atlantic Monthly* in 1880, and at the end of its run was published in book form the following year. The germ of the story, as Mr. James informs us in the preface to the collected edition (1908), was "the mere slim shade of an intelligent but presumptuous girl." The characters are, as their author humorously puts it, "the numbered pieces of my puzzle, the concrete terms of my 'plot.' It was as if they had simply, by an impulse of their own, floated into my ken, and all in response to my primary question: 'Well, what will she do?'" Of all Mr. James's books this has perhaps enjoyed the greatest popularity, and is, in its author's judgment, "the most proportioned" of his productions after *The Ambassadors*.

N the lawn in front of one of those charming Georgian mansions that adorn the Thames valley afternoon tea was being served. The company about the table were Mr. Touchett, a retired American banker, who had spent thirty years and grown rich in the English capital, his son Ralph, a more pronounced type of the expatriate, and their neighbor, Lord Warburton. The two younger men were bachelors, and the elder, though possessed of a wife, enjoyed very little of her society, since for many years she had elected to live mainly in Florence. The conversation turned upon marriage, and Lord Warburton was advised to find himself a wife, but was cautioned about falling in love with Mr. Touchett's niece. This young lady was the more readily a subject of humorous conversation as she was an entire stranger to all three. The absentee, Mrs. Touchett, a week previously had announced by telegram one of her periodical visits to the family roof-tree. But the point of her departure, instead of being Florence, was the United States. It was Mrs. Touchett's habit to pay her native land an occasional visit, and it was known to her son and husband that she was on one of these visits, but little further had been communicated, until she sent the following rather inscrutable telegram:

Tired America, hot weather awful, return England with niece, first steamer, decent cabin."

Mrs. Touchett had found her niece in Albany, a young woman who had grown from childhood since she had last seen her. Mrs. Touchett's habit of differing with her family had expressed itself in a violent quarrel with her brother-in-law after the early death of her sister. For years she had taken no interest in the family her sister had left, but being lately apprised that the objectionable brother-in-law had himself died, she determined to seek out her nieces. Two of them were married, but the youngest, Isabel Archer, was left without fortune. Mrs. Touchett generously determined to do something for her; but her plans advanced no further than a purpose to take Isabel abroad and give her some of the opportunities afforded by society in Europe. Hence the proposed visit to Gardencourt, the home of Mr. Touchett.

Isabel's success there was immediate, both with her uncle and with her cousin. A new life seemed to be brought to these two valetudinarians; for Ralph Touchett, though not much more than thirty, had suffered much illness and looked forward to a shortened career. She was even successful with Lord Warburton and his sisters, at first charming them, especially Lord Warburton, by the freshness of her outlook on life and the keen interest that she took in a social situation that presented not only novelty but anomalies to her unsophisticated mind. As she was much interested in the picturesque, Lord Warburton invited her to Lockleigh, his country place, not far off, and took great pains to exhibit not only his house but himself in lights that might be ingratiating to her. It must be owned that only an innocent and unsuspecting nature such as hers could have failed to see that he took far more pains to please than he would to one who was simply a stranger in the land and a niece of a much valued neighbor. But before he had time to declare himself to the extent he evidently contemplated, Isabel's situation was complicated by the arrival in England of an American friend, Henrietta Stackpole, a newspaper correspondent of advanced views, who was destined to play an important part in Isabel's struggles consequent upon her endeavor to adjust her new and enlarging opportunities to old ideals of life. The lady correspondent, it appears, had crossed on the steamer with a young American, Casper Goodwood, who had been an earlier suitor of Isabel Archer's, and who now came to press his claim upon her attention. He represented the best type of American youth, with fortune and prospects of commercial success; but it is very likely that he had ever failed to touch the imagination of this young lady in whom romance had been a predominating quality. She received a letter from Casper Goodwood, asking for an interview. She was reading this on the lawn at Gardencourt one day when Lord Warburton appeared. Fate had perhaps not made his visit well-timed, especially for his offer of marriage. She asked for time, not wishing to seem indifferent to the honor of his proposal; but she found that she could not marry Lord Warburton. The idea failed to correspond to any vision of happiness that she had hitherto entertained, or was now capable of entertaining. She was conscious of liking him—indeed, she liked him too well to think of inflicting, upon a man who offered so much, a wife with a tendency to criticize.

Shortly afterward she despatched a courteous letter declining Lord Warburton's offer. The courage and independence that she showed in declining one of the finest places in England had its effect upon her uncle and her cousin and led to very important results.

The smoothly flowing life at Gardencourt was interrupted by a visit to London. Miss Archer wished to see the sights, and Miss Stackpole was anxious to secure more "life" for her American newspaper letters. They were accompanied on this journey by Ralph, and stayed in a modest hotel, the gentleman going to his father's house in Winchester Square. It was at the time of this London visit that Casper Goodwood made his appearance. Though his errand was the same as Lord Warburton's, it can hardly be said that he received even the same consideration. Casper stood his ground through a long and determined siege, but he failed to elicit more than a sort of sympathetic kindness from Isabel. Before they parted she gave expression to the keynote of his character. Casper was asked to leave her entirely alone for at least two years.

"If there is a thing in the world that I am fond of," she said, "it is my personal independence. I am not in my first youth—

I can do what I choose—I belong to the independent class; I have neither father nor mother; I am poor; I am of a serious disposition, and not pretty. I try to judge things for myself; to judge wrong, I think, is more honorable than not to judge at all. I don't wish to be a mere sheep in the flock; I wish to choose my fate and know something of human affairs beyond what other people think it compatible with propriety to tell me."

Casper wondered at all this, but accepted his fate. He agreed to go, and he promised to come back wherever she was, two years later.

The return to Gardencourt was made without Henrietta. When Ralph and his cousin arrived there they found a visitor, on the ground, a Madame Merle, a friend of Mrs. Touchett's, who had lately come from her home in Italy. Isabel was fascinated by the perfection of manner this woman displayed, by her social accomplishments and by the exquisite faculty she seemed to possess of serving her friends.

Meantime old Mr. Touchett's health grew worse and the London doctors summoned in consultation gave an unpromising verdict. He rallied, however, to afford strength for talking with Ralph about the future and the disposition of his fortune. Ralph urged that in bestowing his fortune his father should consider the state of his own health and not burden him with the care of too much money. His idea was that Isabel, who had been remembered in the will, should have something splendid.

"I should like to make her rich," he said.

"What do you mean by rich?" asked his father. "I call people rich when they are able to gratify their imagination. Isabel had a great deal of imagination."

He further appreciated that Isabel wanted to be free, and reflected that being rich would keep her from marrying for money. He had not left it unconsidered that she might fall into the hands of fortune-hunters, but he was prepared to take the risk.

During these days Isabel cultivated the friendship of Madame Merle and heard much about the great world, concerning which her curiosity was abounding. Madame Merle talked in an ironical view of men like Ralph Touchett, who had no position—was simply "an American who lives in Europe." She spoke of another, a Gilbert Osmond, whom she promised Isabel should know.

"He is exceedingly clever, a man much to be distinguished; but, as I say, you exhaust the description when you say that he is Mr. Osmond, who lives in Italy. No career, no name, no position, no fortune, no past, no future, no anything."

Mr. Touchett died, and Isabel became possessed of a fortune of seventy thousand pounds. Mrs. Touchett presently set out for Italy, though she made a stay in Paris *en route*. This was effective in enlarging Isabel Archer's social horizon, though the only person she met, destined to be intimately connected with her future history, was Edward Rosier, an amiable dilettante, and a variant of the type of American expatriate whom she was principally coming to know. In good time her aunt proceeded to Florence.

Madame Merle was as good as her word in bringing about the meeting between Isabel Archer and Gilbert Osmond, and the glimpse we get of her in the first act of the process shows that lady in the light of a matchmaker. Gilbert Osmond, being a delicate and highly cultivated product of civilization, had to be carefully prepared for the proposal. He refused to meet the newcomer unless she should be "beautiful, clever, rich, splendid, universally intelligent, and unprecedentedly virtuous." Isabel was declared to meet all his requirements, and the end of their conversation, which carried implications of previous relations and entailed obligations, was, that Osmond should call at Mrs. Touchett's house, the Palazzo Crescentini.

There he was presented to Isabel by Madame Merle. The impression he made was so strong and so aroused her interest that she went not long afterward with Madame Merle to visit his house, which stood on a hill-top overlooking Florence. Here he lived among his things—the rare and beautiful bibelots, furniture, and fabrics he had managed, with the taste and skill of a connoisseur, to collect at small cost. With him lived his daughter Pansy, a frail and beautiful convent flower, just emerged from that discipline.

When Mr. Osmond began to visit at the Palazzo Crescentini it was apparent to Mrs. Touchett that he had taken it into his head to marry her niece. This idea was not pleasing either to her or to her son Ralph. Mrs. Touchett easily remembered that the girl had refused an English peer; and that a young lady for whom Lord Warburton had not been up to the mark should content herself with an obscure American dilettante, a middle-aged widower with an overgrown daughter and an income of nothing—this answered to nothing in Mrs. Touchett's conception of success.

Mrs. Touchett read her niece in a very shrewd way, and found her capable of marrying Mr. Osmond for his opinions. "She wishes to be disinterested; as if she were the only person who is in danger of not being so! Will he be so disinterested when he has the spending of her money?" Madame Merle was appealed to, but showed herself discreetly ignorant of what might be the intentions of Gilbert Osmond, yet she did not refrain from presenting him to Mrs. Touchett in a favorable light, but without convincing that lady in the least.

Isabel had no idea that her relations with Osmond were being discussed. Their acquaintance progressed, and when it was proposed that the process of her European initiation should involve a visit to Rome, she hinted to Osmond that he should go there at the same time. In Rome other things happened besides the inspection of ancient monuments. One day, after wandering in the Forum, Isabel sat down on a prostrate column, when Lord Warburton came in sight among the ruins. This gentleman confessed that he was returning from a six months' journey in the East. It was natural that he should convey the impression of unhappiness, but this did not much move the young lady, whose thoughts were mainly engaged in other directions. She exacted the promise that he would be silent on the subject of their earlier difference; and when this basis was adopted the Englishman made an interesting addition to the party then "doing" Rome. Complications were inevitable, however, when Gilbert Osmond arrived. The two gentlemen met on several occasions; but Lord Warburton easily discerned that the field was likely to be held by the American, and he cut short his stay.

The Roman visit did not end before Osmond had declared his affection for the rich young American. He received no ready acceptance, but at least his fate in no wise resembled either that of Lord Warburton or that of Casper Goodwood. When they parted, Isabel to make an earlier return to Florence, she promised to go to see his little daughter.

She went back to Florence, but it was only the starting-place of new journeys to Bellaggio, then Paris, afterward Switzerland, then London. Then to Italy again, but she found the zest for travel still unsatisfied and there was a further flight to Greece and Egypt, this time in the company of Madame Merle. From these journeyings there was another return to Rome. A few days later Gilbert Osmond came down from Florence and remained three weeks, during which the fact of her being with his old friend, Madame Merle, in whose house she had gone to lodge, made it virtually inevitable that he should see her every day.

About the last of April, two years from the time she had left Albany with Mrs. Touchett, Isabel Archer, a young American woman who had accumulated experience of life, was once more sojourning under Mrs. Touchett's roof in Florence. She awaited a visitor whose coming and going would sweep away the last impediment to the new life she contemplated. This was Casper Goodwood, who came and was received with the bright, dry gaze with which she rather withheld than offered a greeting. Their conversation began in a minor key. He told of his arrival the night before, and complained that the "Italian trains go at about the rate of an American funeral."

"That is in keeping—you must have felt as if you were coming to a funeral," Isabel said, forcing a smile, in order to offer such encouragement as she might to an easy treatment of their situation.

"No, I don't feel that; because I couldn't think of you as dead. I wish I could!" said Goodwood.

"I thank you immensely."

"I would rather think of you as dead than as married to another man."

He asked whether the marriage was one that her friends would not like, and she replied that she really hadn't an idea; that she didn't marry for her friends. He tried to consider who Mr. Osmond was; and after much parrying she admitted ironically that she was marrying "a nonentity," and asked Mr.

Goodwood not to try to take an interest in him, since he couldn't. Goodwood explained his long journey as having been taken simply because he wished to see her again as she was, and that before she had married. He wished to hear the sound of her voice, and Isabel retorted that she fancied he found it said nothing sweet. Yet she declared that she had not deceived him, since she had been perfectly free. He reminded her that she had said she would probably never marry, and had said it so positively that he almost believed it.

"You told me that if I heard you were engaged, I was not to believe it," Casper went on. "I heard it twenty days ago from yourself, but I remembered what you had said. I thought there might be some mistake, and that is partly why I came."

Beyond that he said he wished to hear what she would say in explanation of having changed her mind; but she retorted that she was not bound to explain. He turned away, saying that he should not trouble her again for a long time; that he should leave Florence to-morrow. To this she answered passionately:

"I am delighted to hear it!" But five minutes after he went she burst into tears.

Casper Goodwood being disposed of, Isabel forthwith informed Mrs. Touchett of her engagement, and that lady received the confirmation of her own surmises with her habitual sardonic frankness. Gilbert Osmond's value was not appraised very highly, and Mrs. Touchett, who chose to see marriage as a partnership, thought this one too one-sided. Isabel admitted Mr. Osmond's lack of money, and declared her wish that he should have some.

"Give it to him, then; but marry someone else."

Mrs. Touchett believed in letting people do as they pleased, and did not press Isabel after she had freed her mind. But she threatened to come down on Madame Merle, who she thought had deceived her after having virtually promised to prevent the engagement.

Isabel had still to reckon with Ralph, who came up from Corfu in a few days, looking sadly ill, and was told the news by his mother. He was distressed and disappointed. He never had liked anything less. What could he do, what could he say?

To try to persuade Isabel that the man to whom she had pledged her faith was a humbug would be decently discreet only in the event of her being persuaded. Days passed before the two came to talk. Ralph began by apologizing for not having congratulated her, and explained that he had hardly got over his surprise. She was the last person he had expected to see "caught." A year ago, he reminded her, she valued her liberty beyond everything. She wished only to see life.

"I have seen it," said Isabel, "and it doesn't seem to me so charming."

But Ralph had supposed she wished to survey the whole field. She corrected him with her discovery that one couldn't do that. "One must choose a corner and cultivate that."

But it was not the kind of corner Ralph would have her select. He told her he thought there was something small, narrow, and selfish in Osmond. Isabel retorted that Osmond's tastes were exquisite, and Ralph asked whether she ever had seen an exquisite taste ruffled.

"I hope it may never be my fortune to fail to gratify my husband's," said Isabel.

But Ralph answered with passion that she was "meant for something better than to keep guard over the sensibilities of a sterile dilettante."

Such a reply aroused her, but she subdued her anger in order that her idea might be fully presented. She admitted that Mr. Osmond was not important, but declared him a man who was supremely indifferent to importance. Such an attitude she called large—the largest thing she knew. She loved him not for what he really possessed, but for his poverties dressed out as honors.

An interval passed, in which Isabel's marriage to Mr. Osmond was accomplished. Several years later they were in Rome, in the Palazzo Roccanera, surrounded by an elegance that was largely the expression of Gilbert Osmond's tastes. From certain circumstances it might be inferred that all was not as well for Isabel as the roseate dream of the future promised. Mr. Rosier, whom she saw in Paris some years since, had fallen in love with Pansy Osmond. He appreciated some of the difficulties in the way of pressing his suit for this young lady, and sought the aid of Madame Merle. Such assistance as she was able to afford she promised the young man, at the same time advising him not to involve Mrs. Osmond, since for her to take a hand in his affairs might only serve to multiply the points of difference between her and her husband.

The Italian season was at its height. Isabel kept her house open to visitors on Thursdays, and at one of these Lord Warburton presented himself. He informed his hostess that he had but lately arrived from England, having brought Ralph Touchett, who was very ill, plainly past much hope, but had decided to try Sicily for the winter. Ever since Isabel's marriage Ralph had been trying to learn whether he had judged rightly of its probable outcome. But in this pursuit he came to feel that he had been a fool to put the girl on her guard. He believed that he should see nothing, he should learn nothing; for him she would always wear a mask. His curiosity led him to take this journey, ostensibly to Sicily but really to Rome; for once there he decided to remain even against prudence. His health would hardly bear it, but he protested he was not interested in his health and was deeply interested in Mrs. Osmond.

There would have been much to see, if Ralph Touchett had not been the invalid he was, so as to be banished from the scene of Mrs. Osmond's doings. Lord Warburton became a frequent visitor at the Palazzo Roccanera, and even confessed to Ralph Touchett that he was strongly attracted by Pansy Osmond. His attentions were probably magnified in importance by Edward Rosier, who came to view the Englishman in the light of a rival and took his fears to Madame Merle. But instead of taking them to a place of safety, he probably went to the worst of markets. Madame Merle at once told Gilbert Osmond that Lord Warburton might be regarded in the light of a *parti* for Pansy, and she at once washed her hands of interest in little Mr. Rosier's affairs. Isabel happened to come in upon the conversation when this hint passed between Madame Merle and Gilbert Osmond, though she heard nothing of what was said by them. Her husband quickly withdrew and gave Madame Merle the opportunity to learn from Isabel that she had observed something that rendered plausible Edward Rosier's cause of jealousy. When Isabel and Gilbert Osmond discussed the subject he plainly gave her to understand that he desired the match between his daughter and the English nobleman, and that he wished his wife to exert whatever power she possessed from her present friendship or her past relations with that gentleman to bring about the result.

Following this colloquy Isabel had a long period of reflection. She examined the relations that had long subsisted between herself and her husband, and felt that he hated her, because he had discovered that she was so different, that she was not what he had believed she would prove to be. He had thought at first that he could change her, and she had done her best to be what he would like. But, after all, she was herself—she couldn't help that; and now there was no use in pretending, playing a part, for he knew her and he had made up his mind.

The effect of her reflections showed itself at a party to which she took Pansy three nights later. There she saw Edward Rosier, who was not permitted to dance with Pansy, because her father had forbidden it. She did dance with Lord Warburton, who, however, gave the larger share of his attention at other times to Mrs. Osmond. During one of their colloquies she drew from him the information that he intended writing Osmond to ask for the hand of little Pansy. Isabel not long afterward pointed out the disconsolate Rosier; and when Warburton expressed his wonder that Rosier, who appeared to be an attractive young fellow, should meet with no favor from Gilbert Osmond, he was told by Isabel that Osmond had "larger ideas" for his daughter. This information was bound to produce its result on Lord Warburton, though he gave no immediate sign.

Meantime Isabel did her best to carry out the wishes of her husband without surrendering any of her own delicacy. She went to see Ralph Touchett—a thing that Gilbert Osmond disapproved of, without having yet come to the point of asking her to discontinue her visits to her cousin. From Ralph she endeavored to find out what move Lord Warburton was likely to make. But Ralph only told her that Lord Warburton was in love with her; and he tried to ascertain just where she stood with her husband. Isabel, save for one glimmering moment, kept up her mask. They parted in some heat, for she perceived with displeasure what he was driving at. Her next move was to go to Pansy and endeavor, without influence or even suggestion, to learn whether she looked upon Lord Warburton as a suitor. Pansy was entirely clear on the point; so much so that her lucidity, together with her unwillingness to entertain the likelihood of Lord Warburton's ever preferring her, left Isabel still in a difficult position in regard to what she knew her husband expected of her.

When she and her husband next talked, an interval of several days had passed without Lord Warburton's expected letter. Osmond was in a bad temper, and accused Isabel of working against him. Their conversation had not proceeded far when Lord Warburton himself entered the room and announced his immediate departure for England. This of course settled the question of his future relations with Pansy. But it did not settle Gilbert Osmond. That evening when they had returned from a late entertainment, he accused Isabel of preventing Pansy's marriage to Warburton, of doing it while she was pretending to take an interest in bringing it about, of even stopping Warburton's letter on the way. Her disdain only permitted her to say:

"Oh, Osmond, for a man that was so fine!"

At this time Isabel was treated to a visit from Henrietta Stackpole; and to her she confessed that she was miserable, that her husband did not like her. Miss Stackpole advised a separation; but Isabel declared that she couldn't change that way, couldn't publish her mistake.

"I married him before all the world; I was perfectly free; it was impossible to do anything more deliberate. One can't change, that way."

At the same time Casper Goodwood made another visit to Rome. The company of old friends surrounding Isabel were becoming too numerous. It was irritating to feel that so many were watching. So when Ralph Touchett announced his intention of returning to England Isabel made Casper Goodwood promise to go with him. Henrietta went also, as a voluntary service. But before their departure Casper wrung from Isabel the second confession. His words were a fervent confession of his undying love, and he asked whether he might pity her.

"Should you like that?" she asked.

"To pity you? Most assuredly! That at least would be doing something. I would give my life to it."

"Don't give your life to it, but give a thought to it every now and then."

When the three had gone from Rome, Isabel was not to rest easier. Madame Merle came to see her, and questioned her about the sudden withdrawal by Lord Warburton of his interest in Pansy. She showed the same suspicion of her that her husband had shown, ended with the assumption that Isabel had brought about the rupture in order to keep Lord Warburton for herself, and urged her to give him up. Yet her insolence was not so bad as a worse horror that thrust itself forward.

"Who are you—what are you?" Isabel murmured. "What have you to do with me?"

"Everything!" answered Madame Merle, and in these words Isabel saw that Mrs. Touchett had been right. Madame Merle had married her.

There were still more things for Isabel to hear, and worst of these came after a stormy interview with her husband. Word had come by telegraph from England that Ralph Touchett was dying and wished to see her. Of course her impulse was to set out at once. Her husband strongly opposed because he hated Ralph, and he was led to believe that her going would in his eyes constitute a rupture. Just after leaving him she was joined in her room by Osmond's sister, the Countess Gemini, a guest in their house. She told Isabel that Osmond's first wife had died childless, and that Pansy was the daughter of Madame Merle. She told her this, she said, because she was so tired of Isabel's not knowing. The Countess Gemini was not noted either for delicacy or for morals, though her heart was somewhat better than either of these others.

Isabel was more determined than ever to go to England; but before leaving she went to bid farewell to Pansy. Pansy, at her father's instance, had returned to the convent. He thought all young girls needed an occasional "retreat," but he really wished to subdue her spirit and make her forget Edward Rosier. Isabel saw that this had been accomplished. The delicate little creature was prepared to obey her father in all things, but she begged Isabel not to desert her.

Going from the convent, Isabel encountered Madame Merle; and there was talk about Ralph Touchett, when Madame Merle completed Isabel's day of illumination by telling her that it was through Ralph that she had her large fortune from her uncle.

Isabel sat by Ralph the last night of his life on earth, and was comforted by hearing him say as almost his last words:

"I don't believe such a generous mistake as yours—can hurt you for more than a little."

JEROME KLAPKA JEROME

(England, 1859)

PAUL KELVER (1902)

This story is largely autobiographical, and in it Mr. Jerome utters the heartfelt protest of the man who has been labeled "humorist" and never can be allowed to be serious thereafter. It is a book to make a man's reputation, but although it was appreciated by the few, to the many it was a mistake "because it wasn't funny enough." When Mr. Jerome was traveling in the United States he met a clergyman who, after praising his *Three Men in a Boat*, a book of which Jerome was heartily tired, said: "Did you ever attempt anything serious?" "I wrote a novel once—*Paul Kelver*," said Jerome. The clergyman began to shake with laughter. "You are not serious," said he. "*You* wrote a *novel*?" "Strange as it may seem," said Jerome, reddening with anger, "I did write a novel." "A serious novel?" continued the clergyman, going off into a peal of laughter. "As serious as I could make it." The clergyman could not get over it, and when a few minutes later someone else came up, the reverend gentleman said, amid interruptions of his own laughter: "Jerome—has—actually—written—a novel—ha! ha! ha! ha!"

OF my father I knew very little until I was seven or eight years of age. My mother and my aunt and I lived in the country, and I did not even suppose I had a father. I knew that one who was called my mother's husband lived in London and now and then wrote to her; but that he bore any relation to me I did not realize until after a conversation with my nurse one afternoon, and then I learned that the man was my father and that he was working hard in London in order to earn money, that we might at last come to live with him. He had lost his money in a mine, and had it all to make again. I remember dreading the thought of leaving the beloved places where my mother and I had had so many delightful times; but when my mother heard that we were to join my father she acted like a child and danced about the house for joy.

We went to live at the East End, where rents were low, and

my first impression of my father was favorable. He had an eye that no one could fear, and he seemed very glad to see my mother.

If at that time which followed our new life I had been called upon to define the phrase "husband and wife," I should have said that they were two persons who were constantly seeking excuses to be together; and that if one entered a room in which they were, one should first make a "noise without"—as stage directions read—in order to enable them to assume absurdly stiff and unreal positions as far apart from each other as the room's limits permitted; and that it was well to keep one's feet raised when at table, in order to avoid pressings meant for other feet.

That father's fortune was slow in the making is shown by the fact that one egg sufficed for father's and mother's breakfast, each clamoring for the white as being "more nutritious."

After we had occasion to discharge our maid for drunkenness we did without one while we were waiting for the right one to come; and when father himself opened the door to a visitor he would call down-stairs, "*Where* is Mary?"

My father and I were congenial companions because he was the youngest being I had ever met. And how manfully he intended battling with the wicked Dragon that was keeping my dear mother in want. With his strong right arm he was going to slay him, he said. But in the end it was the Dragon that overcame.

One day a man named Hasluck called on my father and gave me a half crown, and from that day our luck changed.

Hasluck dropped his *hs*, and he was certainly vulgar-looking, but he was kind to us, I could see that, for his mere coming seemed to bring us good fortune. Before he called again we had a maid in cap and apron, and new oilcloth in the passage, and father took to wearing his Sunday clothes on week-days.

Through Hasluck I (who had had one or two childish loves, if one can so call street children with astonishing vocabularies and dirty though pretty faces) met the Princess of the Golden Locks and fell in love with her. Her name was Barbara, and she was Hasluck's daughter.

Thanks to the good luck that Hasluck had brought to father, I now was sent to a boarding-school, and there I met Dan.

Dan was a boy with a code of honor all his own. Naturally that fact did not tend to make him popular with either boys or teachers, and yet much might be said in favor of his code. He was a good fighter, and yet he never fought because it was the correct thing to do at a particular time, and he always fought lazily, if effectually. Once he was thrice provoked by a street boy, and to an ordinary lad the only issue would have been a fight to a finish, but he received all the indignities smilingly and passed on, saying to me: "I'm glad he didn't insist on fighting." And his reason for gladness was, that he was going to a party that night.

Dan and I became chums, and later in the term I told him that I had prayed that I might win the history prize. This, he told me, was beastly unfair—it was like Achilles' winning his fights by his invulnerability. This was a new way of looking at things, and it made a great impression on me. Whatever the reason, I won no prize that year, but Dan did.

Father's fortunes continued to mend. The bulk of his law business came from Hasluck, and he began to talk of moving to more commodious quarters in a better neighborhood.

I remember one evening when mother gave a dinner-party —a real dinner-party—and at the last moment the maid bolted and there was no one to serve the meal. Mother was in despair, and my aunt suggested turning it into a picnic and eating in the kitchen. And then the Princess of the Golden Locks became a fairy godmother. She had come to help mother dress, and when she learned what had happened she went out to get a maid whom she said she knew, and brought her back in her own fair skin. And a winsome-looking maid she was and shed luster on our feast.

That was almost the last happy time we had together; for father's proverbial ill luck began to pursue him soon afterward, and dinner-parties were not even thought of. And a shadow, a new shadow, crept into the house, for my lover parents began to quarrel. That each one wept bitter tears of remorse at unconsidered speeches the other did not know; and by turns I was angry at father and mother alike, when I saw how deeply each wounded the other.

The shadow had come between them at the dinner, and the name of the shadow was jealousy. The young wife of Mr. Teidelmann was at the dinner, and she was more modish, more regularly beautiful, than my mother, and my mother knew it. Whether my father knew it or not I cannot tell; but shadows are by nature incorporeal, and it takes very little to make a most portentous one. Matters were not mended when the sudden death of Mr. Teidelmann made the presence of my father at the house of his widow obligatory.

It was a strange thing that brought about the peace that had been in the house. Mrs. Teidelmann was going abroad, and she had sent for my mother to come and bid her good-by, as she was suffering from a severe headache. When my mother arrived she was shown with me to her boudoir where Mrs. Teidelmann lay asleep; and in her sleep she began to murmur my father's name and to say "We must not, Luke, darling!"

My mother sent me out of the room, but she herself did not come down for half an hour, and from that time there were no more harsh words for my father. She wrote long, long letters to Mrs. Teidelmann (never saying a word about it to father), and peace came once more to the house.

But mother was not well. Dr. Hal Washburn (our doctor, a great, bluff fellow between whom and myself a friendship quite ideal had grown up) said that nothing was really the matter with her, only weakness, and that a change of scene and air might be beneficial. And as father was too busy to leave London it came about that mother and I went back to our old home on a visit. And there in a few days came to us dreadful news, news that made my mother forget she had ever felt jealousy. For father came to us, looking buoyant as he always did when luck had turned against him, and told us that he was a doomed man—had but a year or two to live. Then my mother went to him, and the memory of her doubts had vanished in a moment.

My father lived a brave man's life until the end, and we were more like brothers than like father and son. For a time I did not realize that he really was going to leave us forever, and then it came on me suddenly when I was on my way to the city to meet him, and I could not hurry fast enough for fear I should find that he had gone from me. I think he understood what was in my mind when I flung myself on him, although he said nothing. After his death and when my education was completed I took up law, going into a house in which my father had been employed as assistant solicitor.

Within a short time of my dear mother's death our little all was swallowed up through the rascality of a much trusted and widely honored man, and, knowing that the end was near, I kept from her all knowledge of it. When she was gone I was not only alone in the world but had to begin at the beginning, for the man that had robbed us was my father's employer.

I obtained a place with a Mr. Lott at fifteen shillings a week, and found that he and Mr. Miniken, my fellow-clerk, were characters whose study furnished me with pleasure. As I had literary hopes, these facts were not unimportant.

I had begun to send out manuscripts to the magazines, and they had begun to come back at about the same time. I continued to send them out, and they continued to return to me with a regularity that was aided and abetted by the editors of some of the best periodicals.

I also learned to smoke and to drink, giving to each vice an amount of patience and determination that would have won success in any art. Nauseous as tobacco and wine and whisky seemed to my inexperienced palate, I felt that I never could become a genius unless I became proficient in their consumption, and therefore I persevered.

While in pursuit of conviviality I fell in with Miss Rosina Sellars—and had not the good sense to fall out with her at once. Several musical and literary Bohemians had been present, and I had found that I could now pay some attention to various liquors without undue distaste and with a feeling of warmth toward the world in general that made me look on all mankind as my brothers and sisters.

I do not think Miss Sellars was the type of young woman who would have called forth warm encomiums from my mother. I think Miss Sellars might have shocked my mother, although she was a harmless enough girl; but when one has partaken of unwonted champagne his taste in female loveliness undergoes a deterioration, and as I sat beside this transcendent being on the sofa, holding her hand and with her head on my shoulder, I murmured words that in spite of their thickness entered her comprehension and awoke phrases that burned with ardor; and finally when I tried to kiss her she so aided me and held me so fast that the entire company saw there was no doubt of our being intended for each other, and so Miss Sellars explained it to those who were for making me out "no gentleman." As for myself, my brain was beginning to be hazy. I remember telling her, at her dictation and before the whole company, that I loved her ardently, and that was all she cared for in the way of an avowal, and everybody seemed satisfied that I had but claimed my right in kissing her.

Next morning I followed a time-honored course, and when my heavy eyes finally opened to the broad daylight I was ashamed of having allowed myself to get drunk—I did not spare myself the use of the ugly word—drunk at nineteen. What would be the inevitable result? One drunkard's grave filled by my form.

And I was affianced to—to Miss Rosina Sellars. Something told me that, although the particulars were nebulous. Miss Sellars, barmaid—to Mr. Paul Kelver. It was a nice prospect—a pretty result to follow on a few glasses of champagne.

My fellow-clerk advised me to let her wait. My idiotic self allowed me to answer in person a note she wrote me, and she made my chains heavier. We went walking together, and she took me to her mother's house, and there I met her friends and relatives. As I was a fastidious youth, my gorge rose at sight of them, and I would have given worlds to be released from my bonds.

By the advice of my friends I resolved to escape from her by giving up my lodgings and my clerkship and that part of London, and going on the stage as a member of the chorus.

Although my voice was very ordinary, I succeeded through the good offices of a friend in obtaining a place at "thirty shillings a week, half salary for rehearsals."

After our first performance I met my old school-friend, Dan. He was dramatic critic on a London paper, and he had recognized me as soon as I came on. We exchanged histories, and I found that his life had been most varied, he having been by turns a circus performer, a footman, a waiter, and a journalist. He suggested that we pool our incomes and set up an establishment of our own, and I gladly assented, as I had always liked Dan and his individual point of view.

Dan was a born cook, and for two years we lived a very comfortable life, nor needed woman's ministrations. The opera in which I had appeared made a hit, thanks mainly to the natural and half unconscious comicality of a fishy-eyed young man in the chorus, and it was followed by another in which the fishy-eyed young man appeared as a principal, and my salary was increased.

In all this time I heard nothing of Rosina. I had escaped out of her clutches with the greatest ease. Meanwhile a short story of mine was accepted and printed. Oh, the joy of the first acceptance! It is a theme for a great poet. There is no joy just like it, and to him who has not had it no words can communicate its quality.

During these years in which I had been doing new things I had not forgotten the Princess of the Golden Locks. Now, having become in a measure independent, I felt that I could write to old Hasluck without his misconstruing my meaning, and in answer to my letter I received a most cordial note. He told me that Barbara had just returned from abroad and would be delighted to see me. I still loved her, loved her more than when I had last seen her, but I allowed a week to elapse before I went to Hasluck's house.

I met Golden Locks in the garden, and, following a sudden impulse, I kissed her hand. She seemed half pleased, half contemptuous, and said: "So you are still in love with me?"

And then it came out that she had always known that I loved her and wished me to tell her about it, much as if we were talking of my love for another woman. I told her I would that she were some great queen of the olden time, that I might be near her, serving her. Laughing, she said she would be my queen, and that I should adore her, worship her blindly, kneel at her feet, and "the Queen could do no wrong."

"You understand, Paul, the Queen can do no wrong," she said, with a note of appeal in her voice.

And then she allowed me to sit beside her and tell her my history, and I did not omit anything, not even the episode of the barmaid. Then she told me her story, and I learned that she was going to make a loveless match with a Spanish noble, and that in return for an assured place in the *haut monde* her father was to settle on her husband a great deal of money.

She did not love him, she said, and she did not know that he loved her. My love, she said, was something to sniff at, like incense, with her nose in the air; but the love of a husband—bah! she did not wish that. Social ambition, money to buy it. Her father a butcher in the Mile End Road at the beginning, and she a countess at the end. It was worth while, she said.

And then I learned that there was one man she could have loved if he could have attained social success, because he was every inch a man—Dr. Hal Washburn, my old friend.

The Queen can do no wrong. And I loved Hal. But the years that followed were to see the Countess Huescar tire of her loveless life; were to see her run away from the Count—with Hal; were to see the Count come and beg for her of Hal, when she and Hal had come to the end of their passion; were to see Hal, filled with pity for the man he had wronged, leave her to her husband—to her husband, who promptly obtained a long-sought revenge by divorcing her publicly.

But I run ahead of my story. Hal was to live a score of years before he, dying of consumption, told me all these chapters in the life history of the Queen who could do no wrong. Yes, I loved her, but it must have been calf love, for it did not break my heart when she married the Count.

Among the artists whom I knew was a middle-aged man named Deleglise, a fellow of originality and charm, the father of an awkward chit of a girl who promised to be beautiful if her features changed enough. She was a frank little thing, and I used to enjoy talking to her, she was so very much herself.

There was also among my acquaintances a young man who took me seriously. Now by the world at large—or such of its members as knew me—I was supposed to be funny. At school I had had that reputation, although I had wished to excel as an athlete. This man took me seriously. He had no sense of humor.

One day he came to me with the suggestion that I act as manager for a provincial company he was going to get up, and I accepted with delight.

I could go on writing, and I had an assured income. The only drawback to the arrangement was the necessity of parting with Dan. The time came to go, and I found myself reluctant to leave my friends, found myself thinking of Norah, Deleglise's daughter.

I went to bid her good-by, and the talk fell on love, a subject that we discussed quite dispassionately, even academically. She told me the kind of man who would fall in love with her, after I had told her that he would be a good-natured, commonplace—

She cut me off. "He'll be alive, and he'll want me, and I'll want him."

And so we parted with a business-like handshake.

I left London, full of hopes of success. I came back to London a year later, defeated, disgraced. For reasons of his own, Urban Vane had not cared to have his name appear as the real manager of the company, and it was some time before I found out why. The play we used I had supposed to be his, and I had helped him rearrange it for production. Too late I learned that he had stolen it from the desk of a well-known dramatist. The man had been taken ill, and Vane had hoped he would die, in which event his robbery never would come to light. But the dramatist recovered and came to England, and then it was that Vane told me his story.

I was amazed at his dishonesty. He smiled, and told me that I was equally involved; in fact, in the eyes of the world I was the sinner. Was not my name on all the play-bills? I was shocked, angry, impotent.

And then Vane disappeared and I learned that the company held me responsible for salaries and would not accept my explanations. He had poisoned their minds against me.

Back to London I came, disgraced. There I fell ill, alone, and if I had died I should not have cared. When I was convalescing I met Norah one day in a park, and told her my tale.

She asked me how much I owed the company; and I told her it was about one hundred and fifty pounds. She gave me to understand, and her tone was rough, that if I rested until I had paid every penny, I was no man. But how? By writing funny stories, she told me. They must be funny, and she would market them for me. But until I had paid the uttermost farthing she would not shake hands with me.

It was three years before I won that handshake; and in those three years I won something else—the reputation of being a writer of humorous sketches. She was a good agent. She bolstered up my prices, and sold my stories under an assumed name to Dan, who was now editor of a paper.

In that time I was invited to the wedding of Miss Rosina Sellars, the lady from whom I had fled. I had almost forgotten that phase of my career, but I went to the wedding and to the wedding breakfast with a thankful heart. I might have been the husband if I had not realized in time that the better part of valor was discretion.

I climbed steadily upward. It had not been my ambition to become a humorist. I knew full well that the man who has the tag "humorist" fastened on him is never allowed to do better things; but humor paid me, and I needed the money, and so I fell. It is always so that the man who can make folk laugh feels that he has missed his calling and wishes that he could instruct them; but if he once puts his hand to the plow of humor he must never turn back if he would.

From sketch-writing I turned to play-writing, as my old manager of chorus days called for a comic opera. When this was finished—I wrote it in the country, away from noise and suggestion—although I had received suggestions in plenty from every member of the company before I began it—I read it to them amid a silence that was portentous. Most of them had trains to catch when I had finished, and the gloom of all, especially of myself, was very deep. The manager thought it clever, but from the box-office point of view impossible, and he added that he never made a mistake.

One by one the different members gave me their ideas as to how their parts ought to be written, and one by one I took their advice and patched up a fearful thing.

And then when it was done I read the riot act to the manager—told him that he had contracted to produce my opera, and he must produce it as I had first written it. He was welcome to the other hodge-podge, to do what he liked with it, but I had no interest in it. By the terms of my contract I had him, and he produced my original work.

Afraid of the result, I went to the Continent, and it was not until a month later that I learned that my opera was a great success. I also learned that old Deleglise was dead, and Norah was left alone. Back to London I went once more, and received congratulations enough to turn my head. The manager reminded me that he never made a mistake, and that he had predicted great things of me, and the several members of the company were ready with their "I told you it would hit 'ems."

Successful at last, I went to see Norah. And we shook hands.

SARAH ORNE JEWETT

(United States, 1849)

A COUNTRY DOCTOR (1884)

Miss Jewett's father was a physician in South Berwick, Me., and in her childhood she was wont to accompany him in his visits to outlying farms and distant villages. We are therefore justified in believing that he figures in these pages, lovingly portrayed. In all probability, *Dunport* is Portsmouth, N. H.; the river is the Piscataqua; and Oldfields is a picture of the author's birthplace.

ON a November night, the inmates of the farm-houses of Oldfields—women busy with knitting, men, in the intervals of pipe-smoking and cider-drinking—gave prominence in their gossip to Adeline Thacher and her blasted ambitions. With "a dreadful cravin' to be somethin' more'n common," she had left her native village to work in a factory in Lowell, whence she had drifted to Dunport, there to attract by her pretty face the attention of handsome Jack Prince, her superior socially and mentally. His estrangement from his proud family followed; married life failed to bring the realization of the woman's hopes; the couple wandered much and quarreled more, till they were freed by the husband's death in a Western town. Adeline returned to Dunport to bury him, but insolently resented the overtures of the Princes and their pleas for the custody of her little daughter. She struggled along, no one knew how, beset by failing health and an inherited passion for drink, till the battle went wholly against her, and she turned her face toward her old home.

She had reached Oldfields on this particular night, ending, or perhaps simply continuing, her journey on foot; flitted ghost-like in the darkness across fields and pastures, with her child in her arms; barely resisted the temptation to drown herself, and reached the familiar doorstep, where she fell in a swoon. In spite of loving and motherly care, she died before daybreak, after committing little Anna to the guardianship of Dr. Leslie, tested friend of the community and of the countryside—the beloved physician, in truth, who was the repository of more secrets than even the minister of the First Parish Church. His slender figure had the bowed shoulders of an untiring scholar. There was something singularly self-reliant and composed about him, and wherever one might place him he instinctively took command.

The trust was sacredly observed, and Nan, as she was called, remained with her grandmother, though the latter felt herself incompetent to rear such a mischievous though loving-hearted child. The doctor's oversight was nominal; but his interest increased as he watched the little one develop in mind and flower into positive beauty, and in return for his affectionate regard he received an almost dog-like devotion. Nan won also the liking of most of the village folk by her many amiable qualities, and scandalized the rest by her pranks. She devoted more time to coursing over the fields, like an untethered colt, than to discovering what was in her school-books. For a quiet pastime she invented stories about the mysterious aunt in Dunport, painting her as a veritable queen. A remittance for her support came yearly from her namesake—came, but was not expended, for Mrs. Thacher refused to be beholden to the Princes, and as long as she lived she kept aunt and niece apart.

Her grandmother's death caused Nan's transference to the house of the doctor, a childless widower, fortunately to the satisfaction of Marilla Thomas, his housekeeper—Marilla, whose hats were grotesque and whose devotion to the weekly prayer-meeting was sublime. The girl became the doctor's companion on many a long and otherwise lonely drive, and believed his assurance that she was indispensable. She acquired a more than superficial knowledge of methods of procedure in cases of illness, and when one day he jestingly asked, "What are you going to do when you grow up?" she gravely answered: "I should like best to be a doctor." His delight in her surprising interest in medical matters was not shared by his intimate friends. He won over, it is true, his old classmate, Dr. Ferris, who had known Nan's father when in early manhood the latter had been an assistant ship's-surgeon; and he almost convinced his valued neighbor, Mrs. Graham, who—housed by lameness, white-capped, serene, always seated in the same chair, by the same window—looked upon his frequent and unprofessional visits as events. To his remark that he intended to help Nan to keep, not to break, the law of her nature, the lady gave answer:

"Don't you think that a married life is happiest?"

She hoped to hear no more of such plans; but she knew the doctor too well to question his wisdom.

The time came for the girl to be sent to boarding-school; and, this period of exile ended, she returned to Oldfields, but only to exist, with no satisfactory reason for existing. Occupations formerly attractive interested her only for the time; she was adrift without a compass, and continued to drift until, as she rested in one of her old playgrounds after a ramble, perplexing herself as to her place in the world, there came a sudden realization of the fact that she had lost sight of the work God had peculiarly fitted her to do. The decision to take up medicine being seriously reached, a new day dawned. She began her studies under the doctor, as eager to learn as he to teach, and with his loving tutelage advanced so rapidly that her services as assistant or as nurse became invaluable.

The Oldfields training was supplemented by a course at a city medical school, and there Nan took another important step—that of writing to her aunt, having come to look upon the relationship with clearer eyes, and to feel a longing to know her only near relatives. A brief note, "very respectful and lady-like" in the opinion of Captain Walker Parish, Miss Prince's cousin, was answered by one equally brief, devoid of sentiment, inviting Nan to spend a few days if it were convenient. Without doubt, the girl was merely a copy of the ill-bred woman "who had beguiled and ruined poor Jack"; but Miss Prince would do her duty.

On reaching Dunport Nan grasped no welcoming hand. Unescorted, she rode to the great colonial mansion that sheltered Miss Prince and her heirlooms. She saw the shipping, the wharves, the narrow streets where her father had played when a boy. A vast inheritance of memories and associations was dimly brought to mind by the breath of the sea, for her Grandfather Prince had been a ship-master. She entered the house as one with as much right to domicile as the portraits on the walls, and by her beauty and well-born manner won an easy victory. Overcome by the family resemblance, Miss Prince capitulated tearfully, instantly, and with the confession: "I did not think I should be so glad to see you." Later, as she smiled across the tea-cups at her guest, she murmured to herself: "Blood will tell."

Nan was displayed at church next morning, not as a family skeleton, but as a relative to be proud of. The best families examined her critically and then accorded the recognition that was due to her charm and her charms. The young people of Miss Prince's set welcomed her as a delightful companion. Invitations succeeded invitations; boat-rides followed picnics. The visit was prolonged, for Miss Prince was loath to part with one who seemed so necessary to her own happiness. Cherishing the hope of keeping Nan permanently in Dunport, she, as a means to that end, encouraged the evident interest in her niece that was shown by young George Gerry. He was the son of an old lover, separated from her by a misunderstanding. The father was dead, but the young man was his living image and therefore was deeply beloved by Miss Prince, who intended to make him one of her heirs. Gerry was a well-established lawyer, and had everything to his credit. An ideal match, if it could be made, thought the lady, and in that opinion Captain Parish concurred. He expressed his sentiments to the young woman herself, in a confidential chat, and could not understand her attitude, though she aptly used the simile of a ship richly freighted and nearing port, only to be taken "where its cargo would be next to useless."

Nan could easily have loved George Gerry, and for a time after coming to Dunport she almost forgot her "mission," so alluring were the womanly, sheltered fashions of life toward which she had been thankful to see her friends go, hand-in-hand. Nevertheless, she anticipated with dread the time when she should have to hear her admirer's avowal. He, like Miss Prince and her friend, Mrs. Fraley, who held that a dining-room, not a dissecting-room, was the proper place for a woman, believed it possible to dissuade Nan from following any profession. He blamed Dr. Leslie for encouraging her mannish proclivities. He could not understand her self-reliance, her evident ability to get along capitally well without him. At last he made his declaration, at twilight, while they were boating together.

She listened to his pleas, his arguments, his almost sarcastic protests, but was not shaken by them, much as her heart inclined to him.

"I could not marry the whole of myself, as most women can," she said; "there is a great share of my life which could—only hide itself and be sorry."

Though he suffered defeat, his whole soul was filled with homage in the midst of its sorrow, because this girl stood nearer to holier things than himself. Her language had been free from cant, but she had expressed her conviction that she was called of God to this special work, therefore no backward steps could be taken. When he had left her at the door, she listened to his footsteps as he went away. They were slower than usual, but she did not call him back.

Dr. Leslie, having received short letters of late, surmised that Nan was passing through some new experience, but he waited patiently. She would bring this important question to him, with her usual frankness. He could not bear that she should lose any happiness that might be hers, and he shrank from forbidding her to grasp it. She told her story calmly, without regrets, and he rejoiced anew in this brave young creature, to whose glorious future all his heart and hopes went out.

Refusing more than one appointment in city hospitals, and postponing the pursuance of her studies at a school in Europe, Nan spent another year at Oldfields. Here was a teacher than whom no wiser could be found; here were the fast friends of her girlhood, mostly of the homespun variety—Jacob and Martin Dyer, who, though brothers and almost inseparable, always had inexhaustible topics for conversation; "Mrs. Jake," who invariably had the mate to any complaint she had heard of; "Mrs. Martin," too optimistic to be troubled by "narves."

She gave herself a holiday one November morning, and took a path across well-known fields. Pausing on the doorstep of the house that had been her grandmother's, she saw her early life spreading itself out like a picture. As she tried to follow herself back into the cloudy days of her earliest spring, she rose and went down the pastures toward the river. She passed the graveyard where her mother lay, her evil deeds buried with her, the mother who in shame and sorrow had brought her to Oldfields on a drear November night. Comforted by the hope that in a better world some lingering love and faith had given the true direction at last, Nan proceeded to the river bank to gaze across the river and beyond it to the hills. The soft air and the sunshine came close to her; the trees stood about and seemed to watch her; and suddenly she raised her hands in an ecstasy of life and strength and gladness. "O God!" she said, "I thank thee for my future."

SAMUEL JOHNSON

(England, 1709–1784)

THE HISTORY OF RASSELAS, PRINCE OF ABYSSINIA (1759)

Dr. Johnson wrote this story in the evenings of one week, to pay the expenses of his mother's funeral. It was printed from the manuscript as first written, and he received from the publisher one hundred pounds. Aside from his great Dictionary, it is his most celebrated work. His first literary work was a translation from the French of Jeronimo Lobo's *Historia de Ethiopia* (entitled, in the translation, *A Voyage to Abyssinia*), and the knowledge thus obtained probably gave him the idea of *Rasselas*.

IT was the custom of the monarchs of Abyssinia to seclude the young princes and princesses in a spacious valley. There, in a private palace, Rasselas, fourth son of the Emperor, was confined. The entrance to the valley was through a cavern that passed under a rock, the opening at each end being carefully hidden. The valley supplied its inhabitants with the necessaries of life, and the luxuries were added at the annual visit of the Emperor. Here the sons and daughters of Abyssinia lived to know only the soft vicissitudes of pleasure and repose. They lay down at night, and rose in the morning, pleased with one another and with themselves—all but Rasselas, who in the twenty-sixth year of his age began to withdraw himself and to delight in solitary walks. On one occasion, a wise man who was a member of the community of the happy valley followed him and heard his utterances.

"What makes the difference," he said reflectively, "between man and the rest of the animal creation? Every beast around me hungers and thirsts as I do; it eats, drinks, and is satisfied. But I am not satisfied. Man surely has some latent sense for which this place affords no gratification, or some desire, apart from sense, that must be satisfied before he can be happy."

The old sage, believing that he now understood the cause of his disquiet, endeavored to give him counsel.

"You, sir," said he, "are the first to complain of the happy valley. Look around, and tell me which of your wants are without supply. And if you want nothing, how are you unhappy?"

"That I want nothing, or that I know not what I want," said the Prince, "is the cause of my complaint. I have already enjoyed too much; give me something to desire."

"Sir," said the sage, "if you had seen the miseries of the world, you would know how to value your present state."

"Now," said the Prince, "I shall long to see the miseries of the world, since the sight of them is necessary to happiness."

The suggestion of the sage served to extend the reflections of Rasselas over a wider space and to lighten the burden of life. He busied himself so intensely in the visionary bustle of a world he never had seen that he forgot his real solitude. And thus passed twenty months of his life. At the end of that time he became aware that, although he had resolved to leave the happy valley, he had not taken a single step toward doing so.

"Twenty months are gone; who can restore them?" he exclaimed with sorrow. The next ten months he spent in fruitless searches for a means of exit, and, although discouraged, he held to his purpose and studied all expedients.

Among the inhabitants of the happy valley was a man eminent for his mechanical powers. Rasselas often visited him, and on one occasion found him deeply interested in a contrivance for flying. This at once suggested to the Prince a means of escape, and with intense excitement Rasselas watched the perfecting of the artist's invention. But when the experiment was made the wings were useless to sustain the inventor in the air, and Rasselas perceived that he must depend on other means if he would ever really get beyond the encircling mountains.

While occupied with melancholy thoughts, the Prince became interested in a poet named Imlac, who had been much in the world and had retired to the happy valley for the remaining years of his life. From him Rasselas drew the story of his experiences.

"My father," said the poet, "was a rich merchant. He had two desires—to be rich, and to conceal his riches, lest he should be despoiled by the governors of the province."

"Surely," interrupted the Prince, "my father must be negligent if any man in his dominions dares take that which belongs to another. Name the governor who robbed the people, that I may declare his crimes to the Emperor."

"Sir," said Imlac, "your ardor is the natural effect of virtue animated by youth. But no form of government has yet been devised by which oppression can be wholly prevented."

"This," said the Prince, "I do not understand. But continue thy narration."

"My father often expressed his hope," continued Imlac, "that I should be the richest man in Abyssinia."

"Why," asked the Prince, "did thy father desire increase of his wealth, when it was already greater than he dared discover or enjoy?"

"Those whose real wants are satisfied must admit those of fancy," said Imlac. "I engaged in commerce, but, as I was rich and ignorant, my companions saw me robbed and plundered, even without advantage to themselves."

"Stop a moment," said the Prince. "Is there such depravity in man as that he should injure another without benefit to himself?"

"Envy," said Imlac, "feels not its own happiness but when it may be compared with the misery of another. Wherever I went I found that poetry was considered to be the highest learning, and I became ambitious to add my name to the illustrious fraternity of poets. All the appearances of nature, therefore, I was careful to study."

"In so wide a survey," said the Prince, "you must have left much unobserved. I cannot take a walk within the circuit of these mountains without seeing something before unheeded."

"But the knowledge of nature," resumed Imlac, "is only half the task of the poet. He must also be acquainted with all the modes of life. He must know many languages and many sciences, and must familiarize to himself every delicacy of speech and grace of harmony."

Imlac was proceeding to aggrandize his profession when the Prince cried:

"Enough! thou hast convinced me that no man can be a poet."

Imlac then recounted his travels and said that, having acquired great wealth and much learning, he returned home, after twenty years, expecting the approval of his father and honor from his fellow-countrymen. Alas! his father had been dead fourteen years, his countrymen suspected him because they regarded him as a foreigner, and he hastened to the happy valley to escape from the world and find happiness at last.

"Hast thou found happiness?" asked the Prince.

"Great Prince," answered the poet sadly, "I am less unhappy than the rest, because I have a mind replete with images."

"My dear Imlac," said the Prince, "I have long meditated escape from the happy valley. Thou shalt be the partner of my fortune, my sole director in the choice of life."

Imlac finally agreed, and after much study a way was devised of piercing the mountain, a feat that was at last accomplished. Then Rasselas, his sister, the Princess Nekayah, and her favorite maid, with Imlac, crept through the opening and emerged on the outer mountain-side. The Prince and the Princess had an immense fortune concealed in their clothing in jewels, and the little company went to Cairo. There they were at first stunned by the noise and offended by the crowds. Imlac purchased a house, and after two years the Prince and the Princess became versed in the language, instructed in the use and value of money, and used to the new conditions. Rasselas had a great hope that he should now determine a choice of life.

"Very few," said the poet, "live by choice."

"My birth," said the Prince, "will enable me to determine for myself. I have here the world before me. Surely, happiness is somewhere to be found."

He sought the young and gay. But he soon left their society. Their mirth was without images; their laughter without motive; their pleasures gross. He never could be happy in a life of which he would be ashamed. He then turned to a sage who discoursed with energy on the government of the feelings, exhorting all to arm themselves against the shafts of misfortune by invulnerable patience. But later he found the old man overwhelmed with grief at the loss of a daughter. All his fortitude was gone, and Rasselas, although his courtesy would not allow him to insult misery with reproach, was convinced of the emptiness of rhetorical sound.

Hearing of a hermit who lived near the lowest cataract of the Nile, he went, accompanied by Nekayah and Imlac, to visit him, to learn whether the happiness vainly sought in the resorts of pleasure and the temple of learning was to be found in solitude. On the way the party passed a beautiful palace, were invited to enter, and were elegantly entertained. "Here," thought Rasselas, "is happiness." But the host mournfully told him that he was living in hourly fear of being plundered by the officers of the Bassa of Egypt, whose envy he had aroused by his wealth. So the travelers left him, grateful that his conditions were not theirs. When they reached the hermit they discovered to their amazement that, although he had left the world because he was disgusted with society, he was now even more disgusted with solitude, and had but one wish, to return to Cairo. He dug up his treasure, and shed tears of rapture when, having returned with his guests, he once more saw the streets of the city he had left.

Deeply impressed by the change in the hermit's choice of life, Rasselas questioned the learned men whose society he sought as to their opinion. Some thought that he should have paid for his foolish choice by being condemned to persevere in it; some thought him a hypocrite; some considered him a deserter from duty; some maintained that a man earns a right to rest after years of labor; one believed that his choice was not yet final, that he would return to solitude, and then again to society; one dogmatically asserted that the way to be happy is to live according to nature.

"Let me only know," said the Prince modestly, "what it is to live according to nature."

"It is to concur with the great and unchangeable scheme of universal felicity; to coöperate with the general disposition and tendency of the present system of things," was the philosopher's answer. Rasselas perceived that he was one of the sages who are the less to be understood the more they say. So he bowed in silence. The philosopher supposed him satisfied, and departed with the air of a man who had coöperated with the present system.

The Prince and the Princess next determined to divide their search after the abode of happiness. The Prince should frequent the halls of the great; the Princess the homes of the lowly. The Prince soon discovered that the Bassa was surrounded by spies and traitors in the guise of flatterers. In fact, he was just then carried in chains to Constantinople.

"Is only the Sultan safe and happy?" thought the Prince.

While he reflected thus, word came that the Sultan had been murdered by the Janizaries, and again the mind of the seeker after happiness was perplexed.

Nekayah, on her part, found that many evils infest humble life. She discovered that in homes of seeming affluence the daily struggle is to conceal poverty; that parents and children seldom act in concert; that age looks with anger on the temerity of youth, and youth with contempt on the scrupulosity of age; that some husbands are imperious and some wives perverse; that though marriage has many pains, celibacy has no pleasures.

"What then is to be done?" asked Rasselas. "The more we question, the less we resolve. I have become convinced that quiet is not the daughter of grandeur or power. Surely, the humble man, whose abilities are adequate to his employments, who chooses by his own knowledge all whom he trusts, has nothing to do but to be virtuous and happy."

"Whether perfect happiness could be procured by perfect goodness," said Nekayah, "this world will never give us the opportunity of deciding. But this, at least, may be maintained—that we do not always find visible happiness in proportion to visible virtue."

The conversation turned upon the married state, and Rasselas was inclined to think that it must be intended by nature to be a means of happiness.

"I know not," said the Princess, "whether marriage be more than one of the many forms of human misery."

"I cannot forbear to flatter myself," said the Prince, "that prudence and benevolence will make marriage happy. Whenever I shall seek a wife, it shall be my first question whether she be willing to be led by reason."

"Thus it is," said Nekayah, "that philosophers are deceived. Wretched would be the pair who should be doomed to adjust by reason the minute details of a domestic day. Long consideration is often fatal to action."

At this point Imlac entered, and urged the young people to visit some of the great monuments of antiquity.

"It seems to me," he said, "that while you are making a choice of life, you are forgetting to live. Ignorance, when it is voluntary, is criminal."

They visited the great Pyramid and were astonished at its extent. As they were about to enter, Pekuah, Nekayah's favorite, trembled and drew back. So she was allowed to remain outside in the tents with the women who had accompanied the guides. When the party had finished their survey and had returned to the tent, they were met with the shocking tidings that Pekuah had been carried off by a band of Arabs. All means were taken to recover her, and after two months of fruitless search, Nekayah declared her intention of entering a cloister. But before she carried out her purpose, news was brought that the lady Pekuah was in the hands of an Arab chief and would be given up for two hundred ounces of gold. Payment was quickly made, and the Princess embraced her favorite unharmed. When Pekuah described the wearisome days she had spent in the chief's castle, where she was treated with the greatest consideration, Nekayah said:

"There were women in your Arab's fortress. Why did not you partake their diversions?"

"Their diversions," said Pekuah, "were only childish play, by which a mind accustomed to stronger operations could not be kept busy."

"How," said Rasselas, "can the Arab, whom you represent as a man of more than ordinary accomplishments, find any pleasure in a seraglio of women like these? Were they exquisitely beautiful?"

"They do not want that unaffecting and ignoble beauty

which may subsist without sprightliness or sublimity, without energy of thought or dignity of virtue," said Pekuah.

"You have reason to think yourself happy, lady," said Imlac, "that you have been so easily dismissed."

Rasselas now announced to Imlac that he had resolved to make solitude, enlivened only by the pursuit of science, his choice of life.

"Before you make your choice final," said Imlac, "you must converse with some of those great scientific men who have grown old in their own society. I have just left the observatory of one of the wisest men in the world. His comprehension is vast, his memory capacious and retentive, his discourse methodical, and his expression clear. His integrity and benevolence are equal to his learning."

"Surely," said the Princess, "this man is happy."

"We were sitting last night in the turret of his house," continued Imlac, "when he addressed these words to me: 'I have long discharged an office that I shall soon quit and shall rejoice to devolve upon you. I have possessed for five years the regulation of the weather and the distribution of the seasons. The sun has listened to my dictates, the clouds and the Nile have obeyed my command. The winds alone have denied my authority. I have administered this great office with exact justice.'"

"'How long, sir,' I said, trying to conceal my amazement and doubt, 'has this great office been in your hands?'"

"'About ten years ago I began to think of the blessings I could confer if I had the power of the seasons. Since then I have possessed and every day exerted it.' He then gave me minute instructions as to the use of this power when it became mine."

The Prince heard this narration with seriousness, but the Princess smiled and the Lady Pekuah was convulsed with laughter.

"Ladies," said Imlac gravely, "few can attain this man's knowledge, and few practise his virtues, but all may suffer his calamity. This, sir, is one of the dangers of solitude—fictions begin to operate as realities."

"I will no more," said Pekuah, "imagine myself Queen of Abyssinia."

"And I," said the Princess, "will no more play the shepherdess in my waking dreams."

"I will confess," said the Prince, "to an indulgence of fantastic delight more dangerous than yours. I have frequently endeavored to image the possibility of a perfect government, by which all wrong should be restrained, all vice reformed, and all the subjects preserved in tranquillity and innocence. I tremble at the coldness with which I have considered the death of my father and brothers that I might work out my plans of reform."

The lady Pekuah expressed a great desire to visit the astronomer, and as she had studied the heavens under the direction of the Arab chief, she was able to converse with him intelligently. The Princess accompanied her, and the old astronomer was delighted with their visits. They induced him to visit the house of Imlac, where he proved himself a most instructive companion. The Prince and his sister became so convinced of his wisdom that they asked his advice as to a choice of life.

"I am not able to instruct you," said the sage. "I can only tell you that I have chosen wrong. Even of those prerogatives which I have obtained above other students I begin to doubt the reality."

From these words Imlac perceived that the mists that had gathered over his intellect in solitude had begun to disperse as he mingled with society.

Nekayah expressed a wish to see something she had not yet seen, and it was decided that all should visit the Catacombs. While they were inspecting those ancient abodes of the dead, the conversation turned on the views held by the Egyptians of the relation between the soul and the body.

"It is commonly supposed," said Imlac, "that the Egyptians believed that the soul lived as long as the body continued undissolved."

"Could the wise Egyptians," asked Nekayah, "think so grossly of the soul?"

"The Egyptians would doubtless think erroneously," said the astronomer; "but some say that it may be material who nevertheless believe it to be immortal."

"Some," answered Imlac, "have indeed said that the soul is material; but all the conclusions of reason enforce the immateriality of mind, and all the notices of sense and investigations of science concur to prove the unconsciousness of matter."

"But the materialists," said the astronomer, "urge that matter may have qualities with which we are unacquainted."

"We know that matter is inert, senseless, and lifeless," said Imlac. "If that which is known can be overruled by that which is unknown, no being that is not omniscient can arrive at certainty."

"Does immateriality," asked Nekayah, "necessarily include eternal duration?"

"Immateriality," said Imlac, "seems to imply a natural power of duration as a consequence of exemption from all causes of decay."

"But," said Nekayah, "the Being who made the soul can destroy it."

"He surely can destroy it," said Imlac. "But that it will not be annihilated by Him that made it, we must humbly learn from higher authority."

"Let us return," said Rasselas, "from this scene of mortality. Those that lie stretched here before us were, perhaps, snatched away while they were busy like us in the choice of life."

"To me," said the Princess, "the choice of life is less important. I hope hereafter to think only on the choice of eternity."

They then hastened out of the caverns, and under the protection of their guard returned to Cairo.

It was now the time of the inundation of the Nile, and they were confined to their house. They diverted themselves with comparisons of the different forms of life they had observed, and with various schemes of happiness which they had conceived. But of the wishes they had formed they well knew that none could be obtained. And as they had discovered that neither youth nor age, solitude nor society, affluence nor poverty, high station nor humble birth, learning nor ignorance, marriage nor celibacy, can give assurance of happiness, after deliberation they resolved, when the inundation should cease, to return to Abyssinia.

MARY JOHNSTON

(United States, 1870)

TO HAVE AND TO HOLD (1890)

This novel, the author's second romance, was dramatized shortly after the book was published, and was produced in New York City. But, notwithstanding its great success as a novel, it was a failure in its dramatic form, and was quickly withdrawn.

IN the midsummer of 1621, when Indian uprisings in Virginia were common, I took the advice of my friend Rolfe, who had wedded and lost an Indian princess. He advised me to go to Jamestown, and, with one hundred and twenty pounds of tobacco, to buy myself a wife, as a ship had arrived bearing threescore damsels sent over to wed the early settlers of the New World.

In truth, I was lonely. At thirty-six years of age a man should have more company than his books, his dogs, and his gun can give him. So I threw dice to see whether I should marry, and it came out that I should. With my man, Diccon, I left my home in Weyanoke Hundred and went to Jamestown, where I saw a maid of amazing beauty and rare distinction, who had recently landed from the newly arrived ship. Later I came upon her in the cedar wood, where I found her struggling with a man who tried to kiss her. I knocked him down, and as he fell near the stream, with the toe of my boot I lifted him into it. She laughed, and then, seeing other men coming toward us, her eyes met mine with the look of a hunted animal.

"Will you marry me, madam?" I demanded, of a sudden impulse.

She asked me whether I lived in the town, and I told her I

lived some miles away. "Then, in God's name, let's be gone!" she cried.

Beside a grassy hillock we were married by Master Jeremy Sparrow, a godly minister, once a player and a favorite of Ben Jonson's, with a frame like a giant and a voice like an organ. When he asked her name, after a deep silence she said softly, "Jocelyn Leigh," although on shipboard she had borne another name. We then got into my boat, but in spite of my efforts at conversation she refused to talk and feigned sleep until we arrived at my wharf. My men, headed by Diccon, had prepared a bridal feast and decorations within the house. I led her to her room, and then waited for her in the great room where the feast was spread. She was so long in coming that I went softly to the half-open door and looked within. She was kneeling in the middle of the room, her arm upraised, and on her face such a look of terror that I stole back, feeling guilty to have seen it. Presently she came out, showing no trace of anguish. She made scant pretense of eating, and then told me how she came to be here. She said that she was not safe in England; that she had joined the boatload of Sir Edwyn Sandys's damsels in the guise of her own maid, and had come to Virginia to escape a great wrong. Then, in a voice of exceeding sweetness and humility, she asked that I hold her as she held herself—simply as a guest within my house. She threw herself upon my mercy and my honor; and before I could prevent her she was kneeling at my feet. I took her hand and told her to rise, assuring her she had nothing to fear. On her way to her room she brushed against the rack whereon my weapons hung. Seeing a small dagger, she tried stealthily to detach the blade; but she did not understand how to do it, and was passing on when I crossed the room, loosened it, and presented it to her with a smile and a bow. She blushed deeply, but took it.

As I was chosen burgess for this hundred, I was obliged to live in Jamestown. Mistress Ralph Percy, my lady wife, wished to go with me, so I took her, her maid, and Diccon—once a cutthroat and gamester, whom ten years before I had saved from being broken on the wheel. Dale had sold him into slavery, and I bought him because he asked me to, and because he had been a horse-boy in my regiment. Once, when I caught him looking at Jocelyn, I had to remind him of this and to make him take an oath to hold my wife in all reverence. He took the oath. On our way we met Master Jeremy Sparrow, who asked us to stay with him at the minister's house, where he lived. I accepted gladly, and when we came to the palisades we found the gates open and the warden gone, and within the town not a soul was to be seen, as they were all at the port watching a ship just come in. The Governor demanded my attendance, and leaving Mistress Percy in Sparrow's charge, I departed.

On came the English ship, banners flying, music playing. The first man that came ashore after she anchored was Lord Carnal, the King's latest favorite, the handsomest man I ever saw. He it was who had supplanted Buckingham. As he came to the spot where I stood beside the Governor, I felt a touch upon my shoulder and turned to see my wife's face, deadly pale and with eyes aflame. With her hand on my arm, she asked me in a fierce voice to remember that she was my wife and to bring both sword and wit to her service.

Lord Carnal presented the Governor with a packet from the King, and told him that his Majesty wished him to assist him in the quest that had brought him there. He then caught sight of Mistress Percy; his excitement attracted every eye, and in a breath he was bowing over her hand, exulting aloud that his quest had ended when he thought it had just begun.

She said in a clear voice: "My lord, permit me to present you to my husband, Captain Ralph Percy; I think you know his cousin, my Lord of Northumberland."

He and I looked in each other's eyes and understood that the gauntlet had been thrown. Turning to the Governor, Lord Carnal told how a jewel had disappeared from court, a jewel promised to him by the King, who had sworn by his kingdom that it should be his. He added significantly that he meant to find it and wear it, turning his bold eyes upon the woman beside me.

Surprised to learn that these two had met at court, the Governor asked my wife her name. Here I interposed with insolent banter with my Lord Carnal and a reckless reference to his birth, hinting at the story of the well-known affair of the late Lord Carnal with a serving-woman in the employ of the

French Ambassador's wife. At this his rapier was out and he thrust at me. The next minute I sent it whirling to the Governor's feet. Men rushed between us in an instant, warning me that if I hurt a hair of the King's favorite I was lost. We parted, with a secret understanding that our duel was but postponed; and my wife and I made our way to the minister's house.

When we were left alone she asked whether I had no questions to ask. I said: "None, Madame."

"I was the King's ward!" she said. I bowed.

Then, seeing that I would not speak, she asked me to listen to the reason why she came to wrong me so. Her mother had died when she was born; her father while she was still very young. She was the King's ward and a favorite of the Queen. Shortly after she was sixteen years old the King promised her in marriage to my Lord Carnal. To escape this hateful bondage she had fled in the dress of her waiting-maid and embarked under her name. Then she added: "The one man who approached me with respect I gulled and cheated, and I allowed him to give me his name, behind which I shelter myself. You cannot despise me more than I despise myself."

I told her that my sword was at her service; that what was mine was hers; that I had pride in keeping my name untarnished, and that I feared not to leave it in her keeping. From excitement and exhaustion she fainted. I did what I could for her, then called her maid and stepped out of doors.

From a trusty friend who called soon, I learned the will of the King. He demanded that the lady be sent back to England immediately in the ship just arrived, and that the man she had married be sent back in irons on the same ship. "If he swears he is innocent of her station, and gives her up, he will be sent back to America honorably, with money enough for another wife; otherwise he will have to deal with the whole court—and my Lord Carnal."

I learned that the Governor had demanded that the King's commands should come through the London Company as usual; that the Company always obeyed the King, and that we must obey the Company; consequently, the ship was to return, carrying the humble petition that his Gracious Majesty should continue to send his commands as usual, and they should be most obediently carried out.

All this was told to me as I sat outside our dwelling; as I turned toward the door, hidden by the vines, I found that my wife had overheard all our talk and had learned also of my duel with Lord Carnal, which was to take place the next morning at sunrise. She begged me to make peace while I might, and refused to have my blood upon her soul, while thanking me for my forbearance and courtesy. I poured out a cup of wine, held it to her lips, and commanded her to drink. Then I put it to my own. Thus we drank of the same cup.

Our duel the next morning was interrupted by the Governor, who commanded us to desist and gave us our choice of giving our word of honor that we would not draw swords upon each other until the King had made known his will to the London Company, or being kept in strict confinement, I in jail and my Lord Carnal in the Governor's house. We sheathed our swords and gave our word to suspend animosity.

I believed my Lord Carnal capable of any act of revenge, and so I never left my wife unguarded during that summer. One day in early autumn, wearied of her confinement, she asked leave to take her maid Angela and slip across the strip of sand to explore the woods on the other side. On the morrow I promised that she should go, accompanied by her maid, Master Sparrow, and Diccon. Just before daybreak I was summoned to the Governor's house. He was fearful of an Indian uprising, and I was ordered to go with a dozen men and bring the Paspaheghs to their senses. I hurried back to the house for my horse, and on the way was subtly warned by a good friend of mine to beware of Lord Carnal's Italian doctor, whom I had kicked off my place the day before on finding him spying around. Arriving home, I roused Diccon, ordered my horse, went to my room, armed myself, and found that Master Jeremy Sparrow had been called away. I cautioned Diccon that his mistress was not to go to the woods the next day. "This is a trust, Diccon," I said. He saluted me as his captain and said he so understood it. Satisfied, I rode away.

Arriving at the village of the Chickahominies, Rolfe and I were received with savage ceremony and hellish noise. Nantauquas greeted us. He was the brother of Lady Rebekah, the wife of Rolfe, who loved him for his own and his wife's sake. We learned from the great Chief, Opechancanough, that we had nothing to fear from the Paspaheghs, and that he was our friend. Hearing this, we decided that Rolfe should remain at the blockhouse with half our troop, while I should report to the Governor.

I left him, and after making my report to the Governor, I hastened toward home. On the way I met the Italian doctor and a moment later Lord Carnal, who started with surprise at my unexpected return. Then I met Master Jeremy Sparrow, and learned that Mistress Percy, Diccon, and Angela had gone to the wood in spite of my words. As I looked toward the fort and the river, I missed the *Santa Teresa*, which was not anchored in midstream off the big spring. Saddling our horses Sparrow and I set out on our search. Hearing some one coming, we hid in a clump of sumach. Presently my Lord Carnal appeared. Then the Italian doctor came cautiously toward him. There we overheard that they had my lady safe in the woodland called "the haunted forest," and that when evening came they intended to row her out to the *Santa Teresa* and sail for England. Then we heard the Italian doctor say that he had hoped to poison me ere this, and Lord Carnal, with many curses, said he wished he knew my whereabouts at that moment.

"In the forest!" I said, as I rode into view with the minister beside me.

In a moment the giant strength of the minister had swung the Italian to his mare's neck, where he bound the creature's hands with his scarf. I was off my horse, and, mindful of my oath, wrestled with Lord Carnal and threw him. I tied him to the young maple under which we stood and left him, telling him that the knot that bound him was a peculiar one taught me by an Indian, which by diligent work might be undone by nightfall! Deeper in the woods we found my lady and Diccon, who was bound. With the help of the minister's strength and clever ventriloquist power, which so frightened my Lord Carnal's knaves that they believed that all the ghosts of the forest were after them, escape was easy. The minister's kind heart would not allow him to draw the Italian's cords tight enough, so the rascal got away after we left.

When I reached home, I learned that Diccon had not told my wife my desire that she should not go to the woods in my absence. He said he had not thought the Indians would trouble her, and he did not wish to alarm her or to deprive her of her pleasure for nothing. I replied that I might pardon a disobedient servant, but that he had shown himself a soldier faithless to his trust. Taking my whip, I struck him several blows until my wife cried to me to stop. He left us in sullen silence, and Mistress Percy said she feared I had made another enemy.

Shortly after this adventure in the forest, Lord Carnal tried to kill me with poisoned wine. I was thinking of this as I sat alone one afternoon at sunset. A fire was burning fitfully, and the light left great shadows in the room. Glancing at a small Venetian mirror on the wall opposite me, I saw a man enter the room; noiselessly he came toward me and bent over me with a dagger uplifted to strike. I sprang up and caught his wrist. The room was almost dark. I had the dagger and the man at my mercy. I let the dagger fall and scrutinized the man. It was Diccon. I went to the table, and taking my tablets from my doublet I wrote out the guaranty of his freedom, and gave it to him, saying, "You are no longer a man of mine. Begone!"

He crumpled the paper. "I was mad," he muttered. "I could believe it," I said. "I shall never strike you again. But begone!"

He went, but later in the evening Mistress Percy found his paper of freedom torn to bits upon the floor.

Not long after this the English ship returned bearing his Majesty's commands. Sir George Yeardley's petition to be released from the governorship of Virginia was granted, but he was to remain in office until the arrival of the new Governor, Sir Francis Wyatt. I was to be taken into custody six hours after the reading of the papers and was to be returned on the ship in irons, while my lady was to go on the same ship with all pomp and dignity. On arriving in London, I was to go to the Tower, she to Whitehall.

Diccon heard all this before we heard it, and came to warn us, slipping away before we could thank him for his magnanimity. Mistress Percy said she should refuse to obey the King's commands; so while I was arming myself she gathered a bundle of clothes, and together we went out into the night. We were joined by Master Jeremy Sparrow, who insisted upon going with us. His boat had been filled with stores for weeks, and was tied to the piles of the old deserted wharf.

When we reached the boat, I got in first. The minister gave Mistress Percy into my outstretched arms. I put her down beside me in the boat, turned to give my aid to Master Jeremy Sparrow, and faced—Lord Carnal! He whistled, whereupon lights appeared along the lane. I started to cut the boat's rope, and Lord Carnal shouted to his men to hasten, and himself sprang down the steps. Sparrow caught him, striking his head, and flung him into the boat, where he lay unconscious. Then the minister sprang in; I cut loose, and we were safe, as no more boats were there in which our pursuers could follow us. Soon I discovered the faithful Diccon, crouching behind the sail. These were strange shipmates—the wife who was wife in name only; the man who would kill me to marry her; the servant who would have stabbed me, and the minister, who was once a play-actor!

After several days and nights of danger beyond description, while we breasted the angry and perilous sea, our ship went to pieces in sight of land. Then Sparrow, who swam like a fish, took Mistress Percy in his great arms and swam to a beach which proved to be about three leagues from the mainland of Accomae. Neither food nor water was to be found there, and I had made up my mind that, if worse came to worst, I would put my wife out of her misery. She was too weak and wretched with the perils she had passed through to realize the horrible possibilities; and like a child she turned to me for comfort.

Leaving her guarded by Sparrow, to whom I had given Lord Carnal's sword—he now being one of us to fight our common enemy, Death—I walked along the beach. Presently I saw, to my amazement, lying anchored out at sea, a heavily armed ship. Looking across to shore, I perceived a boat drawn up on the beach. When I reached the point above the boat I saw men digging a grave. I surmised that they were pirates and were about to bury their captain. From what I could overhear, I learned they were going to fight for the captaincy of their vessel.

I crept back to Sparrow and instructed him, should I come back alive, to take his cue from me. I returned to the group on the shore, and presented myself to the astonished and villainous-looking combatants as the famous Captain Kirby, the blackest pirate king unhanged, with a ship just sunk. In turn I fought each man, and gloried in their defeat. Finally with all five rogues at my heels, submissive and admiring, I rejoined our party and told Sparrow how I, Kirby, had found these rovers. I introduced Sparrow as my mate, the lady and Lord Carnal as my prisoners, and Diccon Demon as one of my crew.

The ship became our stage, with danger lurking on every side in the shape of meeting shipwreck, and the perils of the pirate life, which we pretended to follow, ready to seize upon the first chance to escape from our distasteful companions. Within sight of Cuba we struck fierce storms, and in the state cabin I held a council of war. With four of us present, I told Lord Carnal that he had been heard the night before plotting an attack upon us with one of the pirates, called simply "the Spaniard." He said sneeringly that I dared do nothing, for should I cry out or make a signal the pirates would break in the door to come to his aid. I replied that if all such arrangements had been made, I agreed that it was time we were gone. "But," I reminded him, "when I bid the world good-night, my wife goes with me." Then I restored to him his sword, and flung my glove at his feet, having decided to kill him then and there. We made ready, but suddenly the door was burst open and excited voices bawled "A ship!" We went on deck. A league away lay Florida, and between us and the glistening beach lay a disabled English merchantman. "An easy prize!" said some of the crew. After desperate commotion, I finally told them that I never would fire upon an English ship, as I was an English gentleman. Immediately from our forecastle came flame and the thunder of guns. I drew my sword; Diccon and the minister moved nearer to me, and at my side stood Jocelyn, the King's ward, white and brave.

Just as the pirates were mercilessly bearing down upon the disabled ship, I nodded my head to Sparrow. He struck the helmsman to the deck with one blow and seized the wheel, jamming it to starboard so that the reef lay across our bows. Amid shrieking and cursing and attempted murder, the boat struck. One of our crew fired point-blank at me.

The next thing I knew I was lying in the blackness of a ship's hold with a torn shoulder; Jeremy Sparrow lay near me in irons, but with free hands to serve my wants, as the crew thought me dying. He told me that my lady was with the gentlewomen aboard; that the ship was the *George*, on the way to Jamestown, and that Diccon had been pressed into service, as they were short-handed. Lord Carnal came to gloat over my suffering and the pirate's death awaiting me. I know not how I knew then that my lady loved me, but I did know it, and when Lord Carnal taunted me about her gaiety and friendliness with him, I told him that he lied, and I knew that what I said was true.

When my wounds had sufficiently healed, I was taken to the state cabin to face my judges, the new Governor of Virginia, his officers, and Lord Carnal. When I said that I had not fired upon the English ship I was told that I lied, and then the cabin-door opened and the Governor's wife entered with the King's ward, who, standing in the center of the semicircle of listeners, told unfalteringly the whole story of Lord Carnal's mad, unscrupulous pursuit of her, her narrative showing the network of his lies. The Governor said her story might have won pardon for her husband had he not fired upon the English ship. A deep silence prevailed. Lord Carnal rose and faced Jocelyn, and she bade him tell the truth. He agreed to do so upon the condition that he might kiss her lips. She consented. Then he told of his unscrupulous passion, and said that the guns were fired without my knowledge and that I had sunk the ship to save the *George*. He then stepped forward and took his reward while I stood by with murder in my heart.

The Governor rose and made me an apology before them all, but would allow me no word with Lord Carnal. With a half sob and a laugh, my wife hid her crimson face upon my breast. All eyes were upon her as I lifted her head, kissed her, and gave her into the keeping of the Governor's wife. Lord Carnal reminded the Governor that I had resisted arrest, and then left the cabin.

I was assigned to better quarters, and I then asked for the

release of the Rev. Jeremy Sparrow, well known to the Dean of St. Paul's.

Spring came, and found me in jail awaiting commands from the King, as my story was sent to him on our landing. Diccon was allowed the freedom of the jail, and Nantauquas, who in the autumn before had promised to tame a panther for my lady, came with a message from Rolfe, who wished to see me alone. Rolfe was admitted to see me, and with him was my wife, who came disguised. He left us alone. In all my life I had kissed her but once, but then I kissed her again and met a warm response. It was an hour of solemn happiness; but she left me with great foreboding of my ruin in her gentle heart.

Diccon slept on his pallet in my room, Since fate had thrown us together again, after our temporary anger, we never wasted words. Late that night the jailer entered with a note for me. It was from my wife, bidding me as I loved her to come to her at once to the deserted hut in the neck of land nearest the forest. With it was a pass in the commander's hand, signed, allowing the bearer to pass beyond the palisade.

With the aid of gold I left the jail unmolested with Diccon, who said that either he should go with me or alarm the house. We passed beyond the palisade and became aware that a panther was following us; it appeared to be a tame panther, probably the one Nantauquas had tamed for my lady. We reached the hut. I forced the door, and saw seated before a dull fire a figure draped in a black cloak. "Jocelyn!" I exclaimed, as I bent over the lonely figure. The head was raised, the cloak fell back, and I looked into the mocking eyes of Lord Carnal's Italian doctor. A warning cry from Diccon roused me, and my Lord Carnal himself entered by the door beyond, and in an instant the room was filled with Paspahegh Indians, my old enemies. I sprang at Lord Carnal and caught him by the sword-wrist and the throat. To and fro we struggled, first one uppermost, then the other, so that the Indians feared to be too bold lest they strike the wrong man. Diccon fought the Indians beside me. With fury I drove Lord Carnal toward the corner of the hut where the panther lay. He gave it a savage kick. At that moment I brought Carnal crashing to the ground, but just as my sword was at his throat my arms were jerked back.

A dozen hands seized and bound me. Lord Carnal rose and stood over me, smiling. "Good night, Captain Percy, a dreamless sleep!" he sneered.

"Have a care!" called the pinioned Diccon. "The panther!" Like a catapult the maddened beast leaped to bury its claws in the handsome face of the man who had kicked it; the claws entered the flesh below the temple and tore downward and across.

Taking Diccon and me captives, the Indians bound us and marched us through the darkness toward a village where torture at the stake was promised us. From this we were saved by the unexpected appearance of our sworn friends, Nantauquas, son of Powhatan and nephew of the great Chief Opechancanough, who, with his warriors, was already at hand. This emperor of the forest asked me to smoke the pipe of peace with him, so for five days I chafed against the delay that kept me from Jamestown and remained among the Indians, although there was horror in the air. On our last night Nantauquas gave us knives and warned us that on our way home we might be murdered, for in three days all the tribes would fall upon the English at Jamestown. I was in an agony of impatience to be off, and at last, laden with gifts and accompanied by our three guides, we were allowed to depart. We saw the guides were bent upon going slowly, so that we should arrive too late to give warning to the English at Jamestown, so at the first opportunity Diccon and I killed them. Then, alone in the forest, we made our dangerous way with what speed we could. A ball from an Indian's musket entered Diccon's side. I bent over him, and took his hand. "Diccon, my man!" I said. I raised his head upon my arm and thus he lay content until he died. I kissed him on the brow, left him in the forest, and stumbled on my way alone. For two days and nights I had not tasted food. Torn and bleeding, I entered Jamestown and made my way to Sir Francis Wyatt, now the Governor. I went to the great room, where Rolfe and others were assembled, discussing a fruitless search for someone. Rolfe turned and saw me.

"God in Heaven!" he exclaimed.

The Governor sprang to his feet. All was consternation. I told my story, gave my warning, then all sound ceased, everything grew black about me. When I regained consciousness I found that an alarm had been given because my wife was lost, having gone with Jeremy Sparrow to the forest in search of me. This blow unmanned me for the moment; then, when I felt stronger, I set forth on an errand that I had yet to do.

I went to the house of the man I meant to kill. But Lord Carnal could not fight me. He had taken poison, and his Italian vassal lay dead in his room beyond. He had not wished Buckingham to look upon his face with its beauty destroyed by the panther's claws, so he had taken slow poison, so well timed that on the homeward trip he would be buried at sea.

Sick at heart, I went to the minister's house, and there found the packet from his Grace of Buckingham, giving the King's sanction to my marriage. I wept. When the momentary passion was spent, I became conscious of sounds of war without. The Indians had come, but they did not stay long; before our forces they broke and fled.

Back into the forest I wandered, a man without a hope. After days of wandering, suddenly a strangled cry burst from me, and the earth seemed to rock, for before me stood Jeremy Sparrow! He told me not to go mad; that my wife still lived and he had kept her safe from all dangers. I took his hand and raised it to my lips. He made a gesture toward the isle of pine-trees, but I could not stir. Then she came slowly, softly, and lifted her eyes, and when she saw me I fell upon my knees; and there I listened to the words I never had hoped to hear again. I rose, and she came to my arms like a bird to its nest.

On our way home in the boat, which Jeremy rowed, while Jocelyn's head lay on my breast and her hands in mine, I told her of the letter from England and the promised honors awaiting us at court.

RICHARD MALCOLM JOHNSTON

(United States, 1822–1898)

PEARCE AMERSON'S WILL (1898)

Although this story was written simply for its own sake as a story, it has added historical value in the pleasant picture it presents of the customs and people of a period and locality little touched by literature. The scene is in the author's native State, Georgia, and the time of the action covers several years in the second quarter of the nineteenth century, before the issue of slavery had led to the great Civil War. The story, published first in *Lippincott's Magazine*, appeared in book form in 1898.

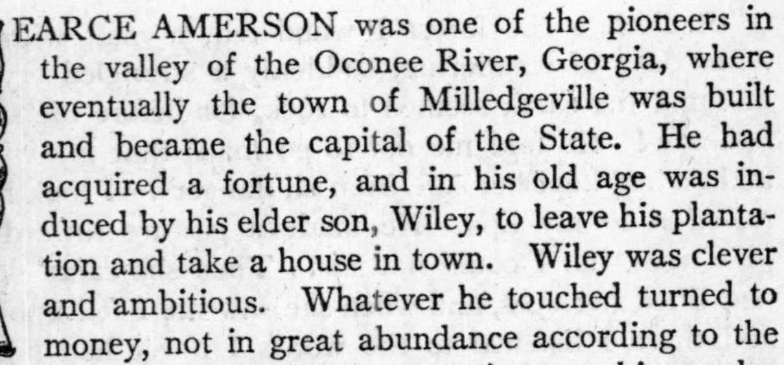

PEARCE AMERSON was one of the pioneers in the valley of the Oconee River, Georgia, where eventually the town of Milledgeville was built and became the capital of the State. He had acquired a fortune, and in his old age was induced by his elder son, Wiley, to leave his plantation and take a house in town. Wiley was clever and ambitious. Whatever he touched turned to money, not in great abundance according to the standards of to-day, but in such wise as to increase his surplus comfortably from year to year. With a growing material fortune, he sought to rise socially, and to that end he arranged a marriage with Julia Marston, daughter of an aristocratic family that had met with financial reverses.

Until this time, Cullen, the younger son of Pearce Amerson, had appeared to be the favorite with his father; but the old man's pride was stirred by the success of the elder son, and he came to feel and manifest displeasure amounting almost to scorn for the younger. Wiley, as he himself would have put it, had raised the family by a judicious marriage; Cullen, on the other hand, had married a girl as poor as himself, whose family had no social pretensions whatever. She was Hannah Enlow; and her beauty had been a temptation to Wiley, but he refrained from courting her because his mind was steadfastly set on self-advancement. Hannah did not lack for suitors, however, Among them was Arthur Dabney, a promising and upright young lawyer; but she chose Cullen, and their married life was of the happiest, the only clouds being the disfavor of Cullen's father and the covert hostility of Wiley.

There was no open breach in the family. Occasional visits were exchanged, and when the brothers met they spoke to each other politely, though the most casual observer could have seen that there was no cordiality in their greetings. The fact was, and Cullen was well aware of it, that Wiley had always, even as a boy, regarded his younger brother as an interloper. They never had been companions, and after Cullen's marriage Wiley openly informed his father that there could be no real social intercourse between the two households. The reason was that "that piece," as he designated Hannah, was not recognized in the social circle to which the Amersons were now welcome through marriage connection with the Marstons. Old Pearce rebelled a little at this attitude; he thought Hannah was a nice girl, every bit as good socially as he and Mother Amerson had been at her age; but Pearce was ambitious, too; he enjoyed the favor that money and his son's cleverness brought him; and so the estrangement was established. Cullen was settled on a farm about ten miles from Milledgeville, where by unremitting industry he made a comfortable living.

In this unhappy relationship there were three persons who did all they could to check the growth of bitterness and bring about concord. These were Cullen's mother, his wife, and, strange as it may seem, Wiley's wife. Julia, aristocrat born, was as whole-souled and sweet a woman as ever lived. She saw far beyond the artificial barriers of society, and held affection and honor as more to be prized than wealth and position. And Julia early came to a deep disappointment, which her pride caused her to conceal. She could not fail to perceive that Wiley was not the kind of man she had supposed him to be; his conduct as a husband was reprehensible in many particulars, and it was only too evident that the love he had professed before marriage was merely a formal pretense to give his courtship and wedding what he conceived to be the proper tone. Julia learned these things too late, and bore them in dignified, uncomplaining silence.

The elder Mrs. Amerson, accustomed always to obeying the will of her husband, had little influence with him in this matter. Moreover, she was in feeble health; she declined steadily after moving into town, and sorrow for her younger son undoubtedly had much to do with the steady debilitation of her powers. Julia could not do much, for the reasons indicated; she, too, had little influence with her husband. Hannah was the most active in the campaign for reconciliation. She always greeted Wiley pleasantly when he called; for he did call at his brother's occasionally. Pearce had acquired considerable land beyond Cullen's farm, after the removal to town; Wiley often had to go out to oversee work upon it, and at such times he would drop in at Cullen's. Pearce sometimes called, too, and whenever Hannah had occasion to go to Milledgeville she called on the families there, and always she was as cordial as if relations were the happiest. She strove consciously, nay, with great deliberation, to win over not only old Pearce, but Wiley. Hannah had her own little ambitions. She wished sincerely that Cullen might be on good terms with his father, but that generous desire did not and could not prevent her from longing to be in town society; and to live in town, and meet those whom she wished to meet, would be impossible, she was fully convinced, unless Cullen should have his proper share of his father's property.

All the contrivings of the peace-makers availed nothing against Wiley's persistent exercise of hostile influence upon his father, until the birth of Hannah's son. Wiley had no children; and this was Pearce's first grandson, and he could not help being interested when he heard the news. He felt a glow of appreciation when he learned that the little fellow had been named for him. Of course he went to see the baby; and the baby won the victory that his elders had struggled for in vain. Pearce's wife, shortly before she died, had the satisfaction of knowing that her husband had wholly overcome his displeasure with Cullen; and she knew that he meant to revise his will to the end that his property should be divided between his sons.

Wiley accepted the reconciliation with outward composure,

but he did not share in it. His demeanor toward Cullen remained as before, and Cullen was quite as obstinate as he.

"You don't know Wiley," he would say to Hannah, when she upbraided him gently for not trying to be pleasant with his brother; "he was always against me, and he always will be. He has a mean nature, and it cannot be changed. What does it matter? Father has destroyed the will he made in Wiley's favor, and in proper time we shall have what is our right."

Pearce lived about four years after the birth of his grandson. He did not make a new will, for Wiley persuaded him that it was not necessary.

"If you die intestate," he said, "Cullen and I will be entitled to equal shares in the property, and we can divide it without the expense and bother of administration."

As is usual in rural communities—for the State capital was little more than a country village in those days—everybody knew every other body's business to a considerable degree of accuracy; and it was common knowledge, therefore, that Pearce Amerson had forgiven Cullen and destroyed the will that cut him off with a mere pittance. What was the amazement of all the neighborhood, then, when Wiley offered a will for probate about a month after his father's death! Not only was there a will, but it gave Wiley all the property except the little farm that Cullen occupied and two thousand dollars in money. The document bore the names of three witnesses. One was dead. Another, Owen Carruthers, was confined to his bed with rheumatism at the time when the will was offered in court. The third, a quaint old rustic known as Lishy Flint, as honest as the sun, but as simple, not to say ignorant, as a sunflower, attended court and acknowledged his signature. The will was dated more than four years prior to Pearce's death.

Cullen, hearing of this from a passing neighbor who had been in Milledgeville, marketing, consulted Arthur Dabney.

"I know that my father meant to revoke that will," he told the lawyer. "I heard him only a short time before his death speak with satisfaction of having destroyed the document."

Dabney had to assure him that the law would have to recognize the document.

"If we could prove," he suggested, "that your father was of unsound mind—"

Cullen interrupted to say that his father's mind was perfectly unimpaired to the end. The lawyer then expressed his indignation at the terms of the will, and promised to look after Cullen's interests, but he could see little hope. The utmost that might be accomplished would be to bring the pressure of public sentiment to bear on Wiley, so that he would offer some sort of compromise.

"Which I will not accept, whatever it is," said Cullen.

Julia heard about the will from a neighbor. She was deeply distressed—more than that, and worse, she was suspicious. She knew beyond possibility of doubt that Pearce Amerson did not mean to leave his property in that way, and as soon as she saw her husband she told him of her doubts.

"You stupefy me!" he cried, in a manner that appeared to be expressive of virtuous indignation. "The will exists. As an honorable man, I could do nothing but offer it for probate. It is true that my father destroyed a similar will. There was a time when he thought better of Cullen and asked me to get his will. I did so. He read it over, and then threw it on the fire. But it appears that afterward he made another, and, I suppose, being an old man, he forgot it."

His wife was not at all satisfied with this theory for the existence of a will that belied Pearce Amerson's manifest intentions and wishes; but she could do nothing more than warn her husband against the presumable consequences of wrong-doing. She could not charge him directly with fraud, for there was no evidence of it. But she was inwardly convinced of it, and the anguish of this conviction undermined her health, which had not been robust for years.

Wiley called at Cullen's one day not long after this, and Hannah received him with her accustomed cordiality and sent a messenger to her husband, who was in the field. When he came to the house Wiley, after feebly protesting that he could not help his father's preferences, called attention to the fact that the law allowed a year for the settlement of the estate.

"But there's no use in waiting so long," he added, "and I

have brought you your money share," and he offered Cullen twenty one-hundred-dollar bills.

Cullen not only refused to accept them but ordered his brother from the house.

Hannah could not give up trying to effect some sort of understanding between the brothers. She believed that a compromise would be better than this quarrel, and it was pretty well known that Wiley was willing to give Cullen more than the will directed. Accordingly, when she heard that Julia was feeling ill, she called on her, and while there tried again to arouse in Wiley a kindly feeling for his brother. Their conversation took place in the garden behind the house. Julia, who was not yet a confirmed invalid, had purposely gone to a neighbor's, so that Hannah might have opportunity to plead with Wiley alone. But Wiley did the pleading. He never had overcome his youthful attraction toward Hannah, and she was now more beautiful than ever. He suggested the pleasures of town life, and her fitness for them. As he went on, his passion flared up, and before Hannah realized the trend of the talk he had seized her in his arms and kissed her. Hannah fled to the house, agitated and humiliated, while Julia, returning just then, unobserved by either of them, saw the end of the episode.

Events then moved rapidly. Cullen was stricken with an acute illness, and died in a few days. Julia, as if the discovery of her husband's utter faithlessness were the last straw, succumbed to her long-standing ailment. No power of resistance was left to her, no desire to live. Her one wish was that the unhappiness about the estate might be taken from those who would survive her, and before she died she asked her husband to marry Hannah. She told him what she had seen, and, in spite of her undiminished affection for Hannah, she had thought that the scene in the garden betrayed love on Hannah's part for Wiley. Her husband was embarrassed, as a better man might have been, and he tried to satisfy her by assurances that Hannah and her son would be provided for properly. Then, before death came, Hannah visited Julia and told her exactly what had happened in the garden; and Julia fervently thanked God that she had learned the truth.

Lawyer Dabney was more eager, if possible, after Cullen's

death to effect a fair division of the property than he had been before. It was not only a case now of widow and orphan against intrenched greed, but the fact that the widow was one for whom Dabney still felt the deepest affection stimulated his efforts. Still, there was the will, legal to the last dot, invulnerable. Nevertheless, he did not give up. He tried to find evidence to break it; but when he talked with Lishy Flint, he was almost convinced that effort would be time thrown away. In his eagerness to leave nothing untried that might be effective, he consulted Seaborn Torrance, a shrewd old practitioner, who was glad to help the young lawyer because he had a grudge against Wiley on account of the latter's sharp dealing in a case that had been tried some years previously. Under Torrance's guidance, Dabney quietly worked up a case on lines that had not been clear to him before, and presently Wiley and his lawyer were astonished by being served with notice of application on Hannah's part for letters of administration of Pearce Amerson's estate. This appeared like an audacious move to force a compromise, and they so regarded it.

Wiley was willing enough to compromise. He even thought of his wife's suggestion of marriage as the easiest way out of annoying difficulties, but, as in his younger days, he decided that if he married again he should look higher than Hannah. But one day he called on her to suggest terms of compromise, and when he saw her his old love flamed up again and carried away his judgment. He proposed to her frankly, and was unspeakably mortified when she indignantly refused him. Hannah also made it clear that compromise with her was just as impossible as it had been with Cullen.

There was nothing to do, then, but await the issue of court proceedings, and at last the day for hearing Hannah's application for letters of administration came. The courtroom was crowded, for popular sympathy was wholly with Hannah, though only Dabney and Torrance knew that there was any reason to hope for success. Wiley was present, confident of his position and wondering what old Torrance and Dabney could possibly be thinking of. Torrance, who conducted the case, soon showed him. He called only one witness, Owen Carruthers, one of the witnesses to the will, the one that had been confined to his house by illness at the time the document was admitted to probate.

Carruthers was a well-meaning, rather elegant, and rather shiftless young man, whose only source of income was derived from odd jobs, so to speak, as a clerk. Wiley Amerson had often employed him, for he was an expert penman, and Wiley was extraordinarily careful in keeping the records of his business. He always had important papers copied, and for years this copying had been done by Carruthers.

Torrance asked him formal questions about the drawing up of the will, how it was signed and witnessed, and how Pearce Amerson afterward declared that he meant to destroy it. Of course the other side objected that such a declaration could not stand in face of the actual will. Torrance blandly replied that he knew as much law as that, and asked the clerk of the court to produce the will. This was done, and it was handed to Carruthers.

"Is that the document Mr. Pearce Amerson signed?" asked the lawyer.

The witness looked at it a moment, and replied: "No. This is a copy that I made at Mr. Wiley Amerson's direction."

There was a sensation in the court, which was subdued quickly, for all were eager to hear Carruthers's further revelations.

"I followed Mr. Wiley Amerson's unvarying rule in such matters," he said, "which was, to make the copy look as like the original as possible. So I imitated the signatures of the testator and the witnesses when I made this copy; but there are plenty of indications here that this is not the original."

He was not called on to tell what they were, for Wiley Amerson suddenly left the court, and his lawyer arose and shamefacedly withdrew from the case. He had not suspected fraud on his client's part, or he never would have consented to advise him. Old Lishy Flint was in torment. In spite of the orders of the court officers, he insisted on making a speech to the judges, bewailing that he had sworn to a lie, for so he regarded his evidence when the imitation will was offered for probate.

"You kin send me to the pen'tenchary," he sobbed, "but you can't never say I meant it."

The old man was made to understand at last that nobody charged him with intended deceit, and the proceedings came to an end amid great rejoicing on the part of the entire community.

Wiley never was seen in Milledgeville after that day. He hid himself in a lonely cabin on some property of his at a distance. Hannah declined to prosecute him, and as nobody else undertook to bring the law to bear on him for his fraudulent conduct, he was unmolested. Time passed on serenely, and the day came when Dabney felt that he could renew the suit of his youth. A few days after he and Hannah were married, Wiley's dead body was found in the Oconee. It was never known whether his death was voluntary or accidental.

MAURUS JOKAI

(Hungary, 1825–1904)

TIMAR'S TWO WORLDS (1888)

The Danube has long been an important highway between several countries, notably, Turkey, Servia, and Hungary. For long stretches it runs along frontiers, one country on the left bank, another on the right. In the old days, as perhaps now, smuggling was a regular occupation of dwellers along the watercourse, and governmental regulations on the one side and the other brought about habits of life that may not be duplicated elsewhere. Jokai used these general facts as a background for his romance, the action of which begins about the year 1825, before steamboats and railways were known in that part of the world.

MICHAEL TIMAR was captain of the *Saint Barbara*, one of a fleet of merchant-vessels owned by Athanasius Brazovics, of Komorn in Hungary. On a voyage up the Danube he had two passengers and a full cargo of grain. One passenger was set down on the waybill as Euthemio Trikaliss, owner of the cargo, and the other was his young daughter, Timéa.

A Turkish gunboat was in pursuit, and violent head winds taxed the skill of the navigator. By daring such as made his seasoned sailors gasp, and by skill such as made them worship him, Timar overcame all perils and anchored at last where the waterway was like a lake. He had trustworthy information that the Turk had given up the chase; but here Timéa fell ill of nausea aroused by the roughness of the broad river. She had interested Timar deeply, and it occurred to him that she would recover if she could have a night on land. Moreover, provisions on board were exhausted.

The vessel lay near an island of which Timar knew nothing. He went to it in a small boat, and found several acres of cultivated garden land, and, at the base of a huge rock, a rude dwelling where lived a woman and her daughter, the only inhabitants, who occupied the island in default of ownership by anybody else. The land had formed, unnoticed by officials, after an overwhelming flood had left the huge rock in midstream to catch and retain soil brought down by the current in other floods. The woman was known as Thérèse, and her beautiful young daughter as Noémi.

They welcomed Timar, readily agreed to supply his vessel with provisions, and consented to give the passengers shelter for a night, but would take no money. They lived by barter. Money was of no use to them, but grain was; so were salt, materials for clothing, and household utensils. Thérèse would exchange for grain a fair amount of fruit, flour, kids, cheese, and garden produce. She explained that smugglers and the country people roundabout traded with them regularly. Timar accordingly had grain brought from the vessel, and obtained provisions for the rest of the voyage to Komorn; and the passengers spent the night on the island.

In the evening there was another visitor, a young man who was evidently not welcome either to Thérèse or to Noémi. He claimed acquaintance with Timar because of some meeting at a port down the river, and he addressed Noémi as his "little *fiancée*." The girl, who was hardly a year older than Timéa, shuddered whenever he approached her. The newcomer's name was Krisstyan. A couch was made for him in the open air, but he did not sleep. When the others had retired he entered Thérèse's room and threatened to report the existence of the island to the Turkish Government if she did not give him money. When Thérèse answered that she never had money, and that he knew it, Krisstyan suggested that she get it from her guests.

"That I will not do," said she, "although I know it is in your power to ruin us."

Timar, trying in vain to sleep in the loft, overheard this conversation, and after the voices had ceased, he went out of doors, where, to his surprise, he found Thérèse. Krisstyan had departed. Timar expressed his sympathy for the woman, confessing that he had heard her resist Krisstyan's threats, and she thereupon told him her story.

She had been the wife of a well-to-do land-owner, who had

indorsed notes given by Krisstyan's father to Athanasius Brazovics. Timar listened without saying that Brazovics was his employer. The elder Krisstyan had defaulted and run away, deserting his little son, whom he had proposed as the future husband of Noémi. Thérèse's husband could have met the notes if only their face value had been required of him; but they were so framed, being for advances on prospective crops, that the holder could by law demand compensation for his losses through failure to receive the shipments of grain for which the notes were security. Brazovics insisted on the letter of the law, and every scrap of property was taken from Thérèse's husband, who thereupon committed suicide. The widow found herself deserted by friends, the law, and the Church—for the priest refused to bury her husband in consecrated ground; but she was not utterly defeated, and, knowing of this ownerless island, had camped upon it and supported herself and her child by gardening.

Timar could do no more than express his sympathy. The journey was resumed early in the morning, and that night Trikaliss summoned the Captain to his cabin and made a startling disclosure.

"I have just taken poison," he said, "and am dying of it. If you do not interrupt me, there will be time to tell you matters of great importance. I am not a Greek, but a Turk, and my right name is Ali Tschorbadschi. The Sultan destined my daughter for the harem, and designed to confiscate my property. Therefore I am a fugitive. I could not let my daughter enter the harem, or myself be made a beggar. Although I am taking with me nothing that is not my own, technically I am a thief, for I am carrying away property that the Government had decreed confiscate. Therefore, if I should reach Hungary and be discovered and properly identified, I could be extradited. So I bought a cargo of grain, that being the best way to preserve my character as a merchant as well as a safe way to invest my money. And I hired this vessel because its owner, Athanasius Brazovics, is a connection of mine. I have been of service to him; now he can repay me.

"Listen sharply, Captain, for time is short. That man who came to the strange island where we passed the night is a spy of the Turkish Government. Be sure he has gone ahead to give warning, and when we reach Pancsova officers will come aboard to arrest me. I shall then be dead, and you will have buried me in the river. This I do to save my daughter, and my property for her. Swear to take care of her. Go straight to Komorn, and conduct Timéa to Brazovics. Ask him to adopt her. In the casket on the table are about a thousand ducats. Give the money to Brazovics; also this paper, which declares that all my property is in the grain. The paper will clear you from any possible suspicion. Tell Brazovics to be present personally when the grain is unloaded. Be sure to tell him this."

When the dying man tried to speak again, his mind seemed to wander. All he could say was something unintelligible about the "red crescent," and with these words on his lips he died.

When Timéa knew that her father was dead, she was as one suddenly benumbed. As her father had foretold, officers came aboard at Pancsova and demanded the person of Ali Tschorbadschi; but Timar reported his death and burial, and the vessel proceeded. Komorn was almost in sight when the *Saint Barbara* struck a submerged tree. A great hole was torn in her bottom, and she sank so quickly that it was only with the greatest difficulty and at his own peril that Timar saved Timéa and the casket containing her little fortune.

He hastened with her to the house of Brazovics, arriving in the early evening. The master himself was there, and Sophie, his wife, Athalie, their daughter, and Lieutenant Katschuka, Athalie's betrothed. Timar was on the friendliest terms with all, and he was doubly welcome when he explained who his companion was and how he came to bring her. This, however, before he had time to report what had happened to the *Saint Barbara*. Then an ominous change came over Brazovics and Sophie. The master, from calling the hapless child his daughter, turned to grumbling that the thousand ducats in the casket were not enough to educate her; she must be a menial in the household; and he berated Timar soundly for carelessness, vowing that he would prosecute him. Timar merely called the owner's attention to the fact that the vessel was insured for her full value.

"We shall lose time scolding," said he. "Not a minute

should be wasted; for the longer the cargo remains under water the less valuable it will be."

Brazovics replied that he cared nothing for the cargo of drowned grain. Timar protested that as it belonged to Timéa everything possible should be done to get something for it. Brazovics stubbornly refused to trouble himself about it, but he gave the captain a written permit to remove the cargo, and Timar left him, to engage men and appliances for the work. When he had done as much as possible that night, he called on Lieutenant Katschuka, who had requested him to look in.

"I have a suggestion to make," said the lieutenant. "As you know, I am the commissariat officer. The army is in need of considerable bread for the maneuvers. Brazovics will get the contract unless somebody underbids him. His bid is one hundred and forty thousand gulden, with twenty thousand for the officials concerned. Do you put in a bid for one hundred and thirty thousand, with thirty thousand for the officials. Then buy the sunken cargo for ten thousand. When the cargo has been removed and the bread disposed of, your profits will be not less than seventy thousand."

Timar replied that he had never bribed anybody, and disliked the thought of it.

"My dear fellow," said Katschuka, "everybody dislikes it, but it is the only way." He urged further that in this way something would be added to Timéa's little fortune.

Timar said he would think the matter over. When he went to the wreck next day he found that the vessel had shifted her position so that the forward part, with its tiny cabin, was well out of the water. He stationed himself there and superintended the workmen, who toiled till after dark removing the bags of grain. Every bag had a black wheel marked on the sacking. They were opened on shore, and the contents spread on mats to dry. Timar paid the men extra to work late; but at last they were too tired to be tempted with money and they quit in a body. He let them go without protest, for he noticed that the last bag hauled up was not marked with a black wheel; its brand was a red crescent. Timar recalled Ali Tschorbadschi's dying words, and his heart leaped excitedly. The workmen had gone ashore; nobody saw him pull the bag into the cabin and lift it to the table. He cut it open, and good wheat rolled out; but, thrusting in his arm, he felt a leather bag, which he drew forth. The crescent moon shone in at the little window and revealed its contents: sparkling jewels and rouleaus of gold.

This, then, was Timéa's fortune. This was the reason Tschorbadschi had been so insistent that Brazovics should personally attend to the unloading of the cargo. And the cargo was now Timar's, for he had bought it at auction for ten thousand gulden.

Timar saw the two courses open to him as clearly as he saw the fortune in his grasp. His honorable habit, for he never had done a dishonest act, bade him take the gems and money to Brazovics, as Timéa's guardian. The tempter assured him that Timéa would lose by that course, for Brazovics would speculate with the property and, if he did not lose it, would divert it to his own uses, not to hers. "If you take it," said the tempter, "you can husband it for her; you might increase it; you might eventually marry her; then she would have all and more than was her due." To this a silent voice replied: "You would be a thief." He lingered long, viewing the two courses, and when he hurried to land he had just time to get in his bid for supplying the army with bread.

The sudden rise of Captain Timar to wealth was more than a seven-days' wonder in Komorn, for the constant increase in his property was a standing sensation. As he had obtained the army contract, his prosperity was attributed to bribery. The disappointed Brazovics, who was the loudest in this manner of talk, instigated an official investigation. This was most searching and resulted in the absolute exoneration of Timar. He then offered the Government a liberal rental for the Levetinczy estate, thirty thousand acres from which no revenue whatever had been obtained in recent years; and officialdom was so pleased with this conduct that Timar was created a baron. He bought seed grain for the peasants on his estate, and turned it into one of the most profitable in the country. He established new enterprises, and invested right and left with such prodigality and apparent folly that his swift downfall was predicted.

But his fortune grew to millions, and he was known as "The Man of Gold."

Meantime he visited Brazovics frequently, to see how Timéa was faring. Poor child! She was imposed on as her protectors would not have dared impose on a hired servant. Athalie and Sophie made her a constant butt for ridicule, for example, giving her clothes of ancient fashion so that everybody laughed at her, Timéa innocently supposing that she was dressed beautifully. But their worst joke, and one that had lasting consequences, consisted in persuading her that Katschuka was paying court to her, and not to Athalie. Timéa's unfamiliarity with Hungarian customs and her ignorance of Christianity made it possible for her tormentors to carry this wicked deception to a fine climax; for, in addition to her ignorance, the child had a trustful disposition. She not only believed that Katschuka loved her, but gave her heart to him, and it was not until Athalie's wedding-day that the real bride brutally disabused her of this fixed idea.

That wedding-day had been subject to many postponements. Katschuka was a business man, in his way. There had been a time when he loved Athalie, but that had passed with the coming of the poverty-stricken Timéa. His one object recently had been Athalie's dowry. Her father had been unable to produce the hundred thousand gulden agreed upon, and Katschuka refused to go to the altar until the money was actually paid. And during all this time, three or four years, Michael Timar, Baron Levetinczy, had been watching Brazovics and planning his ruin. For Timar loved Timéa, and he knew to what cruel ridicule she had been subjected. Matters had become so desperate with Brazovics that he could see success only in following Timar's lead. Timar bought a few acres of land where it was rumored that the Government intended to build fortifications. There was the opportunity for Brazovics! He sold his ships, mortgaged his house, raised every gulden he could, and bought as much land as could be had at any price near Timar's purchase; for it was the rule that the Government paid double the last purchase-price when it expropriated property for public purposes. On Athalie's wedding morning the officials regretfully informed Brazovics that the fortifications were to be erected on land quietly bought by an employé of Timar's in another part of the city. Brazovics committed suicide, and Katschuka returned Athalie's engagement-ring.

In due course all the property in the name of Brazovics was put up at auction to satisfy his debts. Timar bought the house and all its contents; then he formally conveyed them by deed to Timéa, and made her a proposal of marriage. She had always been sensible of his kindly interest in her; she remembered how he had saved her life in the perilous voyage up the Danube; she was now overwhelmed with gratitude, and she accepted him. In the first moment of his happiness at hearing her promise, Timar agreed to grant her an unasked favor. She requested that Sophie and Athalie be permitted to continue to occupy the house with her as before the catastrophe; and Timar, with unexpressed regret, kept his word.

But Timar's marriage did not bring him happiness, and he was not long in divining the cause. If he had been lacking in perspicacity, the defect would have been supplied by Athalie. She knew that Timéa loved Katschuka, and for that reason she hated both. It was her exquisite idea of vengeance to hope for long life to Timar and Timéa, that both might suffer as much misery as possible. Timar wooed his wife as best he could; he overwhelmed her with gifts, he was patiently attentive, but never could he win from her the response to his affection that would have been dearer to him than his wealth and station. She was always grateful, patient, willing, beautiful; and however much he might infer the secret of her heart, it was impossible to imagine her guilty of as much as the shadow of misconduct.

One day Timar took a journey southward to complete a project that had long been dear to him. He went to the ownerless island, where Thérèse and Noémi welcomed him as an old friend. Noémi, particularly, was so ingenuous in her expressions of pleasure that he was charmed, and he allowed two or three days to pass without informing them of his errand. He liked to talk to Noémi, for she was a good listener and hung on his words eagerly. Before he had announced his business, Krisstyan came to the island. As usual, he was on an errand of extortion, and this time he was prepared to compel acquiescence. He showed Thérèse a contract whereby she was to give him all her valuable timber. If she refused to sign, he would forthwith notify the Turkish Government of the existence of the island and that it was inhabited unlawfully.

"You are too late," said Timar, quietly. "I have already notified both the Turkish and the Hungarian governments, and each has conveyed this island for ninety-nine years to the present colonists for a nominal rental."

He did not say how much it had cost him to fix that nominal rental. The official deed of settlement was in his pocket, and he handed it to Thérèse. Krisstyan foamed at the mouth.

"What gives you the right to meddle with the affairs of this family?" he screamed.

"My love!" cried Noémi suddenly, with all the strength of overpowering passion, while she fell on Timar's breast and threw her arms around his neck.

Krisstyan fled the place, cursing. Timar was thunderstruck. There was no question of propriety here. Noémi loved; she knew nothing of conventional restraints; her passion flooded her being and compelled expression. For the first time, Timar knew what it was to have love spoken to him. He bent his head to kiss her brow, and felt her heart throb against his. And an inner voice whispered, "You are a thief!"

A new world had opened for Timar, but he departed from it the next morning. Thérèse and Noémi offered no protest. To them he was a poor ship-captain who must have much to do, but he would return. His landing-place was not many miles from the Levetinczy estate, and, having left his boat at a fishing-hut, he set forth to walk the distance. Krisstyan lay in wait for him in a wood, and shot twice at him. The bullets pierced Timar's hat, who discharged his own weapon in the air, and faced Krisstyan unarmed. It would have been possible and fair to kill the man, and Timar could have done it easily, but his heart revolted. He talked to the fellow, making excuses for him, trying to induce him to adopt an honest mode of life, and gave him an opportunity. Timar was just then embarking on a new venture, the shipment of Hungarian grain to Brazil. He offered to make Krisstyan his personal representative in that country at a high salary. Krisstyan accepted, and sailed with the first cargo. That enterprise prospered, as did all Timar's, and he received from his agents glowing accounts of the industry and integrity of his representative.

This treatment of Krisstyan was in accord with Timar's public character. He was famous as a philanthropist. Hospitals were maintained by him, schools were endowed, and every form of charity found in him a most generous contributor. New distinctions were conferred upon him; he was made a Privy Councillor. But that other world called to him. There was no joy at any of the houses which he might call his home. Through a long winter he struggled against the call of the other world, and at last, when spring was in the air, he departed on a journey of indefinite duration. He went to the ownerless island, and until the frosts came he worked there with Thérèse and Noémi, and these three were happy.

When he returned he let it be understood that he had been in Brazil. Nobody thought of suspecting him. Another winter he spent in the great world, entertaining lavishly, honored, prospering; but he was unhappy and Timéa was unhappy, and Athalie knew it. With spring he was again at the ownerless island.

Thus the years passed. A little boy was added to the colonists of the island, who called Timar "papa," and who crowned his cup of joy. Neither Thérèse nor Noémi ever suspected that he had either a wife elsewhere or more wealth than they. He left his palaces to toil in the fields, and returned with his hands roughened by hard labor.

But this could not go on forever. Timar thought of suicide, and made his will in Timéa's favor. The joy of the other world was too sweet, and he thought of divorce. With this in mind he returned to Komorn, early one winter, wondering whether it might be possible to find Timéa in some fault.

Athalie volunteered to convince him of his wife's faithlessness. Much as he wished to learn of this, her assurance offended him, but he listened. Katschuka had fought a duel on his (Timar's) account. A stranger had ventured to cast discredit on Timar's character, and Katschuka would have killed him, but that his sword broke over the fellow's head. Timéa had sent for Katschuka, and they were to meet that very night. Athalie showed Timar a secret passage that Brazovics had used for spying upon business associates, from which he could look into Timéa's chamber. Timar concealed himself there and at the appointed hour saw Katschuka come in. Timéa stood the length of the room away from him and thanked him for defending her husband's honor. Love burned in their eyes and faltered in their voices; but Katschuka withdrew, leaving the listening Timar to know that his wife was of the rarest in faith and faithfulness.

So, then, nothing was left but suicide. He went to one of his lakes, ostensibly to inspect the business of fishing through the ice. On his arrival he invented an excuse to get rid of his servants, and sat alone in the house. There Krisstyan came to him, ragged, wounded, forlorn. It was he who had fought with Katschuka. He caught up Timar's gun when he entered, and held it at aim while he told his story and made his demand. He had robbed the business in Brazil and had been sent to the galleys. There he had found himself chained to his father, who told him so much about Ali Tschorbadschi that Krisstyan was able to infer how Timar became possessed of his first million. This knowledge had been supplemented by patient inquiry since he escaped the galleys and returned to Europe.

"I have four letters exposing you," said Krisstyan. "One is addressed to the Turkish Government, another to the Hungarian, another to your wife, and the last to Noémi. Refuse my demands, and I will hand them to the priests at the monastery on the island yonder," pointing to an isle in the lake, "and they will see that they are delivered. My demands are simple. Some money which you can spare, but not much. I want the ownerless island and Noémi."

Timar offered him fabulous sums, and Krisstyan laughed at him. Still threatening with the gun, he threw off his ragged clothes, put them on the fire, and donned a complete suit of Timar's. As he asked for money, Timar tossed him a purse. In the end, as Timar refused to yield, he set out across the ice to the monastery. It was night, and some time after he had gone, Timar went also in the same direction. He came to a hole that the fishermen had cut in the ice; it was his door to death. He stooped and drew back suddenly, for Krisstyan's dead face was looking up at him. The scoundrel had unwittingly fallen in where Timar meant to go deliberately.

When the ice broke up in the following spring a body, macerated beyond recognition, was found on the lake shore. It was identified as Timar's by the clothes, the purse in the pockets, and a watch that Krisstyan had taken from the house. There were four letters in the pockets, but the water had made them illegible. This body was buried with honors of state as that of the Baron Levetinczy, and somewhat more than a year afterward Timéa married Katschuka.

The author once visited the ownerless island in search of botanical specimens. He found it inhabited by a colony all of whose members were known only by their first names. A hale old man called Michael and his wife Noémi were at the head of affairs. Their sons had married peasant women from the surrounding country and were bringing up families of their own. The island was large enough to sustain them and many more. All lived by barter, no money ever being accepted for produce or service. I was told that their tenure of the island had fifty years more to run.

ELISABETTA JUNCKER

(Germany, 1830)

MARGARETHE; OR, LIFE-PROBLEMS (1870)

The English translation of this story was made by Mrs. Annis L. Wister, a sister of Dr. Horace H. Furness, the Shakespearian scholar. It was first published in the United States in 1878, and was reprinted in a new edition in 1906.

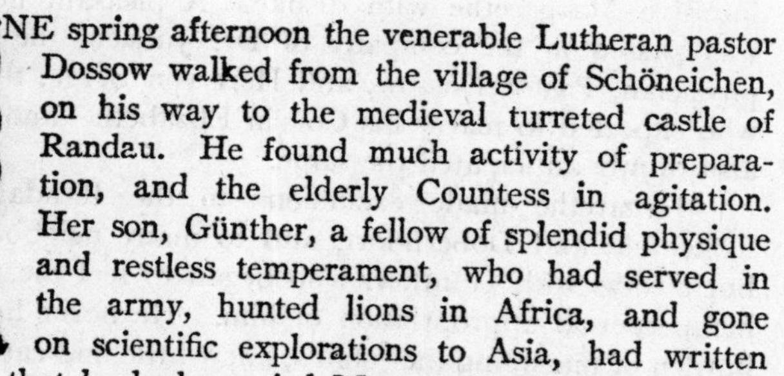

ONE spring afternoon the venerable Lutheran pastor Dossow walked from the village of Schöneichen, on his way to the medieval turreted castle of Randau. He found much activity of preparation, and the elderly Countess in agitation. Her son, Günther, a fellow of splendid physique and restless temperament, who had served in the army, hunted lions in Africa, and gone on scientific explorations to Asia, had written announcing that he had married Margarethe Trentler, daughter of a wealthy manufacturer's widow, and would bring her home that same day. The Countess was grievously disturbed at this intrusion of *bourgeoise* blood into their ancient family.

Elizabeth, the daughter, now entered, a girl of twenty-three, not beautiful, but attractive, with intense life in her gray eyes and a rare charm of intelligence and amiability. She joined the pastor in calming her mother. Presently the carriage arrived, and Count Günther placed his young wife in his mother's arms, and, after one glance at her lovely face, the Countess pressed her cordially, and kissed her brow.

In the evening Günther talked with the pastor about the latter's new book, calling for simplification of the forms of the ancient creeds, in harmony with the advancing knowledge of the times. It had created wrath among the Church dignitaries, and the pastor had been judicially summoned to account for it. But soon the tactful old gentleman, drawing out the newcomer to talk of her family and early interests, helped much to make her feel at home.

Six weeks passed, and the gay little bride was persuaded one afternoon to pay some visits of ceremony. Günther and she visited first his Uncle Berge, who was a prim, old-fashioned man; but he and his gentle wife were charmed with Margarethe, so that the dreaded ceremony easily passed. Then they drove to Uhlenhorst, to call upon Frau von Massow, a dashing widow, who had been a favorite comrade of Günther's. The ladies were mutually polite, but oppugnant — the brilliant, self-possessed widow with a scorn of the child-wife of seventeen, and the intuitive Margarethe with dislike. A pleasant home evening was passed in the company of Dr. Jussien, the grim family physician, Pastor Dossow, and Herr von Berge, the Landrath, who expected to marry his Cousin Elizabeth—and, indeed, she also calmly anticipated the same.

Margarethe made excursions to the Randau estates of Tökenfeld and Doberndorf, and to many neighboring places, but always with Günther, who began to feel the restriction of her perpetual appropriation of him. He never had taken the burden of managing the estates, knew little and cared less about the details, and when old Lüthke, the steward, brought him accounts and requests for instructions, he impatiently put him off.

Elizabeth went one morning to her dear pastor and teacher. There she had a talk with Frau Wessel, his old housekeeper, who said much of baby Willy, the boy, the man, and now the hero of battles and commander of a great ship, that day expected home. On leaving the garden, Elizabeth met at the gate a manly stranger, with fine, bold features and sparkling blue eyes, and so suddenly that she dropped at his feet all her gathered flowers, and then laughingly sent him to his rejoicing father.

Günther had a new plan—disapproved by everybody else—of buying some large meadow-lands, bordering the sea, for a model English sheep-farm, with its buildings. Old Lüthke warned him of its dangerous exposure to ocean storms, and of the great expense; but Günther said it never yet had been overflowed, and the cost he took, with Margarethe's consent, from her dowry. The land was bought, the sheep were ordered, and the buildings begun. This took him away often for inspection; and one day, losing his way in the fog, he found himself at the gates of Uhlenhorst, and went in. Baroness Massow was stormily scolding her children and servants, but welcomed him and offered him refreshment, and soon they were discussing marriage, husbands, exacting brides, etc., with the freedom of old comrades; and before leaving Günther was again under the spell of her fascination.

The next day was Sunday, and there was company at dinner. Captain Dossow, who with his father was present, sat beside Elizabeth at table. He had been hitherto absorbed in his profession, but now found himself succumbing to an undreamed-of attraction; Günther made himself agreeable to Baroness Massow, to the discomfort of Margarethe; but on the whole the party concluded harmoniously.

After this Captain Dossow was greatly changed, rushing to party and soirée for a glimpse of the Countess Elizabeth, knowing the futility of passion for one so far above him, yet reverentially, passionately idolizing her. Elizabeth, seemingly unconscious of this, treated him with kindly regard and confidence, appreciated his fine qualities, but showed no sign of sentiment. One day he met her by the lake, and in their free talk she told him that on her twenty-fifth birthday she should disregard her independent temperament, and, following her reason, become betrothed to her estimable cousin, Hermann von Berge.

"You have not said that you love him," said Dossow.

"No, for that, in the usual sense, is something that I cannot comprehend. Perhaps, like Undine, I shall find a soul only in marriage."

"And upon this he dares to make you his wife? He is insane enough to believe—"

He stopped, and gazed at her intensely. Elizabeth looked at him, and a strange sensation seized her. She saw only his eyes. She suddenly knew that he loved her, and in her heart arose a vague longing for full happiness. But she started up, and they silently returned.

At home, the Captain talked it over with his father: he loved her, but never had told her. For himself, he gave her up, but he never should cease loving her.

Elizabeth spent the next week under a spell. She did not understand herself, but awaited something, she knew not what. Riding with her through the forest one morning, to a picnic breakfast, the Captain cut away the branches from before her face with a little Oriental dagger, which he gave her, and she fastened it in her belt. As they approached the sea he hailed it joyously, explaining that he had requested orders to join the China expedition. Elizabeth turned pale. She had carried these earnest eyes in her heart, and now to see him so calmly, even gladly, ready to leave her was intolerable. She touched her restive horse with the whip and rode off. The little dagger jolted out, and, trying to replace it, she wounded herself in the breast, just below her throat. The blood on her glove made her faint, and Dossow, checking the horses, laid her, unconscious, under a tree. He loosened her habit at the throat and, folding his handkerchief, bound it upon the wound, with her veil over all. She quickly recovered, but, discovering the bandage, she was irritated at the man who had witnessed her weakness, turned back, and sent him on to excuse her absence from the breakfast—"with anything except the truth."

At the evening ball following the picnic Elizabeth was again herself. Dossow, in a dance, was brought to stand near her for a little, and she was very cool. After some fencing, he suggested that she should frankly say that she did not care to see him again.

"And if I should?"

"You would be right, except in one case alone."

"And that?"

"That you loved me, as I love you."

He had not meant to say it, and was shocked at himself. The dance separated them, and when they met again she said wearily:

"Go!"

But Elizabeth's morning absence and now her embarrassed air had been noted by many. Lieutenant von Brinken was busy gathering gossip about it, and finally rushed into a group, exclaiming at "Captain Dossow's insolence to the Countess Elizabeth," etc. Dossow, standing by, called him a lying scoundrel, while Herr von Berge generously offered himself as second to the Captain, who gratefully accepted the service.

The next morning, Günther asked Elizabeth about the difficulty, and she told him the facts.

"Oh, women! women!" he exclaimed. "Here is Captain Dossow, a man, every inch of him, and out of mere whim you treat him so that idle fools get up a scandal to explain it." And he told of the scene with Von Brinken and the coming duel.

Günther went out and Elizabeth sank into a chair. "'A man, every inch of him!' He loves me, and I—I let him be insulted by a fool!"

After the duel, which resulted in a slight wound of Von Brinken, the Captain went to say farewell at the castle, and soon Margarethe went for the mother, leaving him alone with Elizabeth, who approached him, saying gravely:

"Promise me never again to trifle with your life. I exact this from you."

He looked at her, surprised, but with a bitter smile. Deeply moved, Elizabeth continued:

"Because I love you so dearly." He fairly staggered; then, seizing her hands, begged her not to trifle with him.

"God forbid!" she replied. "I have struggled in vain. Early education, my knowledge of another good man's love for me, my own independent nature, all forbade this; but I can no more. Your heart must be my home, and you my all!"

And the strong man wept, so great was his revulsion of joy.

Günther sympathized with Elizabeth in admiration of the man, and promised to help her with their mother, who was sure to be distressed by this second plebeian alliance. Of course all the neighbor-nobles were agitated, but the Landrath von Berge behaved very handsomely, and wished his lost lady all happiness with her chosen man.

Events always appeared to furnish Edith von Massow with emotional crises. Once it was a thunder-storm, in which she and Günther were caught; again, a stag-hunt, in which he saved her life: and, skilfully using these exciting occasions, she fairly bewitched him. The wealthy old General Steinhausen had proposed marriage to her, and she almost got Günther's promise to follow her to Italy if she would refuse the General.

One dreary autumn day Elizabeth and Captain Dossow were married by the good pastor in the little village church. He was to leave in the evening for Williamshaven, where the *Bellona* lay, and whence he was to sail, and they spent the last hours walking in the bare woods. With tears and smiles and happy vows they sorrowfully parted, and Willy strode off to his year of absence. Their marriage was Pastor Dossow's last official act; by order of the Consistory he was suspended from pastoral duties. He appealed, but meantime must share his parsonage with his appointed successor, Pastor Friedmann, a showy, shallow, insinuating man, of the requisite orthodoxy, gifted with sentimental oratory and musical talent.

One morning a book and a note came to Günther from Frau von Massow—awaiting an answer:

"I have refused General Steinhausen. To-morrow he returns to B——, and two days later I set out for Italy! Will not you now shake off your fetters and follow? We will redeem lost years, Günther. We are not like your tame little girl, who, as you say, can do naught save sigh, and weep, and love."

Günther wrote for answer, "Go; I will follow." He thought awhile about this "expedition for a few weeks—harming nobody," and then sallied forth and proposed a sleigh-ride. Margarethe went, with exuberant joy; her day was pure sunshine. Made hungry by the cold, they stopped at a little inn, and found there, to Margarethe's uneasiness, Frau von Massow, General Steinhausen, and Pastor Friedmann. They partook of champagne brought by the Baroness. The General gallantly drank to a pleasant Italian journey for the Baroness, and a happy return to friends, counting the days of her three months' stay.

Immediately the world grew brighter to Margarethe; how she had wronged her husband! When Pastor Friedmann proposed that she should sing, at the old piano in the next room, she willingly consented. He played the accompaniment to Mignon's song, "Knowst thou the land." The gallant General came into the room, listening with delight. Margarethe leaned forward to catch in the mirror over the piano some answering glance from Günther in the parlor, and saw him looking passionately at the face of the beautiful woman whose head was on his shoulder. Pastor Friedmann saw it, too.

The song stopped, and Margarethe staggered to the hall-door, saying that she needed air. Wrapping her cloak around her, she rushed out, Pastor Friedmann covering the break with roulades and trills on the piano. An icy wind swept her, but she hurried along in desperation, her skirts clogged and heavy with the damp snow.

"Oh, if it were but summer, and I could reach the lake!" she cried.

No, it was winter, within and without, and at last she fell by the roadside, where she lay till Dr. Jessien's sleigh came by, and he took her home.

The others did not notice Margarethe's absence, except Friedmann, who went out to find her. The General, moved by the song, said to the Baroness:

"Dear lady, one should not go to Italy alone. Why not ask our friend, Count Randau, whether I ought to bear three weary months until your return, or may not rather go with you as my darling wife to Italy? Count, am I not right?"

Günther hesitated from shame and pain at being deceived. Presently he turned:

"You are quite right, General, in not yielding to such whims, and I cannot believe that anyone will so long delay your promised happiness."

Pastor Friedmann, who had not found Margarethe, now called the General out, and Günther calmly turned to the Baroness:

"Ah, Madame, you have a thoroughly bad heart. Thanks to you, I have played to-day the part of the traitor betrayed. Enjoy life, Madame, until disgust seizes you, of yourself and of the golden calf to which you have sacrificed everything that could make you worth a man's regard."

The two gentlemen here returned, reporting Margarethe's disappearance. A sly allusion to the mirror by Pastor Friedmann gave Günther the clue, and he departed, enraged with himself and all the world. Driving furiously, he vainly searched the roadway. At the castle, Elizabeth told of Margarethe's coming, adding: "Oh, Günther, God only knows what the end may be. Your child cannot live—so prematurely born—and the mother's life is in terrible danger."

Every word stabbed the Count to the heart. This was Nemesis! His fault must be expiated—and not by himself only. If the poor child had but told him of her hopes, all would have been different; but it was his fault alone. And for hours he lashed himself with remorseful thoughts.

The dead child was a boy. The mother, mentally as well as physically ill, faded daily, and after some weeks the doctors found hope only in transfusion of blood, which Günther gladly furnished from his own veins. This saved her; but, at his unconscious wife's bedside, Günther suffered tortures of conscience, and a new tenderness arose within him.

Slowly life returned to Margarethe, stolid and indifferent upon her bed. When danger was past, Günther went to the capital, to the sessions of the Reichstag, to which he had been elected, and, joining the Liberal party, his energetic personality soon made him a commanding figure. Elizabeth sent him daily reports, and his longing for his wife increased as the winter passed.

Margarethe gradually grew stronger, and she now joined the family daily; but on Günther's return she determined upon a separation. When, the first night, he went to her chamber, with self-accusations and a desire to explain the wretched misunderstanding, she sprang up and poured out such a denunciation of him that he stood aghast, while irresistibly admiring the force and fire and good sense of this awakened woman. She furiously refused even to think of living with him again—despised her soul, that had received his false vows, and her body, that had been branded with his kisses. He staggered back, and with bent head left the room.

The next day a letter from him acceded to her desire for separation, but requested her so far to consider the family as to remain until the matter could be quietly arranged. She agreed to this, promising to remain for a year, and to do her social duty; meanwhile asking him not to distress his mother and sister by absenting himself. Margarethe now resumed her duties as mistress of the household; and thenceforward, not as a child-like bride, but as a beautiful, self-possessed woman, she entered upon a new life.

Günther was bound, upon Elizabeth's marriage, to deliver half of her portion, paying her interest upon the other half as heretofore—seventy-five thousand thalers. Of Margarethe's dowry—three hundred thousand thalers—fifty thousand had gone for the salt meadows, English sheep, and several fine horses. This must be repaid when she returned to her mother. He could not sell or mortgage his entailed estate, and he had no salable timber. Therefore, Günther grimly set himself to economies: sold his Arabians; dismissed the expensive superintendent of Dorberndorf and Tökenfeld; and with systematic energy began controlling inspectors, foresters, and clerks, overseeing the hated accounts, making of roads, and repairing of dykes, with numberless other details, besides retrenching needless expenses.

The quiet courtesy between him and his wife and the evident harmony of the household, showing them to be an exemplary couple, prevented possible gossip. Yet the gulf between them widened. Margarethe (who had come upon Edith's letter) cherished implacable pride, although feeling forlorn; while Günther kept his polite distance, although longing for Margarethe. Once she dislocated her ankle, and he made her allow him to set and bandage it. This led to her learning from Dr. Jessien of the transfusion of blood, saving her life; but the very idea aroused her antipathy afresh.

There was to be a celebration of the old Countess's birthday—a morning hunt, an evening ball, and *tableaux vivants*. All their world was invited, and Margarethe had made perfect arrangements. The tableaux, planned by an artist, were exquisite. Margarethe appeared in the last one, "The Sleeping Beauty." It was indeed lovely; but a flaring candle caught her draperies, and instantly she was aflame. Günther seized her, and crushed out the fire, bearing her away. She was unhurt, changed her dress, and returned to her guests; but when they had gone she sought Günther's room and tenderly dressed his blistered hands. Then, under gratitude for his second saving of her life, she said:

"Let there be peace between us, Günther. We have caused

each other great suffering, but much may yet be saved. I no longer insist upon a divorce; let us shape our lives pleasantly—not in bitterness, but in calm confidence. Here is my hand, Günther; take it, and let us be friends."

He made no reply, nor did he take her hand, but said, almost angrily, that he would answer her to-morrow.

The twelfth of November dawned gloomily; the wind, raging all night, was still furious; dark clouds were rising, and Günther, anxious, took horse for the salt meadows. Elizabeth drove over to Hellerbrook. Her long year was ended; the *Bellona* was due, and she was to meet her Willy. Her windows commanded a terrace high above the sea, and she shivered at the rising tempest. By evening she had given him up for the day, when suddenly he appeared, and she was in his arms.

"I ought not to have come," he said, "before the *Bellona* was anchored, but I saw the lights in your windows, had a boat lowered, and came ashore. I must go back within an hour, for a storm is brewing, and even in port I could not leave my vessel in a storm."

They clung tenderly together until, the hour passed, he rose to go. But Elizabeth passionately begged him not to go out into the storm. He implored her not to tempt him. She prayed to go with him, but this was impossible; and, taking his cap and sword, he went to the door. He turned for one last look, and saw her, broken, forlorn. Once more he clasped her in his arms. The lace of her square-necked dress was slightly disarranged, and on her breast he saw the little dagger-scar. He kissed it—and saw visions of the girlish figure at the gate. He kissed it again; and saw her at the altar with him. Again he kissed the cool white breast, and he saw—he heard—no more. The winds and the waves had lost their power to call.

At dawn the sound of a cannon-shot mingled with the roar of the storm.

"The *Bellona*!" cried Willy as he leaped to the window and saw his distressed ship tossing on great waves. Stunned for a moment, realizing that he had been recreant to duty, he showed Elizabeth the ship, with foremast gone, and despite her pleadings, he bade her farewell for a few short hours, and went.

That day Günther had spent at the meadows, strengthening dykes. The next morning intelligence came from coast villages of inundations, and Günther went out early. His letter to Margarethe frankly told her that there was no middle path of friendship for them: it must be all or nothing. He declared his unalterable love, briefly recounted their misunderstandings, his impatience of her tender exactions, and his following of a wild fancy, although asserting that his relations with the Baroness never had been criminal. He told of his disappointment the night before, when he thought she had come to bestow life upon him, and said that, if they were to live separate, they must live altogether apart.

Refugees from the inundated villages soon began to appear, and were sheltered and fed under Margarethe's own supervision. Günther's letter had dissolved her pride, and she was happy in the thought of possibilities in a love purified by suffering. With further news, alarmed by the perils of Günther's labors, she insisted on going to him, with Pastor Dossow. The carriage took them as far as it could, in the devastating storm, and then they struggled on afoot. At the meadows they found sky, sea, and land one indistinguishable mass of foam; most of the buildings had sunk before the waves; the Count was just going with one helper in a little boat, to save the shepherd and his son, now on the roof of the last building. After incredible efforts the men were reached, and the boat came toppling back over the waves. But the shore was gained, and the people sent up a mighty shout, while Margarethe rushed to Günther.

"You—you here, Margarethe?" he exclaimed, as he clasped her, and then with sobs and laughter she hugged him tight, and cried: "Mine, mine once more! My husband!"

The next day when Pastor Dossow traveled through desolation to Hellerbrook, he found the *Bellona* anchored at the repair-dock. The Captain, he learned, had got on board, but had lost four men from his boat. He had saved the ship, but had been struck on the breast by a breaking yard-arm. The surgeon told of the bursting of a blood-vessel, and the unsparing efforts of the Captain, which had greatly weakened him. The Pastor descended, trembling, to the cabin, and found his boy in the peaceful sleep of death.

Elizabeth had had a dreadful day, although learning that the *Bellona* was in with her captain. But when the Pastor came without his son, it was some time before he could answer her rapid questions, and at last, by his tearful speechlessness, convey to her the truth of their crushing bereavement.

The next day the *Bellona* stood out to sea a little, while the good Pastor commended the Captain's body to the deep and his spirit to his Maker, not sparing himself or the tearful crew some reflections on the fact that one small neglect of duty, even by an unselfish and heroic man, might bring fearful consequences. Before he had left Schöneichen, the old man had been restored to his pastorate; but, even with his daughter Elizabeth to console him and to be consoled, his heart went down as his boy's body sank to its watery grave. Yet he did not murmur, but trusted the divine Helper, whom he had brought to other wounded hearts.

HENRY FRANCIS KEENAN

(United States, 1850)

THE MONEY-MAKERS (1885)

The issue of *The Bread-Winners* in 1883, published anonymously, but since attributed to John Hay, gave so degrading a view of the unscrupulous agitators who often misled the labor-unions into violence that it widely discredited the labor movement in general. In the following year Mr. Keenan wrote, as an offset, *The Money-Makers*, which was published, also anonymously, in 1885, giving a broader view of the same period—the 'seventies—when had developed a class of able and unscrupulous men, grasping power through accumulated wealth and using corporate influence to shape laws for their own benefit. It portrayed the conditions under which the laboring classes suffered, and which have inspired their slowly learned lessons of better organization and wiser methods of agitation; but its chief aim was to depict the dangers of moral degradation arising from the getting and spending of unlimited money. It is not so much an offset as a complement to *The Bread-Winners*.

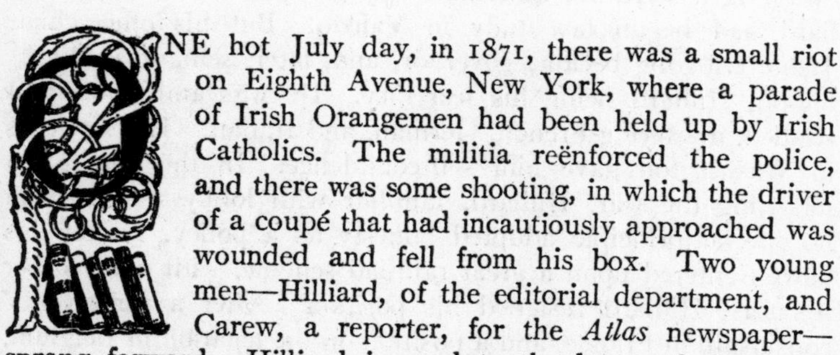

NE hot July day, in 1871, there was a small riot on Eighth Avenue, New York, where a parade of Irish Orangemen had been held up by Irish Catholics. The militia reënforced the police, and there was some shooting, in which the driver of a coupé that had incautiously approached was wounded and fell from his box. Two young men—Hilliard, of the editorial department, and Carew, a reporter, for the *Atlas* newspaper—sprang forward. Hilliard jumped to the box and drove the coupé to safety, declining to give his name to the steady-faced man who got out to thank him, glanced at the lady within and returned to Carew, who had hauled the wounded man into a house. Leaving their cards, as witnesses for the man should he need them, the riot being over they departed.

The next day Carew's report and Hilliard's comments so pleased the manager of the paper that he increased Hilliard's salary and transferred Carew to the editorial department. Also, to each came a letter of thanks from Mr. Aaron Grimstone, enclosing to Hilliard five thousand dollars and to Carew one thousand.

"Whew!" said Carew, "five thousand. That's princely. You can live like a nabob."

Hilliard was disgusted. "Do you suppose I'm going to keep money flung at me so, because I chanced to get the man and his daughter out of harm's way? But now that I know his name, I'm not surprised at it. He is a Western railway magnate—made his money in Valedo, through all sorts of sharp practises. The man might reward a footman so, but not his equal. Your case is different. You helped a poor man, and were practically an agent of law and order. His master may properly offer you compensation."

"I confess I don't understand your distinctions," said Carew. "Grimstone evidently means to be generous, and I shall write and thank him."

But Mr. Grimstone had sailed that day for Europe, and Hilliard could not return the check at once. His reasons for declining it were not quite sincerely given. After college, Hilliard had begun law-study in Valedo. But his office-chief, Judge Killgore, became governor, and, later, senator at Washington, Hilliard being his secretary. He was ambitious, and studied, mastering French, German, and Italian. His six years in Washington gave him self-confidence. In the corruption following the war, Hilliard, familiar with lobby secrets, from no special principle adopted honesty as a policy. When his patron entered upon a great railroad scheme, with many other senators, Hilliard resigned his position. After a three-years' consulship in France, and a position on the legation in Belgium, he returned to New York in 1870, brilliant, scholarly, polished, conceited, and selfish.

Carew, whom he had known in Valedo in boyhood, was doing assignment-work on the *Atlas*, and got Hilliard's help in writing up a French Offenbach opera-troupe. The captivating style of the resulting article—with Carew's telling of his friend's authorship—ended in Hilliard's engagement as an editorial writer. A series of screeds on the *Crédit Mobilier* exposure, involving many leaders of the Optimate party in Washington, whose maneuvers were familiar to Hilliard, gave him instant recognition, and he rapidly advanced. He was a general favorite in literary clubs and socially—yet he had not money, the source of luxury, servants, horses, the play, the opera, books, pictures, leisure.

He had seen, though not known, Mr. Grimstone in Washington. He had known of the family in his student days at Valedo, and in New York heard much of the father's wealth and the daughter's beauty. Thus matters stood when the coupé incident had happened. Hilliard had meant to meet the Grimstones—but with *éclat*, in some drawing-room, talked of as the "Rupert of the Pen"; but to meet them thus, and as Grimstone's beneficiary! He burned to send that check back.

But one day he learned that the English shareholders in the Ontario railway, tired of having the stock a ball of speculation, planned to control it, and a man with a few thousands as margin might clear a big profit on the rise. Excited by the sudden chance, he deposited as collateral for margin the Grimstone check and another thousand, bought Ontario that afternoon, and the next noon learned from the papers that his six thousand had been transformed into one hundred and sixty thousand dollars!

He regained the Grimstone check and at once sent it to Grimstone's address in Valedo.

Alfred Carew had had no such temptation and fall as this in the use of Grimstone's honorarium. He had immediately sent five hundred dollars to his mother in Valedo, for his brother Jack's schooling. He had had five years of the usual struggle to get a footing in New York journalism; but he carefully did his best on every assignment, and had now attained recognition and certainty of employment. One day the coachman he had saved at the riot came in. His injury had ruined his right hand for driving, and Grimstone had let him go, securing him a place, which now he had lost, and he was in want. Fred vainly tried to get him a position in the Custom House, but no official would do anything for an Ultrocrat. So he got him a place in Valedo, and, with Grimstone's other five hundred, he paid the transportation of the family and secured them a modest home.

About this time Fred was sent to the Appalachia coal-region to investigate labor disturbances. At the beginning of winter the operators had suspended work until spring. The workmen were distressed and were forming leagues — as reported, for pillage. Fred spent weeks there, ascertained the capacity of the mines, their output, etc., and then found that coal was dearer than ever, that New England had to import coal despite the heavy duty, that in the West there was almost a coal-famine; yet the operators assured him that the market was glutted. Journalists came from all parts, and were sumptuously entertained by the operators. Fred wrote of this ominous hospitality as indecent and degrading. He learned that the suspension of work had been planned to stimulate a legislative consolidation of the coal interests of Appalachia and Transylvania in the hands of a powerful Eastern syndicate; and the miners had been systematically goaded to outbreaks. He told the truth. The bill was passed, however.

Then Carew had a taste of policy. Birch, an influential leader among the workingmen, laying a sealed envelope on his desk, said it was the sum agreed on for his work in their interest. He indignantly refused it, when Birch opened the door, saying in a loud voice:

"There's the money agreed on; if you're not satisfied you must ask the council for more."

Fred sprang at him, but several others rushed in, and he saw it a prearranged plot to disgrace him, Birch being in the pay of the syndicate. He called the landlord and gave him the unopened envelope to be returned to its owner. But in vain. The next day the story of the "detected bribe" was telegraphed abroad. Fred's chief said he believed his story, but the *Atlas* must be above suspicion, and he dared not retain the young man on his force.

One morning Hilliard saw the names of the Grimstones among the steamship arrivals. He now occupied fine bachelor's quarters on Madison Avenue, and lived in style; he still wrote for the *Atlas*, but rarely visited the office except to take the managing editor to dinner in his elegant coupé.

The *Atlas* at this time was discrediting the leaders of its own party, the Optimates, the party having grown corrupt through long possession of power. Hilliard's Washington experience and his deft pen had aroused public attention. In brief, he stood upon a very comfortable height of self-complacency on the morning when he saw the return of the Grimstones.

While he was thinking matters over, Fred Carew called, and was cordially received. He told Hilliard that he had yesterday been invited by Miss Grimstone to dine with them. He had gone, and was charmed with the young lady's simplicity and frankness. She had asked Fred to tell Hilliard that they would be happy to have him call upon them. After some talk about his own projects, he left his brilliant friend. Carew had had a hard time for months; had met coldness and worse on all sides; had refused good pay from the editor of the *Janus* if he would write some scorching sketches of the editorial corps of the *Atlas;* and had finally met a genial member of the *Atlas* corps, named Rivers, who secured him a place on the *Tomahawk,* where he made himself valued — but anonymously, for the editor had begun investigating Fred's downfall, and, until he had the true story ready for publication, wished him to lie quiet. Through the same friend he had been invited to edit the *Eagle,* an Ultrocratic paper in Valedo, and had about concluded to accept.

Miss Grimstone, whatever her motive, evidently meant to show Fred that the July incident was remembered. He was again invited to dine, meeting at table Mr. McKay Dorr, a millionaire of railways and gold, impassive, audacious, and successful, a partner in Grimstone's schemes. Miss Grimstone seemed not to like him. After dinner, Fred went to the opera with the ladies, and was in the box when one of the many visitors brought in Hilliard and introduced him. The next day he drove in the park with Miss Grimstone, and she begged him to be kind to her brother Herbert, soon coming on from Harvard. At the dinner party, when Herbert came home, Fred met Mrs. Albin Circester, a brilliant widow from Valedo, who also had a son at college, Walter, for whom she asked Fred's friendliness.

Herbert Grimstone's ardent desire, Fred found, was to know newspaper men who could introduce him behind the scenes at the theaters. He professed great admiration for Beauxjambes, the fascinating leader of a ballet troupe, who was now in New York. Fred tried to disillusionize him as to the perquisites of journalists, and at all events proclaimed his own inability to help him, except to know other newspaper men.

The next morning the *Tomahawk* came out with six solid columns, detailing the plot to blast Carew's reputation, including the operations of the mine-owners, the bargain with legislators, names and amounts of bribes, management of newspapers, and the final disgraceful scene and dismissal. Many of the city journalists united in a paper recognizing Fred's blamelessness; it was a complete vindication.

One of the newspaper men to whom Fred had given Herbert a letter had introduced him at the back-doors of the theaters and he had captured the coveted Beauxjambes. Fred had met some of Herbert's gay associates—rather to his own disdain—but had yielded to his urgency that he should preside at a little supper.

That evening Fred dined with Mrs. Circester, and met her son Walter, the Columbia College student, who had just bewitched from his not wealthy mother a five-hundred-dollar check, "for a class-yacht." About eleven o'clock he went to Herbert's supper, arriving as the young men—including Walter—were settling gambling debts of their evening's play. The supper was brilliant and noisy. Beauxjambes and several of her pretty ballet-sisters graced the scene, and Fred left about six in the morning. The last thing he saw was Herbert handing to Beauxjambes Walter's check for five hundred dollars, lost and won at the evening play before supper.

Aaron Grimstone began his career as an efficient blacksmith in the village of Valedo, in 1847. The operations of a company to build a canal had reached Valedo, but they ignored the town in purchases of stores and munitions, in favor of Carleo, a neighboring town, and brought swarms of foreigners for the work. Under stress of haste on that particular section, their horses had worn out their shoes. Grimstone went to Carleo, quietly bought up every ounce of iron and nails in the town; and that night the company's luggers at Carleo, laden with horseshoes, disappeared—as it was supposed, drifted away in that night's storm. The contractor had to give Grimstone the shoeing of five hundred horses, undertaken on condition that the company's stores should be unloaded at Valedo and its laborers preferred to foreigners. The new activity brought people and money to the town; Grimstone secured the blacksmithing for the whole line; and he was the hero of Valedo, which now prospered amazingly.

The money Grimstone made on canal-contracts he invested in land along a proposed railway-line: and now he was rich. He went into railways and other speculations; married; built a fine mansion; had two children, a son and a daughter; enlarged his operations, and became a power in Wall Street and Washington. But he never loosed his grip on Valedo, where he ruled with a rod of iron. As he grew rich he grew close. He built a new opera-house and a new hotel, but cut down the architect's estimates on both, substituting cheaper construction. He owned mines, coal-fields, blast-furnaces, machine-shops, became director in forty railroads and president of two. In short, he was one of that extraordinary group of men grown up in this country after the great war who—to reverse Thiers's famous saying—"Govern, but do not reign."

Before going to Valedo, Carew was sent to Saratoga in "the season," to write it up for the *Minerva*. As everything was new to him he wrote with charming enthusiasm, and the hotel where he lodged was thronged with guests. The Grimstones, Mrs. Circester, Hilliard, and many of his New York acquaintances were there, and he was soon overhead in social pleasures.

Hilliard was not a vulgar fortune-seeker. He was attracted by Eleanor Grimstone, but felt that she did not fulfill his ideal; yet such a marriage would conduce to his advancement. He was puzzled. She, meantime, believed that he loved her, but was prevented from its declaration by reluctance to seem to seek wealth in marriage. She had often seen the longed-for words in his eyes, but they were never spoken.

One day as they walked together she talked of Carew and his poetic notions, and told how she had argued with him against his silly notion that he would not marry a girl with money.

"Did you ever hear anything so absurd? I had no patience with him."

Hilliard's admiration of her honesty and her beauty were aroused afresh. He took her hand; kissed it. Their eyes met; the irrevocable words were on his lips—when her brother Herbert crashed through the bushes and called her to her father, his arm having been hurt by the horses. In fact, Grimstone had heard of their walking off together, and had hastened to break up their *tête-à-tête*. The drive back was pleasant and the parting cordial.

An hour afterward Hilliard went by invitation to Mr. Grimstone's parlor. There he was politely informed that Eleanor was engaged to be married to Mr. Dorr. Should she marry anyone else, it would be against her father's wishes, and she would get not a penny of his fortune.

"I will be frank with you, sir," pursued Mr. Grimstone. "I know your history; I know the first money you made in New York, and how you invested it. I know your tastes and ambitions. Marry my daughter, and you shall never occupy a post of distinction on any journal in the country. On the other hand, if you retire from further pretensions to her, with your abilities I can put you in the way of making a fortune not burdened with a wife that after all might not meet the needs of a nature so refined as yours. Take time to reflect, and then write, or come and say what you will do."

Indignation, wrath, humiliation, crushed Hilliard. He staggered out. Poor fool! He had ignobly stooped, and was under the lash of this pitiless taskmaster, as well as that of his own intelligence.

Blackdaw, his chief, came to his room and said that Grimstone, a large owner in the *Atlas*, had asked him to urge Hilliard to accept a proposition he had made; he knew not what it was, but neither he nor Hilliard could afford to oppose the man. Hilliard laughed bitterly and said he should not dispute Grimstone's wish.

Eleanor, anxious about Hilliard's interview with her father, after vainly trying to communicate with her supposed lover, directly charged her father with coming between them. Grimstone explained Hilliard's insincerities, from when he scorned the check and yet used it for his own purposes to the present, when, on learning the disposition of the Grimstone millions should he marry Eleanor, he had withdrawn all pretensions to her hand. Shocked and distressed, Eleanor refused to believe it. She demanded to be taken to Hilliard. Her father drew her hand into his arm and went with her. She appealed to Hilliard to know whether—but her father put in quietly, saying that his daughter believed that he had deceived her. "I have told her," he said, "that if you married her she should not inherit from me. I want you to tell her frankly that you never loved her; that you do not now ask to marry her."

No answer. Shame, anger, consternation, anything but love, was in his pitiful face. Her eyes wondered and grew to anguish, the horror of the truth freezing her blood; and Mr. Grimstone with his daughter silently passed out.

The season was almost over. Fred settled his affairs in New York and proceeded to Valedo to edit the *Eagle*. Having by contract supreme control, the new editor made a good and interesting paper, which soon enlarged its circulation, not only among the Ultrocrats but throughout the city. Once or twice in his showing up of the leaders of the "party of great moral ideas"—their perfidy, corruption, and dishonor—he ran against great men, like Killgore, who tried to drive him from Valedo with distorted stories of his New York experiences. But all to no end; the *Eagle* continued steadily on its way.

Herbert Grimstone had returned with the family to Valedo, having been expelled from college. As desired by both families, he was practically engaged to Betty, Senator Killgore's pretty daughter. He quarreled with Carew because the editor would not permit his paper to eulogize the seductive Beauxjambes, for whom he had negotiated an engagement in Valedo. Finding that he could neither frighten Fred nor wheedle him, Herbert fomented a strike among the *Eagle's* printers; but Carew secured compositors from the country around, and the strike was a failure. Moreover, he took back the good men after the strike, and so fairly treated the labor unions that they hailed him as "the workingman's friend." This alarmed the corporations, and soon after this Eleanor told Fred of a plan between her father and Mr. Dorr to buy up the stock of the *Eagle* and dismiss the editor.

Meanwhile, most of the corporations had suspended work. Ten thousand men were idle. Trade stood still. Similar conditions spread over the country, and distress was great among the workers. "Society," however, continued brilliant and extravagant. The labor unions began to hold meetings, and agitators spoke evil words. Fred was invited to speak on "Capital"; and, preaching peaceful measures, led the unions to adopt "Free-Trade and Labor-Rights" as their watchword.

The syndicates had their newspapers ascribe the trouble to over-immigration, over-production, and the essentially charitable conditions on which capital had employed labor for years. Speakers addressed public meetings. Among others, Hilliard spoke at a great mass-meeting in Grimstone's opera-house. It was a skilful but not satisfactory speech, and as the meeting was separating in disorder, the sudden movement of the mass broke down the parquet floor. The resulting rush dislodged the frail gallery supports, the crash of timbers and frenzied shouts of the panic-stricken crowd, and soon the roar of flames added to the terrors. How many perished was never known. It was a time of wo in Valedo. Even "the best" ceased their gaieties, hospitals were improvised, and money was lavishly contributed from all parts of the country, Grimstone heading the contributions with twenty thousand dollars.

After the horror had somewhat passed, the *Eagle* pointed out the defective construction of the building and demanded investigation. A few days later, Carew was informed that a majority of the stock had been sold to Archibald Hilliard, Esq.; his own services were commended in a resolution, fifteen thousand dollars (three years' salary) were paid him by the treasurer —and he was out.

Carew immediately established an afternoon paper. Within a fortnight the *Free Press* was on sale, the first week's circulation being more than ten thousand a day. Carew was more radical than ever. He was not only a vigorous writer, but a good editor and a fearless manager; so that, although his foes tried to cripple him by bribed delays of his telegraphic news, poor deliveries of his mail-edition, libel-suits, and other ways, he met and beat them, in the courts and before the public. The *Free Press* throve; the *Eagle* lost ground.

The grand jury's investigation developed Grimstone's interference with the architect's specifications, and the verdict announced that "the responsible cause of the defective building was Aaron Grimstone." This inflamed afresh the popular hatred for the old man and for Herbert, whose dissipations and extravagances were well known. One evening they dragged the young man from the carriage in which he was driving with his light o' love and threw him into the canal. Fred, who was passing, called by the shrieks of the agonized Beauxjambes to save her "husband," rescued him and bore him to Mrs. Carew's house, where he was put to bed and taken care of by Fred's motherly mother, the distracted wife being permitted to remain with him; but Herbert was insultingly angry when he learned that his marital relation was known.

Aaron Grimstone's reflections on reading the verdict may be imagined. Lord of millions, arbiter in courts, Congress, and legislatures—to have the humiliation, the hate and scorn of the sordid masses! He discussed with Killgore some means of disposing of Carew, so that, his restraining influence gone, they might incite a riot which, with the destruction of a few thousand dollars' worth of property, would terrify the sentimentalists captivated by his mad reform doctrines of free-trade and different labor-laws. They parted, and Grimstone went to seek Herbert, who had not been home for several days. In driving about he encountered Fred, who told him of the mobbing, the rescue, and Herbert's presence at his mother's house. Grimstone had the grace to wonder at the magnanimity of this young man, whose ruin he was plotting even then.

That night delegates from all the labor unions in the State met the local unions, three hundred thousand workingmen represented. Inflammatory appeals were made, advising the destruction of the property of railroads and various corporations. The next morning the railroad station and stock were seized, without arms or violence, and the corporations notified to negotiate. No answer. Carew knew of the policy of the corporations, had the violent agitators tracked to Killgore's office, and at the next meeting laid the plan before the delegates, showing that they were to be incited to violence, men had been hired to fire buildings, and all prepared first to excite and then by soldiery to crush disorder. However, collisions came the next day. Sporadic fires broke out; street cars were stopped; shooting began, and many were wounded. In the afternoon a great crowd surged toward Grimstone's Albatross Hotel. The leader demanded that the hotel should be instantly cleared, as they were going to fire it in one hour, "because it has been condemned as unsafe," he said, "and we are determined that there sha'n't be any Academy murder here."

It was cleared and fired. Fred ran in from his office, trying to stop it, but to no avail. Hearing some of the men talking of mobbing a certain Madame Dominguez, in the house, Fred found her, and through incredible exertions—finally crawling through the smoking, fiery cellar—rescued her and took her to his mother's house.

The Optimate journals united in accusing Carew of this outbreak, except the *Atlas*, which not only refrained from that, but commended his gallantry in the rescue of a noble lady. Some strong influence in the enemy's ranks seemed bent on protecting him; one might suppose that even Grimstone had some conscience and sense of shame.

The old man was overjoyed to find Herbert. Eleanor had been to the Carews', and made friends with the terrified Beauxjambes, concealing the marriage from the family. Herbert—who treated his wife brutally and all his helpers insolently—told Eleanor that he should divorce the actress and marry Betty Killgore. He left the Carew house and went home, where he found his father in an apoplectic fit—caused by Killgore, who having heard of Herbert's marriage from some of his young friends, had been in to reproach the old man. Mr. Grimstone partially recovered, and, seeing Herbert, shouted:

"Get out, you dog! You selfish, low-lived ingrate! Go rot in the slime you have wallowed in! Not a penny of mine shall keep you from the slums you have chosen." And the young brute went to New York, where for a time he fulfilled his father's curse.

The riots over, the battle of words continued. Many thinking people changed their opinions; the city was before long carried by the Ultrocrats; the State also; "unjust taxation and the robber-tariff" were increasingly denounced, and two years later the Ultrocrat candidate was elected to the presidency by a popular majority of a quarter of a million—although kept from his seat by the peculiar decision of a commission named by Congress to investigate the contested election.

Aaron Grimstone recovered, and pursued his old trade of money-getting with vigor and success. But in less than a year, just as he, his wife, and Eleanor were about starting for Europe, he shot himself. Herbert successfully contested the will that disinherited him, but could not overthrow the transfer to Alfred Carew, Esq., "for value received," of the majority interest in the stock of the *Eagle*, which, consolidated with the *Free Press*, was thereafter conducted by Carew to influence and success.

Hilliard went to New York and married the daughter of a bonanza king. Herbert allied himself with Madame Dominguez, built her a fine mansion, ruled as despotically as his father had done, and prospered in his evil way. His abandoned wife was supported by Eleanor, whose friendship with Fred was never broken.

And the parable ends in incompleteness. Unmerited rewards and unrewarded merit; hapless love and loveless pleasure; Misery and Greed living together; Money not only the law but the gospel of life.

JOHN PENDLETON KENNEDY

(United States, 1795–1879)

HORSESHOE ROBINSON (1835)

The scene of this story opens, in the latter half of the War of Independence, in the southern part of Virginia and the Carolinas. It was at the most critical period of that struggle, when the bitter warfare between the Tories and the Patriots was at its height.

GALBRAITH ROBINSON, a sergeant in the army of the Patriots, was chiefly engaged in very dangerous secret attempts to trace the movements of the enemy and to encourage the disheartened defenders of colonial independence. He was a blacksmith, a man of large and powerful frame and great shrewdness and courage. But his sobriquet of "Horseshoe Robinson" was derived not so much from his occupation as from the fact that his backwoods dwelling and shop were on a tongue of land (surrounded by a stream) shaped at that point like a horseshoe.

Associated with Galbraith Robinson in these desperate enterprises was Brevet-Major Butler, of the Continental army, dressed as a civilian. Both of these heroes knew well the fate that awaited them, according to the law of nations, in case they should fall into the hands of the enemy.

Before setting out on a perilous journey for Georgia, where the British were then especially active, Butler was moved to make a stop near the Dove-Cote. This was the beautiful residence of a Royalist gentleman, standing alone in a cultivated clearing in a thinly settled country, after the fashion of planters in the South. Mr. Lindsay was a man of culture, a native of England, who had transferred his fortunes to America, and had devoted himself to study after the death of his wife. Although averse to taking an active part in the war, he was heartily with the Tories in principle. On the other hand, and greatly to his sorrow, his daughter and son, Mildred and Henry, were as strongly in favor of resisting the efforts made by Great Britain to crush the rebellion. Whether the fervor of Mildred's loyalty was kindled before or after she first met Major Butler is not on record, nor is there any means now for settling this point. At any rate, owing to her father's well-known sentiments, she kept her attachment secret from him, as she supposed, but found a faithful ally in her brother Henry, a fiery, intrepid youth.

Before setting out on his expedition to Georgia, Butler arranged an interview with Mildred, which was unusually touching, as each realized how many perils must be encountered by him, any one of which might prove fatal. It was a consolation to her to know that he was to be accompanied by a man of such quick resources and cool intrepidity as Horseshoe Robinson, whose prudence it was which at last forced the lovers to separate at this interview. She returned unobserved to the Dove-Cote, while Butler and Horseshoe hastened to the little roadside inn kept by Mistress Dimock. She sided secretly with the cause of liberty, and when satisfied of the character of her guests gave them a warm welcome.

But in the conversation that followed the meal, caution was neglected in the discussion of plans. They were overheard by a man named Curry, a private of the British army, a sharp, stealthy, unscrupulous fellow who was then serving as one of the attendants of an English officer passing under the name of Tyrrel. This Tyrrel was himself something of a spy, who came repeatedly to the Dove-Cote, ostensibly to urge Mr. Lindsay to lay aside his non-combatant methods and devote his energies and fortune to the cause that he professed to favor so strongly. Incidentally, Tyrrel was also a determined aspirant to the hand of Mildred, and of course as determined a foe to Major Butler, of whose love for Mildred he had learned by various crooked methods.

At the very moment when the lovers were meeting in a secluded nook by the riverside, Tyrrel was on one of his visits to the Dove-Cote, and his servants were staying at the neighboring inn. Horseshoe observed a man who was listening on the porch, and, going out stealthily, detected Curry in the act. A sharp encounter of words was followed by a severe fight on the turf. Robinson succeeded in disarming the spy and dismissed him on his promise that he would leave the premises at once. He could not quite nerve himself to kill the spy outright when he had him in his power, which was an error on the part of Horseshoe. He realized the importance of quitting the inn by early dawn; but the mischief had already been done. Curry had heard and seen enough to put Tyrrel and all the Tories in that region on the alert for Butler, to ruin his plans and put the life of both Butler and his companion in immediate peril. The two wayfarers proceeded with great circumspection as they approached the South Carolina line, although they did not realize the possible consequences of the encounter with Curry, not being fully acquainted with the facts behind the espionage of that villain. But the entire region was seething with disaffection, and they desired, by following winding bridle-paths in the dense forests, to avoid the bands roving the wilderness to pick up patriots engaged in enterprises similar to their own.

The Sergeant's first object was to conduct his superior to his own dwelling on the Catawba, near the Waxhaws. They arrived there on the second day; and Butler then exchanged his civilian suit for one more homely and rustic. Thence they shaped a course between the Catawba and Broad rivers, intending to reach the habitation of Nat Adair, a well-known woodsman on the southern side of that river, near its confluence with the Pacolet. It was agreed that, if challenged on the road before reaching Adair's, they should say they were graziers going to the mountains to buy cattle. But if they should meet suspicious characters unlikely to be hoodwinked by such an explanation, Horseshoe would put his hand to his mouth and give a sort of hem, and Butler was to leave the answering of questions to him.

"If worse comes to the worst, Major," said the Sergeant, "the rule is to run or fight. We can manage that, at any rate, for we have had a good deal of both in the last three or four years. It is all a matter of chance, for, to tell you the main truth, I don't know whom to depend upon."

Nat Tyler was a desperate character, and his farm associate, Michael Lynch, was almost an avowed Tory. But Nat's wife inclined the other way, and Mary Musgrove, her niece, who lived with them, was the *fiancée* of a soldier in the Continental army, and hence, of course, entirely to be trusted. The travelers hoped that these various elements in the household of Nat Adair, and his known habit of being influenced at the sight of gold, for he had an itching palm, would carry them safely at least through one night at this lone ranch in the woods. They reasoned that, before he could carry news about them to the enemy, if he were so disposed, they would again be well distant from his power to harm.

But in this Butler and Robinson were sadly mistaken; for Curry and Tyrrel had stolen a march on them and already sent word to Adair of what was expected of him and what would be his reward. While the lodgers under his roof were wrapped in slumber he despatched Lynch to put a well-known band of Tory marauders, commanded by the ferocious Captain Habershaw, on the lookout for a certain Major Butler and Sergeant Horse-shoe Robinson, who were on a spying expedition to Georgia.

Mary Musgrove had observed Adair and Lynch whispering together, and, suspecting what was on foot, managed to get a clue to their plot. After all were asleep, the faithful girl slipped out and, creeping under the window where Butler was sleeping, called to him repeatedly: "Take the turn to the left! Take the turn to the left!" Not daring to remain any longer, she returned to her bed just as Butler, but half awake, crept to the window. Seeing no one, he concluded that it was only a dream, and returned to his straw pallet.

When morning came, and they purposed to leave early, Adair detained them on one excuse and another until Lynch had returned and informed him that Habershaw had put his column of rough-riders in motion to intercept the travelers. Apparently out of a friendly spirit of hospitality, Nat accompanied them part of the way, when in reality he was anxious that nothing should lead them to take the safe turn in the road rather than the one he planned for them. When the fork in the road came in sight he directed them by no means to go to the left but to follow the right turn, if they would consult their own best interests.

As a matter of course, Butler and Horseshoe fell into the trap and were obliged to yield rather than be slaughtered on the spot by an overwhelming corps of troopers. Seeing a way to escape the next morning, the wily Sergeant did not hesitate to seize it, hoping by this means to devise a way for the rescue of Butler. For him to neglect the chance simply meant the sacrifice of both; as it was intended by Habershaw to take them both to the nearest British post to be tried and hanged as spies.

Horseshoe eluded pursuit, and soon afterward, by the aid of a stalwart youth, the son of a patriot, whom he found protecting his mother at home, contrived to bag seven British soldiers, including the lieutenant commanding them, who were carelessly resting in a small shanty, with their arms stacked in a corner. They were regularly trapped, and were led to the boy's house, where they were safely locked up. It then transpired that this officer was the brother of the very Colonel Tyrrel already mentioned as visiting the Dove-Cote, whose servant was the very Curry who had spied on the travelers and caused them to be intercepted. Lieutenant Tyrrel was forced, at the pistol's muzzle, to write a note to the commander of the post, urging that no harm be done to Butler, for his own life would inevitably and promptly pay the forfeit.

As soon as Butler reached the post he was court-martialed and condemned to be shot immediately. But ere this order was executed the note of Lieutenant Tyrrel was handed in. The commander considered or assumed to believe it a forgery, a mere ruse to postpone proceedings; but the brother of the Lieutenant took it in earnest, identified the writing, and insisted on a delay of the execution, to which the commander reluctantly acceded, and Butler was remanded to prison.

In the mean time Colonel Ferguson, a brilliant officer of the army of Lord Cornwallis, had been taking advantage of the consternation produced by the disastrous defeat of the Continental army under Gates, at Camden, to collect an army composed almost entirely of Tories of the Carolinas. With the addition of such a force, the army of Cornwallis would have been indeed almost invincible in that section. But the patriots realized the emergency no less than Ferguson. Quietly and with consummate skill and despatch the various desultory bands of patriots, thirsting to rid the land of such invaders, converged toward the Tory force, under such admirable partizan leaders as Marion, Campbell, and Williams. Unable to escape without a battle, Ferguson seized the slope and summit of a steep eminence springing boldly out of the forest, called King's Mountain. The arrangement of the patriot army was so admirably planned, and the American troops burned with such ardor for revenge, that their attack was irresistible, and the Tory army was dispersed with great loss. Among the slain were Colonel Ferguson himself, Colonel Tyrrel, and Curry, the spy, who was killed in a desperate fight with Horseshoe Robinson.

Mildred Lindsay, who had been to see General Cornwallis himself, to intercede for the life of her lover, was on the way home when the battle began, and saw with mingled dread and hope the terrible scenes of the conflict. She now learned that a corps of British soldiers who were with the Tories had brought the Major with them. In the hurried flight they were unable to hold him, and Mildred had the inexpressible joy of clasping him again to her heart.

One sad incident clouded the joy of the lovers. During her absence her father, Philip Lindsay, had been induced by Tyrrel to join the Tory army, and was desperately wounded and captured by the victors. Before he passed away he withdrew the opposition to their marriage, which had caused so much domestic sorrow, admitted that perhaps he had been in error, and bestowed on them his paternal benediction. After the war they lived happily for many years at the Dove-Cote.

RICHARD BURLEIGH KIMBALL

(United States, 1816–1892)

ST. LEGER (1849)

Though unknown to the younger generation of Americans, this novel was widely circulated in its day. Kimball wrote it while editor of the *Knickerbocker Gallery*, and published it first in the *Knickerbocker Magazine*. Eight American editions in book form followed, two in England; and Tauchnitz published it on the Continent.

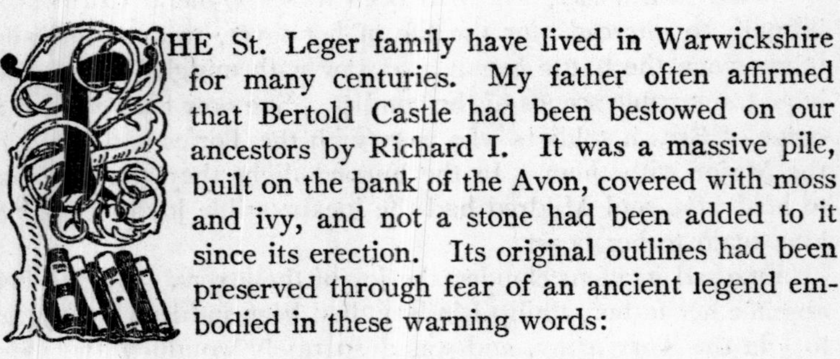

THE St. Leger family have lived in Warwickshire for many centuries. My father often affirmed that Bertold Castle had been bestowed on our ancestors by Richard I. It was a massive pile, built on the bank of the Avon, covered with moss and ivy, and not a stone had been added to it since its erection. Its original outlines had been preserved through fear of an ancient legend embodied in these warning words:

> "When ye Saint Leger shal marrie a virgyn fair,
> Shal build a new castel both wondrous and rare,
> Lett him warnynge tak, for ye last of his race
> Shal hee meet in yt castel, face to face."

So when my father, after marrying the daughter of a noble Warwickshire family, decided to make some modern additions to the castle, the old servants shook their heads and muttered the ancient prophecy. We children, said they, were doomed. My elder brother seemed little affected by the warning, but my temperament was such as to cause me much suffering from fear of these evil forebodings. This, with the fact that my education was conducted at home, made me a thoughtful child for my years.

With us in the castle lived an old maiden aunt, an eccentric woman, always reading or walking alone, kind to us children, but apparently without a spark of affection in her nature.

Until I was sixteen I had been a lonely, meditative child, speculating over the meaning of things. At sixteen I left my home for the first time.

My mother was related to the noble family of Venachoir in Argylshire. They had invited us to visit them in Glencoe, but as my brother had no desire to go it was decided that I alone should accept the invitation.

It was June when I set out, supplied with letters to my father's friends on the way and much good paternal advice. Just before my departure my Aunt Alice gave me a small parcel, and then abruptly left me. I had no time to examine its contents, so I put it into the bottom of my portmanteau and forgot about it.

Early in the morning I took the royal mail-coach to Oxford. Among the passengers was a dark young man of foreign features, whose eyes I caught. An instinctive presentiment that he was to be an important factor in my career led me to examine him more closely. There was mutual dislike in our exchange of glances; I already felt him to be a man of evil mind.

After spending several days in London I pushed on to Glencoe, where my cousins gave me an enthusiastic welcome. Herbert, a lad a year older than I, seemed especially pleased to see me. We became very intimate companions.

Imagine my surprise upon meeting that evening the dark-faced stranger of the coach. He was introduced to me as Count Vantrey, a distant cousin of our family.

The time passed delightfully; Hubert and I hunted and fished together, and often we all played games together. All, I say, except Vantrey, who never joined us. His supercilious airs made him cordially disliked among my cousins. Hubert, especially, whose proud spirit rebelled against Vantrey's superior presumptions, could hardly conceal his antipathy.

Cousin Margaret told me the story of Vantrey's relation to our family. My grandfather, Hugh St. Leger, had had a younger brother, Wilfred, who fled from home to Scotland at twenty years of age. There he met Julian Moncrieff, cousin to Margaret's grandfather, the old Earl of Venachoir. Julian's influence on my granduncle was evil and they were ever implicated in disgraceful escapades. One day they departed together for France. Simultaneously disappeared from her home the ward and relative of the Earl of Venachoir, the beautiful young Isabella Seward. She had eloped with Wilfred St. Leger. In France Julian Moncrieff left the couple, and for a while they lived together happily. But after a time Moncrieff returned, with an Italian wife, and again Wilfred fell under his evil influence, and began to neglect his young wife.

Julian Moncrieff had one daughter by his foreign wife, who married Henri Laurent de Vantrey, and their son was the disagreeable young fellow whom we all disliked.

One day a group of us were playing at putting the bar, a number of our guests being present. Hubert had just thrown, rather unsuccessfully, when Vantrey passed and cast at us one of his habitual contemptuous glances. Hubert was enraged, and made some cynical remarks about our guest. Hot words followed, and a personal encounter would surely have resulted had not Hubert's eldest brother, Frank, interfered, and, in the absence of the old Earl, asserted his authority to forbid further quarreling.

Hubert, unable to bear Vantrey's presence longer, asked hospitality of his visiting friend, which was immediately offered him by a young highland laird, Glenfinglas. But Glenfinglas wanted to do more; he wished to avenge the insult offered his friend. I hurried off and found Vantrey in the garden and tried to persuade him to avoid a meeting with Glenfinglas. As we stood talking, the young laird suddenly appeared, and firmly, though politely, demanded satisfaction. Vantrey's supercilious answer enraged Glenfinglas, who reached out his hand and slightly touched Vantrey's shoulder. I saw the flash of a blade, and the laird fell, wounded in the breast. Vantrey disappeared. During the excitement that followed he left the castle.

Glenfinglas's life had been saved by a buckle; he was not even seriously wounded. He soon recovered enough to go home alone, his servant having disappeared. This boy, Donacha MacIan, had been one of a band of highland cattle thieves. Glenfinglas had once saved the lad's mother from the brutal treatment of some soldiers, and Donacha had become his benefactor's most faithful servant.

At the end of the summer I prepared to return home. While packing, I came across Aunt Alice's forgotten packet. It was addressed to the "Woedallah of St. Kilda." I remembered then that Aunt Alice had often made vague references to the Hebrides, and though I had never dared question her, I had been impressed with the existence of some deep mystery connecting her past life with those islands.

I desired to deliver the packet personally. Hubert volunteered to accompany me on my trip, and we set out together. It was a pleasant autumn journey, and we took our time.

We reached St. Kilda finally, and next day I went forth alone to examine the island. Wandering along the cliffs by the sea, I caught a glimpse of a woman's skirt at the mouth of a cavern. Approaching, I caught the words, in a woman's voice: "I hate you! Leave me, sir; there can be nothing between us."

A man's figure came suddenly into view, and I recognized Count Vantrey, his countenance flushed and agitated. I caught one glimpse of a beautiful, fair face, then turned and hurried away.

The incident created a deep impression on me, besides rousing my keenest curiosity. Chance satisfied the latter. Next day, while wandering aimlessly about the country, I came upon a house, by the gate of which stood an old man, attired in English costume, which, contrasted with his appearance and environment, excited my astonishment. The old man addressed me in English, and we entered into conversation. My first surprise increased to bewildered wonder when he told me that he was the person I sought, the Woedallah of the island. I gave him the packet, and upon beholding the superscription, his hands trembled and his face became livid. He then nervously, though cordially, invited me into his house, saying:

"I, too, am a St. Leger."

Inside, whom should I meet but the beautiful stranger whom I had seen in conversation with Vantrey! The Woedallah introduced her to me as his daughter, Leila.

On returning to our lodgings, Hubert told me that he had met Vantrey, and that they had parted amicably.

From our landlord I learned more of the Woedallah. He had appeared with his daughter six years before, and immediately gained the esteem of the people by his qualities as a healer of disease, for which reason he was termed Woedallah ("God of the Rocks"). At that time a tyrannous steward oppressed the people, and the Woedallah incited them to revolt. He himself fought with them and helped bring the uprising to a successful issue. After the coming of the new steward, the Woedallah led a secluded life. Often he left the island, and once returned with a woman, who soon died and was carried away in a boat.

I visited the Woedallah again and again, and became intimate with him and with Leila. One day, while walking along the cliffs, he related to me his life history.

He was the son of my granduncle, Wilfred St. Leger. He had studied at Oxford, until one day he received an urgent summons from his father in Paris. He answered the summons, and found his father in a repentant state of mind for the miserable life he had led his wife. He blamed Moncrieff, and had determined to fight his evil genius a duel. The son witnessed the fight, and saw his father, who was the better swordsman, deliberately throw himself on his antagonist's rapier.

The death of his father so unnerved him that he began a life of dissipation, but one night at a masked ball he heard my Aunt Alice's voice in his ear saying:

"Reform, or I shall end your life."

He married a fine, pure woman, but lived with her unhappily, through suspicions excited in his mind by plotting enemies. On her death-bed she convinced him of her innocence, and the last few days of her life they spent blissfully together.

The St. Kildans arranged a bird hunt one day, Vantrey and I both being of the party. It was growing dark, when suddenly I saw a figure rush out from the brushwood and hurl Vantrey over the edge of the cliffs. In that glimpse I recognized Donacha MacIan, Glenfinglas's servant. Vantrey's life was saved by his catching on a ledge of rock, but Hubert said, "He is a doomed man."

Two years passed, and the abstract problems of life did not unravel themselves to my ponderings.

I read Spinoza and Kant, and finally decided to go to Germany to study the philosophies of the German savants. My father was pleased, and sent me to Leipzig, where he had studied under Johann von Hofrath.

I found my father's old tutor, who gave me a home with himself and his daughter Theresa. Here I met the great German poet and philosopher, Wolfgang Goethe.

Theresa became my dearest friend. Among the students I made many pleasant acquaintances, but most strongly was I attracted to Wolfgang Hegewisch, known among his fellows as Mephistopheles on account of his solitary habits. We became very intimate, and once, under the impulse of our friendship, he told me the story of his past.

"I am without a heart," he said bitterly. "Listen, and you will know why.

"I am the son of Baron ——, but never mind places and names. We were two brothers, Caspar and I. Caspar hated me, for, as eldest son, I had the prospective privileges of primogeniture. As he grew older, Caspar fell under the influence of a monk, an evil fellow, who taught him craftiness and hypocrisy.

"From childhood I had been engaged in marriage by my father to Meta von Richstein, a girl three years my junior. She had been sent away to be educated, and I rarely saw her.

"One day, when I was about twenty, Caspar came to me in what appeared to me a state of great mental distress. He confessed that he had met Meta, and they had exchanged mutual vows. Meta loved him, not me. Would I relinquish my claims? I consented, and gave him a written statement to that effect, and he went away overjoyed.

"Some time after that I chanced to visit the town where Meta lived. At the inn where I was staying I had heard a conversation through a partition in which I had no difficulty in recognizing the voices of my brother and the monk. I caught enough to convince me that they were intriguing for possession of Meta's dowry and that my note was to be used as a means to accomplish their ends.

"I hurried to Meta and exposed the conspiracy. My note had been elaborated, and was now a plain forgery. Caspar's plot failed; he was sent away, and not long after Meta and I plighted our troth anew. Alas! those were happy days, gone forever.

"Before marrying, I decided to tour the world. For a while I received regular letters from Meta; then they ceased. My anxiety increased and I hurried home. Meta, my Meta, was married to Caspar, and mad, insane, I entered their house, threw Caspar out of a window and took Meta home to my mother. After a long illness she recovered her reason, only to live a few days longer. Alas! Meta was dead. Gone, forever!"

Wolfgang's story depressed me heavily, and I began to realize that there is no philosophy to guard us against such calamities.

One day I received a letter from Leila St. Leger, telling me her father had died after extracting a promise from her to marry Count Vantrey. The tone of her letter was despairing, but showed her firm determination to fulfil her promise.

I set out at once, determined to make all efforts possible to prevent this hideous sacrifice. Leila was then in Dresden, and I hastened thither. On my way I made the acquaintance of a fellow-traveler, an Irishman named Robert Macklorne. He was a light-hearted, rollicking soldier of fortune, whose tales of adventure fascinated me, and our acquaintance ripened into real friendship. I confided to him my mission, and he promised his help.

We had spent a night at an inn several hours out of Dresden. The next morning I heard a familiar voice in the passage, and, most astounding fact, there was Leila, in conversation with a gentleman. She saw me and came to me at once.

In three days she was to be married; and from her face I knew her fate weighed heavily on her soul, though she held herself proudly. The young man, I gathered, was her real lover, Heinrich Wullenroth. She introduced me to him, and we became intimate friends. It did not take us long to realize that we were as one in the desire to prevent Leila's revolting sacrifice.

The possibility of our success seemed indeed hopeless. I had seen Vantrey and made one effort to appeal to his generosity, but he repulsed me in his usual manner.

The day of the marriage came. Only Macklorne seemed

optimistic. Our last hope was in the justice of God above. Surely He would not allow this hideous farce to be enacted.

Leila appeared at church pale, wasted, but firm in her bearing. Vantrey led her to the altar, his habitual sneer assuming an expression of malignant triumph. The ceremony was proceeding, the priest was demanding the responses, when there was a quick, violent commotion in the thronged aisle. A wild, roughly-clad man burst through, sprang up to the altar, and grasped Vantrey's arm fiercely. A steel blade flashed in the subdued light, and Vantrey fell, dead.

The assassin was immediately seized. He was Donacha MacIan. The wretch's oath of vengeance was fulfilled. Such is destiny!

The murderer escaped shortly after, and reappeared before his master, Glenfinglas, dying, but with energy enough to show him his blood-stained dirk.

Leila married Heinrich, and lived with him an ideal life. They are happy.

As for me? Shall I hasten back to Theresa? No, I will not. Come, Macklorne, let us out into life! My resolution is taken!

CHARLES KINGSLEY

(England, 1819–1875)

ALTON LOCKE, TAILOR AND POET (1850)

Championship of the poor earned for the Rev. Charles Kingsley a title, the "Chartist Parson," the significance of which is lost to most readers of the present generation. Chartism was an early demand on the part of English common people for political recognition. It took definite shape in 1838 and endured until 1848, when the movement that was designed to begin a revolution ended in a fiasco as pathetic as it was ludicrous. Its influence, however, still endures. Some of the Chartists' demands have been gained in considerable measure; others are still active questions in British politics. The "People's Charter" called for universal suffrage, vote by ballot, annual Parliamentary elections, electoral districts of equal population, abolition of a property qualification for Parliament, and salaries for the members. Kingsley contributed to the movement by letters to the *Christian Socialist* and other periodicals. *Alton Locke* is a historical novel in the sense that, under the guise of an autobiography, it gives a vivid picture of the conditions that drove English artisans to religious heresy and political rebellion. The events of the story, too, are as true as if they had occurred as related, for precisely such things did happen during the Chartist agitation. Moreover, the book was written in 1849, while all the hopes and disappointments, the terrors and the strivings, the deeds and the misdeeds, of the Chartists were fresh in the memory of the author, who had personally observed and to some extent shared in them.

I AM a cockney of cockneys. With the exception of two journeys, never to be forgotten, my knowledge of England is bounded by the horizon that encircles Richmond Hill. My mother was a widow and a Baptist, a believer in the extremest of Calvinistic doctrines, and under their shadow my childhood passed. From a stern sense of duty she rigorously subordinated maternal tenderness, of which I am sure there were abysses unspoken in her, to the absolute method by which she believed I should be brought up. Until I should be converted, she had no more spiritual bond with me, she thought, than with the heathen or a Papist. She dared not even pray for my conversion, for that would have been inconsistent. Either I was elect or I was reprobate. Could prayer alter that? But she kept the sharpest, most anxious watch over me, and when my childish questions appeared to verge on heretical doubt as to any item in the scheme of God's universe as deliminated by her creed, I was brought by severe whippings to realize my errors.

We were very poor, dependent on my paternal uncle, a prosperous tradesman. He had one son, George, two years older than I, at King's College preparing for Cambridge and the Church, that being the approved method of converting a tradesman's son into a gentleman. My uncle obtained for me a place in a tailor's workrooms, where I was assigned to the special care of one John Crossthwaite. This man was nicknamed by his fellow-artisans "the orator," and I speedily saw that he was in a sense their leader, but for a long time I had no personal knowledge of his remarkable ability as a talker. He said nothing to me beyond what was necessary in instructing me in my trade, but what he did say was on the whole as kind in manner as it was valuable in matter, and I came to respect him highly.

Up to this time my only books had been the Bible, *Pilgrim's Progress,* and missionary tracts, all of which I had read with the greatest avidity. My way between workrooms and home took me past a book-shop where many volumes were displayed on a shelf outside the door. I often paused to observe greedily this, to me, vast collection of literature, and with positive yearning I read the titles of the volumes. One day I opened a book and read a few lines. The next day I opened at the same place and read a little farther. Nobody forbade me, and I made considerable progress, hurrying through *Childe Harold, Lara,* and *The Corsair,* a new world of wonders to me. One evening I fell accidentally on a new book, *The Life and Poems of J. Bethune.* I became absorbed, so that I stood, I know not how long, on the greasy pavement, reading by the flaring gaslight that sad history of labor, sorrow, and death. Presently tears of sympathy rolled down my cheeks, and I was interrupted by a man whose harsh voice bade me "no spoil his books wi' greeting ower them."

I replaced the book and was hurrying on when he called to me in a kinder tone. I submitted to his questions, and thus began a friendship that endured as long as the shopkeeper, Sandy Mackaye, lived. In brief, when he knew what I could tell him about myself, he undertook my education. His was a stern taste, but in no wise a repressive influence. He merely insisted that I should be well grounded, and to that end he made me study Latin, lending me a grammar and Virgil. He also let me take Milton's poems as refreshment from study. Strangely and tragically enough, this led to separation from my mother. She discovered that I was spending the greater part of my nights studying, and she demanded to know what I was doing with these heathen books, and where I obtained them. I told her truly, and she called her spiritual advisers into consultation on my desperate case. They were missionaries and narrow-minded ministers, who suspected that I was reprobate and knew that I was a hardened sinner. My mother forbade me to have anything more to do with Mackaye. I was heavy-hearted enough, but I obeyed faithfully until one evening, when shop duties made me late, she accused me of keeping bad company. When I explained my tardiness she chose not to believe me, and I left her house forever. Deplorable, from every point of view, as was this parting, I at least had the compensation of freedom to study, for thereafter I lodged with Mackaye and had free access, under his guidance, to all his books.

The first holiday I ever took was devoted to a visit to the Dulwich Gallery. I knew nothing of art, and too little of history to understand the significance of what I saw, but I was enthralled by one picture before which I stood for a long time. An elderly gentleman in clerical garb, accompanied by two young ladies, came that way. Observing how I was absorbed in the painting, they spoke to me and told me it was Guido's *Saint Sebastian*. Gently they drew me out, and when they went away they knew all about me that was worth knowing, except one thing—that the beautiful features of one of those young ladies, her they called Lillian, had sunk deep into my heart. I had seen pretty faces before, and knew they were pretty, but they had passed from my retina. This face did not pass away. Day and night I saw it, just as I had seen it in the gallery. I never thought of disparity in rank. Why should I? That could not blind the eyes of my imagination. She was beautiful, and that was all, and all in all, to me. It was impossible to keep my infatuation from Mackaye, and when I confessed, I did so whole-heartedly; and this led directly to the final change in the course of my thoughts which made me what I am and brought me to this pass.

Mackaye sought to divert me from my dream by interesting me in what he called "the Cause." And about this time Crossthwaite began to talk to me. It seemed that both my friends had hitherto refrained from opening my eyes to the miseries under which artisans suffered, preferring to wait until they thought my mind was matured sufficiently to grasp the new thought then rife among the working-classes without miscomprehending it or losing its point in merely boyish enthusiasm. So I read a different kind of books, discussions of economics, and heard much talk of the People's Charter. Meantime, the reading I had done could not have failed to stimulate me to write; and, following my natural bent, for I had dabbled in verse when very young, I took to poetry. My first poems were wild, though perhaps not ridiculous fancies of distant climes—poems of the sea that I had never seen, of countries that I could never hope to visit. Mackaye took me severely to task for this.

"Ay," he grumbled, "sing awa'; get yoursel' wi' child wi' pretty fancies an' gran' words, like the rest of the poets, and gang to hell for it."

"To hell, Mr. Mackaye?"

"Ay, to a verra real hell, Alton Locke, laddie, the hell on earth o' being a flunky and a humbug, wasting God's gifts on yer ain lusts an' pleasures. Now look here!" He stopped before the entrance of a miserable alley. "Look! there's not a soul down that yard but's either beggar, drunkard, thief, or warse. Write aboot that! Say how ye saw the mouth o' hell, an' the twa pillars thereof at the entry, the pawnbroker's shop o' one side an' the gin-palace at the other, twa monstrous deevils, eating up men and women and bairns, body and soul. Write aboot that!"

"Well, but, Mr. Mackaye, I know nothing about these poor creatures."

"Then ye ought. True poetry, like true charity, laddie, begins at hame. If ye'll be a poet at a', ye maun be a Cockney poet; ye maun write, like Jeremiah of old, o' lamentation, and mourning, and wo, for the sins o' your people."

"But all this is so unpoetical."

"Hech! Is there no the heeven above them there, and the hell beneath them? And God frowning, and the deevil grinning?"

And so Mackaye argued, not only with words but with deeds, for he took me to squalid homes and showed me conditions of life and climaxes of privation such as, poor though I always had been, were nothing short of horrible revelations to me. And so I became a poet of my people, and so, when our employer yielded to the greedy trend of the times and reorganized his establishment on the sweating plan, I was one of the few who, led by Crossthwaite, refused to take work home. I could not obtain employment in London at my trade on any other than sweating conditions. Nothing remained for me but to write, and my effusions would not sell. At last Mackaye himself suggested that I try to get my volume of poems published, and that I seek the advice and aid of my cousin, who was then at Cambridge.

To Cambridge, then, I walked. It was my first journey, and for the first time I saw God's green earth and how beautiful it was. George was more than interested. He was, as I partly saw then and afterward knew, an inordinate self-seeker, but what he did for me was done in an apparently generous spirit and under the impulse of genuine desire for my success. Doubtless it was as genuine as was his frank attempt to ride to his own advancement on my astonished shoulders. I met Lord Everton at his room, and as George was too busy to do some correction of proofs for his lordship, I undertook it. The work pleased Everton, and through him my manuscript was brought to the attention of Dean Winnstay. In due course I was summoned to call on the Dean, and I found him to be the clergyman who had spoken to me years before in the Dulwich Gallery. Moreover, the first person I saw in his house was the idol of my dreams, Lillian, and shortly afterward I saw the other young lady who had been at the gallery, Eleanor. My love, which never had burned low, leaped up afresh, and it influenced a most important decision I was called on to make.

Dean Winnstay not only commended my poems, but undertook to get a subscription and a publisher for them, but on condition that I omit the more revolutionary and radical utterances. Incidentally he was interesting himself in my further education, and he had me at his house for days at a time as his guest. Do you see what that meant? I was privileged to be near Lillian, and if I refused to tone down my poems, I should lose all possibility of that privilege. I yielded, much, it appeared, to the disappointment of Eleanor, who, though she disapproved my radicalism, affected to wish me to be brave and consistent. I hardly noticed what she said, however, for I had conceived a violent dislike for her. It was apparent, even to my inexperienced eyes, that she perceived my interest in Lillian, and that she was doing all she could to dissipate my dreams and turn Lillian against me.

At last I returned to London, happy and hopeful. I had to earn my bread pending the completion of the subscription and the publication of my book, and this I managed to do by turning hack writer. But I had also to pay a debt; for, when I was in Cambridge, my cousin insisted that I should dress better than I could afford to do, and, again influenced by the dream of Lillian, I let him have his way. For that reason I owed him money, and in spite of incessant work and privation, I could not accumulate the requisite amount. My delinquency weighed hard upon me at the best, but when one day I made a painful discovery, it became intolerable. I met George in London. I was even then on my way to call on Dean Winnstay, who was in town, ostensibly to thank him for his interest in my book, but really, I fear, to have one more glimpse of Lillian. In the course of our conversation it developed that my cousin was a suitor for Lillian's hand, and in my bungling way I let him know that I was his rival. He affected to disdain me as such, but I knew better. I knew how he had taken advantage of the Dean's interest in me to gain a foothold in the clergyman's house, and I understood my cousin's character sufficiently now to know that he would stoop far to circumvent me.

Mackaye, as usual, wormed my secret from me. He began to fumble in his desk, and I thought he meant to offer me money to pay my debt, but instead, he produced a receipt in full for what I owed my cousin. To my astonished inquiry he answered that the amount was sent to him by a stranger shortly after my return from Cambridge. The remittance was several pounds in excess of the obligation, the anonymous sender—apparently a woman from the handwriting—saying she feared I was in debt for expenses at Cambridge, and requesting Mackaye to pay all bills and hand the balance to me. Need I try to express my joy? Need I confess that my deluded heart leaped to the conclusion that Lillian was my benefactress?

At last my poems were printed and actually published; and I sat staring at a book of my own making, and wondering how it ever got into being. What was more, the book sold, and was reviewed. I tasted the sweets of success. Dean Winnstay invited me to breakfast at his town house, where I met distinguished men to whom I was introduced as "the young man whose poems we were talking of last night." Lillian sat at the head of the table and poured coffee—for Eleanor had married Lord Everton—and I sat in a delirium of silent joy.

Meantime I fell into disfavor with some of my own people, and the success of my book increased their ill feeling. Much of my writing naturally had been in the way of contributions to Chartist organs, and after my acquaintance with Dean Winnstay and Lord Everton, and some others of the upper classes, I perceived that not all aristocrats were wholly bad. I even found some who had intelligent sympathy with artisans. I said so when occasion offered; more, I resented extravagant fanatical attacks on the clergy and the nobility; more yet, I flatly declined to color my attacks on the industrial system with falsehoods about those who sustained and benefited by it. There were plenty to share my views—men like Mackaye and Crossthwaite—but there were others, notably the editor of a radical organ, who accused me of backsliding. This man published attacks, saying that I had stooped to flunkyism, and he made known the sorry fact that I had omitted my strongest utterances from my book. I was wrought upon terribly by this manner of thing, for I was no less eager for the Cause than before, and it did not mitigate the severity of his impeachment that so much of it was true. I had, indeed, yielded to temptation and emasculated my book, but I was as firm as ever in my conviction that the

Charter would right all our wrongs. So now I was hot to do something that should rehabilitate me in the eyes of my fellows, and the opportunity was at hand.

"There is a rising down in the country," said Crossthwaite. "The people are starving, and they are going to have a great meeting. I wish to send somebody down to talk to them. It's a great opening for spreading the principles of the Charter."

I volunteered to go, and I did not hesitate even when he told me that the place was in the vicinity of Dean Winnstay's home. The matter was speedily arranged, and I journeyed across country once more to the place of meeting. It was in a desolate spot, far from any dwelling, attended by women as well as by men, all showing in their scanty dress and pinched features the reality of the wrongs that had brought them thus surreptitiously together. A dozen of them made speeches; some mere rehearsals of wo, others filled with pleas for violence. At last, when riot seemed about to break loose, I forced my way forward and asked for a hearing. I told them I came from London to offer them the sympathy of London artisans. They interrupted to say that they wanted bread. I explained the idea of the Charter, and begged for their help in gaining it. To which they answered that they knew nothing of politics; they wanted bread. I went on, more vehement than ever, to show them how all their misery sprang, as I then fancied, from being unrepresented, how the laws were made by the rich for the poor, and not by all for all, and so forth—you know the arguments; to which they cried that their stomachs were empty, and they wanted bread. "And bread we will have!" they shouted.

"Go, then," I cried, losing my self-possession between disappointment and the maddening desire for influence, "go and get bread! After all, you have the right to it. Wo unto those that grind the faces of the poor! Their cry has entered into the ears of the God of Heaven—"

But I had no time to finish. The murmur swelled into a roar for "Bread! Bread!" My hearers had taken me at my word. I had raised the spirit, and amid yells and execrations, the whole mass poured down the hill, sweeping me away with them. I was shocked and terrified at their threats. I tried again and again to stop and harangue them. I shouted myself hoarse about the duty of honesty; warned them against pillage and violence; and all to so little effect that while I was still shouting I saw them burst open a granary and fight with one another for the food stored there. Even then I persisted in my efforts, trying to limit the pillage to the securing of food; but the spirit of destruction and vengeance was abroad; somebody fired the hay-stacks, and soon the barns were in a blaze. The yard was a pandemonium that endured until the yeomanry appeared, when the whole crowd made off as fast as possible. I did not care to run. I was utterly disgusted with myself and the people; but as I stood there, one of the looters ran by me with a writing-desk, crying madly that he had found the money. I sprang up and seized him by the throat.

"Rascal! Robber! lay that down! Have you not done mischief enough already?"

"I wain't have no sharing," he retorted.

In an instant he shook me from him, and dealt me a blow with the desk that laid me flat. I just recollect the tramp of the yeomanry horses, the gleam and jingle of arms; and when I came to real consciousness I was lying on a truckle-bed in a tiny room with stone walls and a grated window.

The learned barrister retained by my loyal friends, and paid by their scrapings and sacrifices to defend me, plumed himself mightily that he got me off with only three years. I would not disparage his services, but he could not have done so much, and I should have been deported, if not hanged, but for the unexpected, volunteered evidence of a man who was a stranger to me. It seemed I had done him indirectly some trifling kindness. He remembered, and his was the only voice raised at the trial to tell how I sought persistently to stay the mob and prevent the spoliation and destruction of property. And so I spent three unspeakable years in prison, reading when I could get books, which was much of the time, and, when they were not to be had, writing, for the sake of occupation, a straightforward account of my life. And all the while, reading, writing, or waiting for sleep, I was perforce of circumstances becoming a bitterer enemy to the social order than before I was sentenced.

When at length I returned, an outcast, to London, I found my friends preparing for the great uprising that was to accomplish all our desires at one stroke. The date was already set, the 10th of April, and some there were who actually believed that the soldiery were ready to rise and join us. I was much enfeebled in body and embittered in spirit; I was not deceived as to the prospect of military assistance, I was not hopeful, certainly not confident of the outcome; but I entered into the affair with such force as was left in me, perfectly content to die behind a barricade if that should be my share in the enterprise.

It is unnecessary to say more of that lamentable fiasco; for history already knows that the meeting, which was to be numbered by hundreds of thousands, numbered hardly tens of thousands; and that these dispersed piecemeal, cowed by authority and drenched miserably by a pouring rain. For myself, I went to Waterloo Bridge. My madness had driven me to call at Dean Winnstay's after the "meeting," and there I had seen Lillian with her head on my cousin's shoulder. So I looked at the rushing water and was saved, for the time, by an old comrade of the tailor's workrooms who came there and tried to leap in. His act recalled me to life, and I struggled with him. That episode passed, and I returned to my room exhausted. For many days I lived in the dreamland of fever, and when at last I awoke, I found Eleanor caring for me.

I learned many things during my slow convalescence. It was Eleanor who had paid my debt to George—she, rather than Lillian, who had always sympathized with my ideals. Lord Everton, her husband, was dead, and she was devoting her life and fortune to the cause of the people, but in her way, not mine. Mackaye was dead, and by his will his little fortune was divided between me and Crossthwaite on condition that we go to Texas and remain there seven years, after which, chastened and wiser, as we presumably would be, we might return to England and again take up the fight for better industrial conditions. I learned, too, how Eleanor was working out the principle of co-operation among poor people, agitating in her way for association as the corrective of that cruel competition from which my people had suffered. I did not wish to go to Texas, but there was no other way. To speak of no other reason, my one possibility of continued life lay in a change of scene and climate. So, regretfully, I sailed at last, with Crossthwaite as my companion, and at Eleanor's request I occupied the time of the voyage by completing the autobiography I began in prison.

We are now in sight of land, and I hear my fellow-travelers on deck singing that stirring song, "A Good Time Coming." Ah! how should there not be a good time coming? Coming surely, soon or late, to those for whom a God did not disdain to die!

Alton Locke's narrative ends abruptly at this point. Appended to his manuscript, when it came to the hands of his friends in London, was a letter from John Crossthwaite, dated at Galveston, October, 1848, in the course of which was the following: "And now for my poor friend, whose papers, according to my promise, I transmit to you. On the very night on which he seems to have concluded them, we found him in his cabin, dead, his head resting on the table as peacefully as if he had slumbered."

HYPATIA (1853)

This novel is an attempt to present to modern readers a picture of the early Church in Alexandria, and to depict the pandemonium of the dissolving Roman Empire, against which Cyril the Patriarch fought. The picture that Kingsley gives us of the social and political conditions existing in Alexandria in the fifth century is mild—a real picture could not be drawn without offense to decency; still, the historical value of *Hypatia* is great.

IN the early part of the fifth century the young monk Philammon, brought up in the desert monastery of the Laura, on the Nile, felt his heart glow with a great desire to fly into the great world and there, among the throngs of his fellow-men, to do deeds of righteousness—to reform the world and scourge the flesh and the devil. So, with the blessing of old Abbot Pambo, he left the eternal purple shadows of the cliffs on the seas of yellow sand that surged around the fallen temples of the lost Egyptian gods, and at last he stood by the moon gate of Alexandria.

The great city, then the most flourishing seaport in the world, dazzled him with its magnificence.

A manikin of a fellow—a porter lounging by the gate for the chance to run odd errands—conducted him to the house of the Patriarch Cyril, to whom old Pambo had given the youth letters of introduction. But the little fellow did not scruple first to take Philammon two miles out of his way, that he might help to carry a basket he had to deliver, and when the young monk, discovering the trick, expressed a desire to box the fellow's ears, the porter began to explain:

"You must know," said he, "that I am a student of the great Hypatia. I keep the cloaks when the gentry come to her lectures in the museum."

"And who is Hypatia?" asked Philammon. "Is she a friend of the patriarch?"

The little porter opened his eyes wide. "Of the human race in general, my young friend," he said. "The philosopher must rise above the individual and contemplate the universal—Ahem!"

As they walked on Philammon was astounded by the multitude of monks whom they encountered everywhere. At one point they came upon a mob of them trying to break into a place where a Christian was being flogged by order of the prefect on the charge of the Jews that he had tried to incite a riot. "Nitria to the rescue!" they shouted, and beat at the iron gates; but the prefect's soldiers and the stout gates kept them at bay.

"And what does this Hypatia teach?" asked Philammon, when they were beyond the tumult.

"Oh, the philosophy of the immortal gods, whose worship she will presently restore, sweeping away you Christians," said the little porter. "And they say she is going to marry the prefect Orestes, if he will but give up his Christianity. Oh, she is the queen of Alexandria; but Cyril hates her, and he hates the Jews, and he hates Orestes; and his Nitrian savages would tear them all to pieces if they could."

The world suddenly did not present so simple a problem to Philammon as it had amid the sands of the Laura. He already had an experience coming down the Nile which had given him a hint that it was rather complicated. He had fallen in with a splendid galley on which was a party of Goths, gigantic of figure, fierce and rude, who had been south seeking Asgard, the city of the gods of Norseland.

The women were the first Philammon ever had seen. He was astonished by the sight of the fair companions of the Goths.

"Come hither, thou boy monk," Pelagia had cried, "and tell me what and who thou art. From the Laura? And dost thou remember anything before the Laura? Certainly thou wert not born there."

"I am a Greek," Philammon replied, "and remember faintly—that is, I think I remember—a great house in Athens—and a great battle there—and coming in a ship to Egypt."

"Heavens!" the girl cried. "How strange! Girls, which of you was it said he looked like me?"

The Patriarch Cyril assigned Philammon to work with the

parabolani, a band of monks who went through the slums of the city relieving the necessities of the poor.

It was the fashion for the young dandies of the city to frequent the lecture-room of Hypatia. She had built up a cult which she fondly hoped was reviving the worship of the immortals of Parnassus; she wrought to bring back the world to a pure philosophy that would satisfy the intellect and save it from the Christian gospel, which she loathed as being devoid of intellectual food, but which she saw was spreading not only among the common people but among the more intelligent.

Most prominent among her pupils was the handsome young Jew, Raphael Aben-Ezra, who had forsaken the creed of his fathers and turned cynic.

One day as Raphael and Orestes sat in a summer room of the prefect's palace, throwing dice for horses and slaves and dancing-girls, the withered old Jewess Miriam came with a letter in answer to one Orestes had written to Hypatia. "That old hag has the evil eye," said Orestes, "and Hypatia tells me she haunts her all the time. I must see to it that she is disciplined, though I suppose to touch one of your race would stir up all the hornets in Jewry."

"I can't say," replied Raphael. "It might. Or it might stir up Miriam to call in some of her loans."

Orestes winced at the intimate knowledge which the Jew seemed to have of his monetary affairs, and continued: "Well, she always has a batch of handsome dancing-girls for sale, and so shall be forgiven."

After reading the letter Orestes threw it to Raphael. "What am I to do? She asks me to apostatize. In the face of Cyril and his monks I dare not. They would tear me to pieces in the streets. Married to Hypatia, I might become Emperor of Africa. I say, suppose you marry her, and I will make you anything you like."

"Your serene high-mightiness overwhelms me," replied the Jew, bowing; "but as I have never in my life cared for anyone's interest except my own, you must pardon me if at my time of life I refuse to devote myself to yours. But there is no hurry about the answer. You can promise."

As Raphael bowed himself out, old Miriam caught him by

the arm and said: "Does the fool dare? If that Pelagia had as much common sense as Hypatia has in her little finger, I could place her and her Goth on the throne of the Cæsars."

"Pelagia is your most successful pupil, certainly," replied Raphael. The hag suddenly forced a splendid opal ring into Raphael's hand, and said: "There, my son. Take it. Now you are safe. It has the unspeakable name carved on it, just like Solomon's own—and do not call me witch and hag as you often do. I do not mind it from anybody else, but from you—" and the old woman vanished down a by-lane.

As Hypatia went forth next morning in all her glory with a crowd following her, a ragged beggar placed himself in her way and whined for alms. Hypatia glanced at him and started with surprise. The man was Raphael Aben-Ezra!

The night before, thousands of monks had broken into the Jew quarter under the lead of Cyril, and, driving the Hebrews from the city, had looted their houses. Old Miriam had warned Raphael, but he had calmly stayed on to the end, and then giving to the old woman for safe-keeping such portable property as she could take away in jewels and gold, he had dressed himself as a beggar, and now announced his intention of journeying to Italy.

"I am now at the foot of the ladder, most fair Hypatia. You have so often lectured of the blessing of poverty that you should not be surprised if one of your pupils at least makes the experiment," said he.

The reputation of Hypatia had become so great that Philammon begged of Cyril to let him go to one of the lectures and confute and confound her heathen doctrine. But Cyril warned him.

"Do not argue. You will be lost if you try to match wits with her. She is subtle as the old serpent himself. Do not argue. Assert and deny with vehemence, but no arguing."

The scene with Raphael had filled Philammon with the question: "Could it be possible that a Jew or a heathen could actually seek a life of poverty?" He had supposed only Christians capable of self-sacrifice. And now the wonderful beauty of Hypatia, the voice like music in which she poured out her words, and the rapt attention with which her hearers hung on her every expression, so entranced the young monk that for a time he forgot his mission and saw only Hypatia, heard only Hypatia. But, recollecting himself suddenly, he shouted: "It is false—blasphemous! The Scriptures cannot lie!"

"Throw the rustic through the window!" shouted the young gentlemen. "Turn out the monk!"

But Hypatia said: "Let him stay, gentlemen. He is but a monk and a plebeian, and knows no better."

After the lecture she sent for him and presented him with a pass for her lectures.

Returning to the episcopal residence he met Peter the Reader, a scheming, cold, and worldly man, who had the Patriarch's ear and meant to keep it. When Philammon asked to see the Patriarch, Peter said: "Do you think His Holiness has nothing to do but to listen to such youthful wanderers from the desert as you? You shall not see him."

"But he told me to report to him," said Philammon.

For reply Peter struck the boy a blow and at the same time set up a shout of "Help, I am being beaten in the house of the Lord by this barbarian!" And in fact he was, for Philammon had knocked him down. In an instant a mob of monks ran up and at Philammon and he was hustled into the street. He wandered to the museum and sat down on its steps. He knew that Hypatia lived in one of the houses opposite and wondered which. He fell asleep, and when he woke it was broad daylight and the little porter was shaking him by the arm.

"Beloved of the gods," said the porter; "favored of Hypatia, how comes it that you are here asleep?"

Philammon told his story, and the porter took him home and not only fed him but showed him a little room which he told him he might occupy until times were better with him. Philammon had found favor in the sight of the little porter because he had been looked on kindly by Hypatia, and because in a riot between the Nitrians, Jews, and Romans, Philammon had saved the porter's negro wife.

Soon thereafter Philammon became a student in the school of Hypatia. He had not lost his Christianity, but had ceased to practise it.

One day Pelagia with her Goths and her girls drove up to the door of the museum. The girls, gay with saffron shawls, rode in gorgeous chariots, while the Goths rode the small, miserable native horses.

The chaste Athene of the schools bit her lip with vexation when she saw the party of Pelagia. Then with a cold, calm demeanor she forgot their presence and began her lecture. At first Pelagia and her nymphs smirked and giggled at the phrases, to them meaningless, which fell from the cold lips of Hypatia. But one of the Goths silenced them rudely but effectively—and then went to sleep. When the lecture was over, Old Wulf pulled out his purse and laid it at Hypatia's feet. "What is this?" she asked.

"My fee for what I have heard to-day," answered the Goth. "You are a right noble woman, and may Freya send you a husband worthy of you and make you the mother of kings!" Then he marshaled Pelagia's party and retired.

The other Goths agreed with Pelagia that Hypatia was a very foolish person to waste her youth and brains talking to donkey-riders.

But as Pelagia rode away her heart was sad. She was a Greek girl bought as a slave by Miriam and then freed for purposes of her own, and she had all her life had one idea only, and that was pleasure. That there were such facts as right and wrong she had gathered dimly for the first time from the discourse of Hypatia.

Philammon saw down the street an old man clad in the garb of a monk, who raised his hands to Pelagia and, with tears, addressed solemn words to her. The Goths would have driven him off, but Pelagia said, "No, do not harm him," and then to the old man, "Come to-morrow and tell me what you mean."

Philammon hurried toward the monk and saw that it was old Arsenius—once the tutor of emperors and now a monk of the Laura. The youth was eager to know what he had said to Pelagia and why the old man seemed to take so much interest in her.

They walked up a quiet side street, while Arsenius explained. He told the boy that, in the markets of Ravenna, after a raid on Athens, he had purchased him and taken him to the Laura. There had been a sister; and that Pelagia was that sister

Arsenius was almost convinced. Miriam knew it beyond doubt.

"Then," said Philammon, "I am a slave. You can take me back to Cyril, or to the Laura. You can have me scourged. I am your property."

"No," said Arsenius. "Though in the eyes of the Roman law you may be a slave, in the eyes of God you are free. And I, who bought you, say you are free."

"And Pelagia, my sister?" exclaimed Philammon. "I will save her. She must leave this wicked Alexandria and fly with me somewhere—anywhere—into the desert." Then the thought came over him: What would Hypatia think of him if she learned that he was a slave and Pelagia his sister? For in the heathen philosophy of Hypatia there was no room for magdalens or slaves.

Old Arsenius labored with the youth to bring him back to a reconciliation with Cyril. "You will come back to us some day," said the old man, "back to the Laura."

The Goths had been kind to Philammon in their rude way in the galley on the Nile. He decided suddenly that he would seek them and tell Old Wulf all.

And now arose Heraclian, Count of Africa, seeking to rule the Roman world. With a great expedition he set out for Italy, and, landing at Ostia, challenged the imperial legionaries of Honorius. Orestes, the prefect, saw for himself the plucking of the crown of Africa. He stopped the grain-ships, and unloaded many of them, that he might give largess to the poor. He devised games and a great gladiatorial contest and scenic display in the long-abandoned theater. Among the spectacles he would have the dance of Venus Anadyomene, which had not been seen in Alexandria since the Christians had become so powerful. He would have Hypatia, who represented the old *régime,* sit beside him on a throne during the games, and when he was hailed by his hired agents as Emperor of Africa he would share the crown with the beautiful philosopher.

He extracted a promise from Pelagia that she would dance the Venus Anadyomene, the Venus rising from the sea. And at last one day old Miriam sent Orestes a letter saying that Heraclian had conquered.

The great day of the games came. Orestes sat on a throne with Hypatia beside him. Among the people stood Philammon, his heart sick at the thought that his sister was about to give this public exhibition of her shame. Gorgeous spectacles were presented, Nubian captives were slaughtered by hired gladiators—though that was against the law—and the shameful dance was danced while Hypatia, angry with herself and blushing at the part she was playing, yet at the same time striving to convince herself that she was doing all in the cause of the immortals, sat beside Orestes and heard the crowd proclaim him Cæsar of Africa.

As Pelagia finished her dance an elephant, excited by the sight of blood that oozed up where the Ethiopians had been killed, caught her in his trunk and would have killed her had not Philammon burst through the crowd and rescued her.

The Goths arose in their seats. As Philammon bore the girl away they joined him, and the party made for Pelagia's house. A mob was there shouting: "Down with the Arians! Down with Pelagia!" The monks of Nitria and the whole population of Alexandria seemed to be afoot, for the real news had at last been given out, Heraclian had been defeated, and the vengeance of Honorius would fall upon the rash prefect who had proclaimed himself Emperor of Africa. The door of every church in Alexandria was placarded with the news. The Jews had deceived the prefect.

"Come to the little postern gate by the canal to-morrow night," said Old Wulf to Philammon, "and Pelagia will be delivered to you. She herself desires it."

As soon as the crowd had somewhat melted away from the streets before Pelagia's house, Philammon returned to his lodgings in the house of the little porter. Meantime Miriam had sought Hypatia. Much had the fair philosopher endured for the cause of the gods, and now it was all in vain. Only the shame of the amphitheater and what she had been forced to witness remained with her. Vainly she tried to put from her the words of Julian: "Thou hast conquered, O Galilean!" Now came Miriam and promised that if Hypatia would but visit her house that night she would show her, in truth, one of the gods. And Hypatia promised.

Philammon found old Miriam waiting for him when he came home. She told him that Pelagia was indeed his sister. She sat him at a table, where she plied him with wine and rich food and induced him to put off his monk's garb, so that he stood in a white tunic, looking, indeed, like a Greek, as he should—he, the son, as Miriam told him, of a Greek noble, a descendant of Hercules. Then, while the boy's brain was flushed with wine and with the intoxication of Miriam's words, the Jewess suddenly left him, blowing out the light as she went. He sprang to his feet and looked about to see a soft radiance beginning to glow through a gauze veil that covered the door to another room.

There was a sound of soft but stately music, and a smell of incense. The veil was withdrawn, leaving him standing behind an altar on which a fire burned, and before the altar knelt Hypatia, who hailed him as a god.

Recovering his wits, Philammon spoke a few words that undeceived her. Angrily she sprang to her feet—then fainted. But, recovering quickly, she charged him with being in league with Miriam to cheat her, and then fled.

Angry and perplexed, Philammon retired to his room, while the Jewess, who had appeared while Hypatia was in a swoon, hugged to her bosom the long-sought half of a carnelian amulet which she had taken while the maiden swooned. This had been given to Hypatia by Raphael.

"It is for Raphael," said the old woman; "for my Raphael. None can harm him now. He will not give it to the Gentile woman again."

When Philammon went out into the street again he found all Alexandria in a tumult. He followed the crowd and at last stood in the temple.

Cyril, being in the right now and Orestes in the wrong, put into the sermon not only that genius which enabled him to remain so long the ruler of Alexandria, but also the teachings of his religion, which he too often forgot. It was forgiveness that he preached, and he preached it with an eloquence that went to Philammon's soul. With the passionate and impulsive nature of the Greek he burst forward through the crowd, and, never stopping until he found himself at the foot of Cyril's pulpit, he threw himself on his face on the pavement, spread out his arms in the form of a cross and lay motionless.

From behind the pulpit an old man sprang forth and clasped the youth around the neck, while he sobbed: "My son!" It was Arsenius.

"Slave as well as son," replied Philammon. "I have but one more thing to do in Alexandria, and then back to the Laura forever."

The next morning Hypatia, worn out with sleepless sorrow, was trying to arrange her thoughts for her farewell lecture in the museum in the face of aroused Alexandria. A man demanded to see her. It was Raphael, returned from his Italian journey. He told her he had promised that if he found "a man" he would come back and tell her. He had found in Christ both a man and God. He had become a Christian, and was about to marry a Christian maiden, the daughter of one of Heraclian's officers, with whom, after the defeat of the Count of Africa, he had escaped to Cyrene. He, the cynic, had found peace. Why could not Hypatia find peace also and cast the anchor of her soul in a sure haven?

"Come again," said Hypatia finally. "I will hear more. At noon I lecture—take my farewell forever from the schools."

As Raphael went out he saw Philammon standing before the house. "Save her!" cried Philammon. "She must not go forth to-day. It is death."

Raphael, convinced by the earnestness of Philammon, sought to go back and warn her. But by her orders the slaves refused all admittance.

At the appointed hour she came, calm and serene. A great mob waited for her, seized upon the fair virgin, and carried her toward the Cæsarium. There, against one of the great pillars, they slew her, she looking upon the rabble in disdain. Philammon fled, to his dying day he knew not whither. At last, as night was falling, he sought the house of Pelagia. But at the postern gate by the canal, where his sister was to be delivered to him, he found no one. The gate was unbarred and he entered.

He heard voices and went up a steep stairs into a tower, where he found the Goths and Pelagia. The Amal had at first agreed to give her up; but he had faltered in his purpose and was clasping her to his arms, declaring that he would never be separated from her. When he saw Philammon and heard the insolent words with which the youth demanded his sister, he sprang toward him. The two grappled. The mud coping of the parapet against which they struggled gave way, and as they fell the Amal was undermost and his head was dashed against the stones.

Dripping, breathless, Philammon pulled himself out of the canal and lay panting on the ground. At the end of the street he saw the light of torches; a mob was surging there. Then he saw Pelagia come out of the postern door, but ere he could call to her she had fled into the darkness.

Yet in the end both Philammon and Pelagia found their way out of the city of discord. Philammon lived many years in the quiet seclusion of the Laura, until he became abbot. Across a desert space from the Laura lived a recluse—a woman of exceeding beauty, to whom the rude inhabitants of the region brought offerings of fruit and corn. So she grew old as Philammon grew old.

Then one day the aged Philammon said to his monks that a voice called him and, taking the holy chalice in his hand, he went out across the desert. When after a while some of his monks followed to see what had become of him, they found near the cell of the woman anchorite an open grave and in it the abbot and the recluse, lifeless.

WESTWARD HO! (1855)

This novel bears the sub-title: "The Voyages and Adventures of Sir Amyas Leigh, Knight of Burrough in the County of Devon, in the Reign of her Most Glorious Majesty Queen Elizabeth," and it is said to be "rendered into modern English by Charles Kingsley."

N all the steeples of Bideford in Devon the joy-bells were ringing. The streets were filled with people in holiday attire, and the houses were hung with garlands. That stout, blond giant, Amyas Leigh, of Burrough, and four other sturdy men of Devon had just returned from their voyage with Drake, the first English sailors that ever broke into the South Sea and sailed around the world. It was five years since Amyas kissed his mother good-by and sailed away with Francis Drake.

All the gentry of North Devon had gathered to welcome Amyas home. Standing beside his gray-haired, widowed mother was his elder brother, Frank, fresh from court, with court manners and court dress.

Among those who pressed forward to take Amyas by the hand was his cousin, Eustace Leigh, from whom his bluff and sturdy kinsman shrank instinctively. His father had remained a Catholic upon the accession of Elizabeth, and it was whispered that Eustace had served his novitiate as a member of the society of Jesuits—crimes, in those days in England, which were likely to bring a man's head to the block or his body to the stake. However, though Elizabeth occasionally burned Catholics for discipline's sake—as her sister Mary had burned Protestants for conscience' sake and their father, Henry, had burned Catholics and Protestants alternately for his own sake—quiet old gentlemen like Mr. Leigh of Chapel, who paid their tithes to the Established Church regularly and kept their religious opinions to themselves, were occasionally allowed to live unmolested in remote parts of England under the protection of powerful relatives.

Amyas looked for one face only, and looked in vain. Rose Salterne, daughter of the rich Mayor of Bideford—the Rose of Torridge, she was called, after the river that ran through the town—was not visible.

Her father had sent her to some poor relatives in the neighborhood, for her beauty had turned the heads of all the well-born gallants in North Devon, as well as the heads of all the 'prentice boys in Bideford.

Rose Salterne was a thorough specimen of a West coast maiden, full of passionate and impulsive affection and of wild, dreamy imagination.

Years ago, as a schoolboy, Amyas had loved her, a little girl, and now he returned from his wanderings to be told that she had grown into a dazzling young woman of eighteen.

But Amyas soon saw that Frank, too, loved the Rose of Torridge, and he resolved to think no more of her.

Amyas had not long settled down to the quiet life of Burrough when all North Devon was aroused by news that a force of Spaniards had landed on the coast of Ireland and taken the fort at Smerwick; and with a hastily collected party of the other youth of the region he prepared an expedition to fight the invaders. Eustace Leigh also departed—stole away a fugitive, having been discovered in treasonable correspondence with the enemy.

Poor Frank did not dare to go to Ireland without the permission of the Queen, who kept a tight rein upon her courtiers. The well-born young men of North Devon were hardly on speaking terms with one another, on account of Rose Salterne. Not that Rose had given any one of them cause to hope; but neither had she given any one of them cause to despair. The air was full of rumors of duels; for one beautiful woman can bring many brave men to grief.

So Frank persuaded all the gallants who aspired to the love of Rose to come to a dinner with him at the Ship Tavern, and there, when the wine had begun to work, he proposed the health of the Rose of Torridge and made a speech to them. He declared how ill it was that men of Devon, who stood shoulder to shoulder throughout the world, should be at swords-drawn with one another in their native land. He set before them that no one could claim any better right to Rose than another, and proposed that each and all should follow the example of the knights of old and, binding themselves together in fellowship, with one object of adoration, depart in search of adventures, to return after three years and let Rose choose which was the most worthy of her love.

All the young men leaped up and on the hilt of Frank's sword swore friendship with one another and fidelity to Rose.

Amyas sailed with his expedition, and they laid siege to the fort and compelled the Spaniards to surrender. The common soldiers were all put to the sword, as a warning to other Spaniards and the officers were held for ransom. When the Spanish officers were distributed among their captors Amyas claimed as his share Don Guzman de Soto, grandson of that famous cavalier who was with Pizarro in Peru, and who found his grave in the waters of the Mississippi.

At the close of the campaign Amyas sent his captive on parole to Bideford, where Sir Richard Grenville, his father's old friend, agreed to keep him as guest until his ransom should arrive.

Amyas soon was up and away again, sailing with that disastrous expedition of Sir Humphrey Gilbert, which sought to colonize Newfoundland. It was Westward-ho! in the reign of Elizabeth, and from Labrador to the Brazils the "gentlemen adventurers" of England were seeking their fortunes in plundered Spanish fleets and cities or in newly founded colonies.

The family of Don Guzman was poor, Spain was a long way from England in those days, and so nearly two years had passed since the Don came to Bideford, and nearly three since the founding of the Brotherhood of the Rose, when the ransom arrived at last. With the ransom came an order of the Spanish King appointing De Soto governor of the Caracas, as Venezuela was then called, and so he departed. But all that night Rose Salterne lay moaning upon her bed, calling out for him to come back to her.

A few days after the Don's departure Rose was missing She was traced to the hut of Lucy Passmore, an old woman who lived by the waterside and was reputed a witch. But the hut was empty; Lucy also had flown. There were rumors, later, of a tall, Spanish-looking man accompanied by two women, one young and one old, having passed over to the Isle of Lundy in a fishing-boat, and then all trace of the fugitives was lost.

Will Cary, one of the Knights of the Rose who had returned from the Irish wars, raged like a lion; all Bideford mourned for its lost beauty, and old Mayor Salterne sat among his piled-up bales silent and broken-hearted.

Such was the condition of affairs when Amyas Leigh arrived at Plymouth, one of the few survivors of the disasters that had overwhelmed the expedition of Sir Humphrey Gilbert.

Mrs. Hawkins, wife of Sir John Hawkins, the famous old freebooter who originated the African slave trade, received Amyas and supplied his wants.

"And, by the way, Captain Leigh," said the lady, "I have sad news for you from your own town." And she told him of the elopement of Rose Salterne. Amyas dropped back into his chair as if he had been shot.

"You'll forgive me, madam," said he. "I am weak from the sea and your good ale has dizzied me a bit, I think."

After a night of sleepless tossing, Amyas set out for Bideford, swearing to himself: "The man that did that deed I will pursue around the world and take vengeance on him!"

As Amyas and his few followers were making their way from Plymouth to Bideford, they were set upon by a gang of heathen outlaws who were sheltered in the hills near Brent. But the men of the sea laid around them lustily and the wild men were driven off, leaving their leader mortally wounded. As he lay dying he called for a priest, and a priest appeared—a Jesuit who had been concealed near by, a man come to do missionary work among the strange, wild people known as the Gubbings, to whom no other missionaries would go.

With the priest was a younger man, whom Amyas looked at in startled recognition. It was his Cousin Eustace!

Amyas promised Eustace that he would not give information of his presence in the country, and told him of his own adventures and of the disappearance of Rose Salterne. Eustace listened to the story with a white and agonized face. Then,

"Fool, fool that I was!" he shrieked, and springing from his chair stamped up and down.

Amyas was thunderstruck. "Oh, Eustace!" he cried, "and you loved her, too!" When he was calmer, Eustace asked what the Brotherhood of the Rose purposed to do in the matter, and Amyas told him—to seek out Don Guzman in the Caracas, kill him, and rescue Rose.

"Oh," replied Eustace, "to hunt her down like a wild beast because, forsooth, she has dared to love a Catholic! To force her to renounce a religion in which she has doubtless found rest and holiness!"

"Has she found holiness?" retorted Amyas. "That is just what I intend to find out for myself."

The Mayor offered gold for the fitting out of an expedition that should go and rescue his daughter. But Frank and Will Cary also claimed a right to contribute, and the three sailed away with Amyas, Westward-ho!

Among the Bideford men whom Amyas took with him was Salvation Yeo, a fanatical Anabaptist. He had been one of the band of unfortunate John Oxenham, who had met his death by lingering too long in the neighborhood of Panama with the young wife of an aged Spanish official.

In those wilds John Oxenham had left a little daughter, the child of sin, but very dear to Yeo, who had tended her carefully in their long marches through the wilderness. He still called her his "little maid," and believed that one day he should find her again.

It was a fair tropic afternoon when Amyas's ship, the *Rose*, sailed before the port of La Guayra, and saw lying within the protection of the forts an armada of Spain. High on a hill they could see a large house before which flew the standard of Castile —evidently the residence of the Governor of the Caracas—and that Governor was Guzman de Soto.

From some Indians who put out in a canoe they learned that their coming was expected, which accounted for the Spanish men-of-war being there; and also that Don Guzman had sailed eastward to intercept them. Evidently someone had betrayed them. Amyas at once thought of his talk with Eustace. His cousin, doubtless, had given the alarm. The tropic night shut down suddenly; the giant mountains flamed a moment and then turned black. In a window of the Governor's house a light shone brightly. The *Rose* anchored below the town, and Amyas resolved upon a bold move. Taking Frank and a few trusty men with him, he rowed ashore to a deserted part of the beach and climbed the hill to the house where the light was burning. They had reached the thicket that fringed the lawn in front of the building when a female figure, followed by a man wearing a cloak drawn over the lower part of his face, came around the corner of the house. The two were the Rose of Torridge and Eustace Leigh. They were talking earnestly.

"What do you mean by praising my husband thus to me?" said Rose. "Do you not think I know his virtues better than you?"

"Husband!" Frank whispered to Amyas. "Thank God for that!"

"My love for him and his trust in me you can never destroy," continued Rose, and then she rained a torrent of reproach on Eustace, concluding:

"I, Donna Rosa de Soto, bid you leave this place forever."

Eustace whispered something in her ear. Her answer was a shriek. Quick of wit and speaking truer than he knew, Eustace shouted: "Help, slaves! Your mistress is being carried off by bandits!"

At once a great tumult arose and bands of armed slaves came sweeping down between Rose and the Englishmen. The alarm spread to the town, and it was a hard fight all the way back to the boat.

Amyas, hit by a large stone, lost his senses. When he came to himself he was in the boat, where his men had dragged him, and nearing the ship. But Frank was gone—captured by the Spanish—and some were killed.

The discovery that Rose had not been deceived by Don Guzman, but was his wife, put a new complexion on affairs; but hatred for the Spaniard was stronger than ever in the heart of Amyas. He steered eastward to meet that ship in which Guzman had sailed. But, falling in with three other Spanish men-of-war, the *Rose* fought a battle in which she came off victorious, but so damaged that they had to run her into a silent, turgid river and beach her.

There were eighty of them when they landed and began to repair the ship, but the fever of the mangrove thickets seized them, and some died. At last they had to abandon the vessel and repair to the highlands. There an idea seized upon Amyas.

Somewhere, in the forests behind them, was the city of Manoa, the famed El Dorado. He would find it, and, forming his men into a guard, would drill the natives for war, descend at their head upon the Spanish settlements, seize their gold, and put the Papists to the sword.

Long they wandered, but no sight of golden domes greeted their eyes.

At last they came where a tribe of Indians lived in a state of semi-civilization, governed by a maiden whom they called the Child of the Sun. They had found her wandering in the forest toward the Peruvian frontier.

When this maiden came forth from her hut to tell the strangers they were welcome to stay in her territory, the Englishmen were astonished at her appearance. Surpassingly beautiful in a wild, savage way, in face and form, Ayacanora, as her people called her, had the features of a European; and though her skin was browned by the tropic suns it was easy to see that its natural complexion was not that of the Indian.

The adventurers had been eighty when they left their ship. They were only forty now, and way-worn and weary. So in this earthly paradise they rested awhile until Amyas roused his men and continued the march.

There was no thought of finding El Dorado now; only to build boats, float down one of the streams, capture a Spanish ship, and sail home in her.

Ayacanora watched Amyas depart with rage and despair in her heart. Though the Englishman had repelled her advances, he took leave of her with sorrow.

The wanderers made for the Magdalena River, and had almost reached it when they learned from Indians of the approach of a Spanish treasure-train going up to Santa Fé de Bogota. Lying in wait in a mountain path, they ambushed the train, putting the Spaniards to the sword and seizing upon their abundant treasure. Hardly had they set out for the river again when they heard a strange, wild song from the forest, and Ayacanora appeared. She had followed them through the wilderness, and now declared that she would not leave Amyas, but go with him to that far land where his home was and where hers would be also. If he did not take her along, she would kill herself.

So Amyas swore himself and his men to treat the wild girl as a sister, and when they had completed their boats and floated down the stream Ayacanora accompanied them.

Gliding by the Spanish settlements at night, the wanderers came to the mouth of the river and felt the lift of the seas under them once more. Three years since they had left their wounded ship and plunged into the wilderness, and now these men of Devon once more saw the sea and regained their old courage.

In the Bay of Santa Marta they came upon a Spanish galleon, ready to sail for home. That night they boarded her through the stern ports and made her their prize, securing or killing the officers before they could give the alarm. Then, clapping down the fore hatch and yelling "Fire!" they caught the Spanish sailors as they came running, unarmed and dazed, up the main hatch, forced them into the boats, and set them adrift.

Some Spaniards took refuge in the cabin and opened fire. The Englishmen charged them, and Amyas engaged the commander in sword-play. Just as the Spaniard was making a lunge at Amyas that would have done for him a bright blade flashed over his shoulder. The Spanish commander fell, and Ayacanora, with hair streaming over her shoulders and her raised knife dripping blood, stood defiant and savage, threatening all who should come near her Englishman.

By daybreak they had the ship under way, bounding eastward. The signs of the conflict had been cleared away, and Amyas invited his prisoners to breakfast with him. Among the captives was the Bishop of Cartagena. As Amyas and Cary were bandying stately compliments with their Spanish prisoners, in came Salvation Yeo reporting that a woman prisoner had been discovered on board in chains. It was poor Lucy Passmore, who had gone away with Rose when she eloped with Don Guzman.

Rose had been happy with her husband until, urged thereto by charges made by Eustace Leigh, the Inquisition had taken her from Don Guzman and brought both her and Lucy to trial for heresy and witchcraft. The Inquisition had pronounced them guilty and handed them over to the secular arm with a charge that there be "no shedding of blood."

"But, oh!" said Lucy. "They took the poor child out into the market-place and burned her and Master Frank, too."

"Frank!" exclaimed Amyas.

"Yes," continued Lucy; "he was captured alive the night the boat came to La Guayra, and him they burned along with Miss Rose, the two holding each other's hands to the last."

Lucy had saved her own life by a timely conversion, but was being taken to Spain for safe-keeping. Don Guzman, when his wife was taken from him, had resigned his government in a rage and gone to Spain to demand justice of the King. Eustace had fled to the wilderness.

"That man was there at the burning!" suddenly cried Lucy, pointing to the Bishop, "And that one," indicating one of two friars that attended him.

"Is this so?" said Amyas to the Bishop.

"I was compelled to be present—unwillingly to be present. The secular arm—I cannot interfere with that—any more than I can with the Holy Office. I do not belong to either—ask these gentlemen."

But the feeble excuses of the Bishop were vain in the whirlwind of grief and rage that swept over Amyas. Calling his men, he took the prelate and the friar out on deck and hanged them to the yard-arm.

A cabin was assigned to Lucy, decent clothing was found for her in the rich cargo of the captured ship and Ayacanora was assigned to wait upon her. But a week later she died.

One day, as the sailors were at work, old Salvation Yeo started a chanty song—

A randy, handy, dandy O,
Whet of ale and brandy O,
With a rumbelow and a Westward-ho,
And heave my mariners all O!

To the surprise of everyone, Ayacanora, who was on deck,

caught up the burden of the song and sang it over again with all the peculiar intonation given it by Yeo.

For a moment Yeo stood as one dazed. Then he fell at the girl's feet, crying out: "At last, at last! My little maid, my little maid!" He had taught her that song in the wilderness of Panama.

Gradually the past came back to Ayacanora sufficiently to remove all doubt that she was the child of John Oxenham, so long sought for by Salvation Yeo.

Again the bells of Bideford were ringing, bonfires blazing, and the people rejoicing; not this time on account of the return of Amyas Leigh, but because Queen Elizabeth had just cut off the head of Mary Queen of Scots and it was patriotic and pious to make merry therefor. To such an England Amyas came home with enough of captured Spanish treasure to make himself and all who had sailed with him and survived, rich for life.

With saintly resignation Mrs. Leigh bore the news of Frank's death. Old Mayor Salterne, when told the story of his daughter's end, shut himself up in the little room from which she had flown, and was found dead there. Ayacanora, under the care of Mrs. Leigh, became a civilized English girl.

Now came the year of the Spanish Armada, and after the fight that took place when a part of that great fleet met the English in the Channel, Amyas was dubbed knight on his own deck.

In the midst of the fight he saw a tall ship of Spain and, standing high on the poop, Don Guzman de Soto. Amyas attacked with fury, but could not capture the great ship, and when that day's fighting was over the fleets were separated. But when the flight of the Invincible Armada around the north end of the British Isles began, Amyas singled out the ship of Don Guzman and stuck to her through storm and tempest, pursuing her until, separated from her consorts, she came plunging down St. George's channel into the seas that wash the Devon coast.

A tremendous thunderstorm was raging, and by one of the flashes of lightning the men on Amyas's ship saw the Spanish vessel ahead of them go crashing on the rocks of Lundy and sink in a swirl of foam. Amyas seized the helm to guide his own ship clear of the fatal spot, and had just succeeded in doing so when a great crash of thunder and a blinding flash of lightning came together. When the air cleared they picked up Amyas, blind for life, and at his feet lay Salvation Yeo, dead.

They carried blind Captain Leigh home to Burrough, where his mother and Ayacanora tended him; and one day Mrs. Leigh, coming into the room, saw the girl sobbing on his heart. The stricken man had at last returned the long love and devotion of the daughter of John Oxenham.

HEREWARD THE WAKE (1866)

In the summer of 1848 Charles Kingsley made an expedition with the Rev. Frederick D. Maurice to Croyland Abbey, near Peterborough, which, as Mrs. Kingsley says in her *Memoir*, gave him many inspirations for this story—which is sometimes called *Hereward, the Last of the English*—finished many years later. In the main it follows history so far as regards the public events of Hereward's life.

ON a day about the year 1054 the Lady Godiva sat in her bower at Bourne and listened with shame and horror to the complaint of Herluin, Steward of Peterborough, that her son Hereward, with his company of unruly youth, had attacked the monk and taken his palfrey, his fur gloves and cape, and sixteen silver pennies that he had collected for the use of the monastery. He had but finished his tale when Hereward, a noble lad of eighteen, entered. His face was of extraordinary beauty, save that the lower jaw was too long and heavy, and that his eyes wore a strange and almost sinister expression, from the fact that one was gray and the other blue. He was short, but of immense breadth of chest and strength of limb. He met his mother's look of sternness, almost horror, with smiling defiance, the result of long estrangement between them.

"Wretched boy! What wickedness next? Know you not that he who robs the Church robs God Himself?"

"And he who harms God's people harms his Maker," added the monk.

"His Maker?" said the lad, with concentrated bitterness. "It would be a gay world if the Maker thereof were like unto you who call yourselves His people. You forget that I have been behind the screen; that I should have been a monk myself, if my pious lady mother had had her will. Do you forget why I left Peterborough Abbey when Winter and I turned all your priests' books upside down in the choir? And they would have flogged us—me, the Earl's son, the viking's son—and we got hold of the kitchen spits and held you all at bay from the top of the peat-stack, a whole abbeyful of comrades against two seven-years' children? It was you bade set the peat-stack alight under us, and would have done it, too, had it not been for my Uncle Brand, the only man that I care for in this wide world. Do you not think I will pay the grudge I have owed you since then, monk? Do you think I would not have burned Peterborough Minster over your head before now, had it not been for my Uncle Brand? See that when there is another Prior in Borough you do not find Hereward the Berserker smoking you out some dark night!"

"Hereward, godless boy, what words are these?" said his mother.

He looked at her majestic face, once lovely, now careworn, and trembled for a moment. Had there been any tenderness there, his history might have been different, but there was none. Not that she was untender, but that her great piety was outraged by an insult to the clergy, whose willing slave she had become.

"Is it not enough that after all you have done you add a worse sin and drive me to tell your father that of which the very telling will turn my hair gray?"

"So you will tell my father? He is at the old miracle-worker's court in Westminster. He will tell the miracle-worker, and I shall be outlawed."

Hereward went to his Uncle Brand at Peterborough and there remained till Martin Lightfoot, the messenger his mother sent to Earl Leofric at Westminster, returned to tell him that it had fallen out as he had foreseen—that his father had appealed to Edward for justice against his son, who had thereupon been declared an outlaw ("wake").

Accompanied by Martin Lightfoot, who asked to go with him as his servant, Hereward went northward and after a few months was sent for by Gilbert of Ghent. There in Gilbert's house he made a friend of Gilbert's ward, Alftruda, a little girl of eight years, beautiful, precocious, and vain. One day Hereward returned from hunting and found that the great white bear, the "Fairy Bear," had escaped from his den and was standing in the center of the courtyard turning about his long snake neck and cruel visage in search of prey. The court was empty save for Alftruda, who in terror was pounding at the bower door, behind which the knights and ladies had barricaded themselves. As the monster reared and lifted its iron talons high in air for attack, Hereward, with one powerful blow of his sword, cleft the creature's skull.

After that deed Hereward's name was in all mouths; but the knights of Gilbert's household were his enemies; so he rode away with the faithful Martin and was never again seen on Scottish shore. He appeared later on the Cornish coast, and then went to Waterford, in both places adding to his fame.

At last, seized with a great desire to return home, he asked Ranald Sigtrygsson, who ruled the Danes of Waterford, for ships, and received two good vessels in payment for his doughty deeds. His voyage did not prosper; he went through the Hebrides and the Orkneys, but got little booty and lost several men; then in a storm one vessel went ashore and the other was pursued by wild weather, till at last they were driven to the Flemish coast, where Hereward and his men took service with Baldwin of Flanders for his war against the Hollanders.

While they were waiting in the town of St. Omer before setting out on this campaign, it chanced that as Hereward rode through the street on one side of the great Marquis, he looked up to a little lattice in a gable and beheld the dark-blue eyes and raven locks of Torfrida, the fairest and richest damsel in St. Omer, famed for her learning and her skill in magic art. And as Hereward loved Torfrida from that time, so she loved him, once and for all; but they did not meet for a while; and it might have been better for one if they never had met.

When the time of the annual tournament came, Hereward took his place with the knights and sent word to Torfrida that if he chanced to meet her favor in the field he that wore it would have hard work to keep it. He did meet a suitor of Torfrida, Sir Ascelin, wearing her favor, and won it from him. Then he went to her house and, giving her the favor, said it was hers to say what should be done with it.

"Take my favor," she said, binding the ribbon about his

helmet, "wear it before all the world and guard it as only you can."

And she gave him also a suit of magic armor, taken in battle by her forefather Torfrid from an emir, which Hereward wore throughout the campaign in Holland, where it preserved him unhurt, and where he gained great glory and renown.

Torfrida, accustomed to the polish of Flemish and Norman knights, saw his roughness of manner; his boastful self-sufficiency, ludicrous even in her eyes; the lack of charm of manner and range of thought conferred by the influence of classic civilization, which he never had felt; and a rude, boastful, quarrelsome spirit that showed after he had drunk too freely, as he often did. These qualities in him made her often cold, contemptuous, even fierce; but she was brave, and she loved him; so she set herself to train the wild outlaw into her ideal of a perfect knight. As she talked to him she awed him as much by her learning as by the new world of higher and purer morality that she opened to the wandering viking, though there were many relapses, which made Torfrida indignant. Finally, one evening at a feast Hereward, in response to taunts of the knights on his magic armor, declared that he cared naught for armor; that he would undertake an adventure without it. When the banquet was over Torfrida said to him:

"You have made me a laughing-stock for these knights. You have scorned my gifts, said that you need neither helm nor hauberk. Give me them back, then, and go sleep off your wine."

"That will I," laughed Hereward boisterously.

And ere she retired Martin brought to her the magic armor, whereat she cried, and fain would have sent it back. He would be killed and his blood would be on her head, she felt.

Spring and summer passed, and autumn found Torfrida a bower-maiden at the Court of Bruges, when news came that the Hollanders were conquered. And when Hereward returned she threw herself into his arms, speechless with joy to have him again unharmed. The next day they were married.

A year passed. Edward of England died. Duke William of Normandy, who was preparing to sail to England under the Pope's banner. desired Hereward's allegiance; but Hereward made answer that when William should be king of all England, Hereward would be his man. Soon afterward he met his former friend, Gilbert of Ghent, who was on his way to William, and Alftruda, grown so beautiful that for one moment, as he looked on her, he forgot Torfrida. Her look showed no recognition, but as she passed him she looked him full in the face, one instant, and said in a quiet whisper:

"So you could not wait for me?"

Meantime Hereward lamented bitterly the ruin the English had brought on themselves, in giving the crown to Harold Godwinsson instead of to Sweyn of Denmark, while he watched the two great storm-clouds about to burst on his native land—in the south the great force of Duke William, in the north that of Harold of Norway. Then came report that William had defeated and slain Harold of Norway; and close upon that the story that William had defeated and slain Harold Godwinsson.

For two years rumors came of the evil condition of affairs in England, where the conquerors had broken the promise that the English should be ruled still by the laws of Edward the Confessor.

The Countess Gyda, widow of Godwin, sought refuge in St. Omer. In this woman, in spite of all she had suffered, a passion for intrigue still ruled, and she persuaded Hereward that with such a leader as he could be England might still be saved.

Alone with Martin, Hereward went to England, and first to his old home at Bourne, where he found on the gable before the door the head of his youngest brother, and within the hall, seated in his father's place, as Lord of Bourne, a stout Flemish cook. He burst into the hall and with Martin's aid slew the fourteen Normans therein; and when the sun rose their heads adorned the gable. He found his mother, who bitterly lamented her share in outlawing him, and took her to Croyland Abbey. To the men of Bourne he gave his promise to return and lead them, within the year, perchance with a Danish fleet.

He returned to Flanders and angry he was when he heard that the English had proclaimed Edgar Atheling. At last came a Danish fleet to take Hereward to England; but to his disappointment it was not commanded by Sweyn himself, but by his brother Osbiorn. However, he and Torfrida and their daughter sailed with him.

Contrary to Hereward's advice, that they sail northward, Osbiorn tried to take strongly fortified Dover, but was defeated with heavy loss; and the same thing happened at Sandwich. Then, too late, he took Hereward's advice, and sailed for the north, plundering right and left without proclaiming Sweyn king, until the people rose and beat him off. Hereward, his soul black with rage at this wasting of opportunity, proposed that he raise the Fen men and march through Norfolk to meet the fleet; and to this Osbiorn agreed.

Many hardships did Torfrida endure in the wild, rough voyage, but she conquered her sadness and homesickness and weakness for the sake of her love. They went to Bourne and there dwelt while brave men came to join Hereward, who trained them in the art of war, of which they knew nothing. Then they heard that the Danes had been defeated at Norwich, and, after heavy loss, had sailed seaward. Hereward felt that he had deceived his men and brought them into a snare; but they made him their captain and declared themselves ready to follow him, to save England without the help of the Danes.

William crushed every rebellion save Hereward's, and then retired for the winter of 1070–71,which time Hereward passed in bitter perplexity, for he felt himself pent in and trapped; he had calculated too little on the Norman castles that had risen during his absence, which he had no means of attacking. Many fugitives joined him, among them his nephews—Earls Morcar and Edwin—and they took possession of Ely, where Hereward instituted the famous Camp of Refuge.

The Abbot Brand died that winter; and when Hereward learned that Thorold the Frenchman was appointed in his uncle's place, he led the Danes, who returned with the spring under the leadership of Sweyn, and were disgusted at finding no plunder, to Peterborough in order to save the Danish Croyland. They burned the monastery, after sacking it and the minster, and took away enormous wealth. In the hospice Hereward found Alftruda, and, gazing on her, for a second time, a little time, forgot Torfrida. He sent her not to her husband, Dolfin, the Scot, but to her former guardian Gilbert. He himself retired again to the monastery of Ely, where he by consent of all assumed command. For the Danes, deeming their expedition a failure, since they found some of the leaders who should have helped them defeated, and others gone over to William, had sailed for home with the booty of Peterborough as payment.

When William learned that the Danes were gone he marched on Ely, and thousands of his men perished by the giving way of the floating bridge that they made to cross the stream to the island stronghold. He then withdrew.

At Ely the rebels became much straitened; and, knowing not what was to be done, either by themselves or by the King, took counsel, and with them Torfrida, their wise woman, whose advice all received as more than human. Hereward determined to go forth and learn what was going on; so he went to the King's court at Brandon where he found that the King, on the advice of an old witch, was preparing to attack Ely after building a larger and stronger causeway. And he returned from his expedition full of fear; for he believed implicitly in the magic powers of the witch of Brandon.

Torfrida and all the women of Ely walked barefoot to St. Etheldreda's well and prayed for her help. The thought of one resource, burning the reeds about the island, came to Torfrida, and she told it to Hereward, knowing that he would carry it out; but her conscience smote her, despite her belief that St. Etheldreda had inspired the idea, at thought of the agony and death this terrible scheme of defense would mean. At last she worked herself into a religious frenzy; and on the day of the battle so fierce a triumph sparkled from her wild hawk-eyes that the Englishmen looked up to her weird beauty as to that of an inspired saint; and when the Normans advanced to the assault there stood behind the English fort a figure, clothed in sack cloth, with long, black hair streaming in the wind, invoking St. Etheldreda and all the powers of heaven. And opposite, on the Norman tower, the old hag of Brandon howled and gibbered. The Frenchmen thrust out baulks, canoes, and pontoons on the twenty yards of deep, clear water that lay between them and the English—and then there was a puff of smoke and a wisp of flame. The column tried to retreat, but the flames came leaping and laughing through the reeds and upon the bridge. As

Torfrida watched the men turn, flee, and die in agony, she dropped senseless on the turf.

Hereward knew well that another attempt would be made, and Ely would be won in the end. Defections began; first his nephew Edwin, and then Morcar, deserted him. One day when he was away foraging, there came to the monks of Ely a command from the King that they surrender or lose all their outlying lands. As Hereward was returning, Torfrida and his men met him with news that the island was surrendered to the French, and that the Abbot had made peace with the King; and they lay in hiding in the heath, listened to the cries as the sack raged in the town, and watched the flames glare.

"Your stars did not foretell you this, Torfrida," said Hereward in sadness.

"My stars at least foretold me nothing but wo, since first I saw your face."

"Why did you marry me, then?" he asked half angrily.

"Because I loved you, and love you still."

"Then you do not regret?"

"Never, never! I am quite happy. Why not?"

Hereward and his men, nigh four hundred, retired to the Bruneswald and there lived as bold outlaws, though they had law and order of their own. Two years and more passed, and neither Torfrida nor Hereward was the better for them. There were fits of despondency, jars, and mutual recriminations; and though the words were wiped away with kisses, they had been said and would be again. The damp, cold weather tortured Torfrida; she felt that her beauty was gone, and that Hereward was less tender than of old, and so she grew colder.

Finally she learned that Alftruda had written to Hereward, and that he had answered the letter. And the misery she endured in thinking that Hereward had secrets from her hardened her heart. One day, as the men were arming and saddling, she helped Hereward with his armor; but when he offered to kiss her she drew back.

"He was as glad not to kiss me, after all!" she thought.

As he rode away she heard him say, when he looked at two bonny boys wrestling: "Ah, had I had such a boy as that!"

She turned away, her heart dead within her, for she knew

what these words implied. She spent that evening thinking over all her past life and love; and at last, as she went to lie down and sleep, she saw at her feet an open letter. It was from Alftruda, and it congratulated Hereward on having shaken himself free from the sorceress. It said that all was settled with King William, who would receive him as his liegeman at Winchester, and she would receive him as her husband as soon as his marriage could be annulled.

Stricken with intolerable agony, Torfrida fled into the forest and ran for miles. Martin Lightfoot overtook her and led her to Croyland Abbey, where she dropped at Lady Godiva's feet and told her all. She assumed a nun's dress, and became a nun thenceforth. And Martin put on the monk's frock in Croyland to be near his Lady Torfrida.

Hereward had loved Torfrida with an overwhelming devotion, and he had become aware that his feeling for Alftruda was strangely like, yet strangely unlike, his feeling for Torfrida. Still, he knew that he cared more for Torfrida's little finger than for Alftruda's body and soul together; yet he could not help thinking, as he was returning, of Alftruda, whom he had just seen. When he learned what had happened he raged and blustered to hide his shame. With forty men-at-arms he journeyed to Croyland; but neither Lady Godiva nor Torfrida would see him, though each sent him a message.

"Tell him who calls himself my son that my sons were men of honor, and that he must have been changed at nurse."

"Tell him that I have lived my life and am dead. If he would see me, he will see only my corpse. He knows what Torfrida dare do."

Torfrida served Lady Godiva. All pride, fierceness, care of self, passed from her. In humility and gentleness she went on, never smiling, but never weeping. Her heart was broken, and she felt it good for herself to let it break.

Hereward left Croyland like a man stunned, and thereafter things went ill with him. He became William's man, and, being besotten on Alftruda, humbled himself to him. His marriage with Torfrida was broken because of the practises of sorcery to which she confessed in order to free him; and he married Alftruda and became Lord of Bourne. But his heart was gnawed with remorse for the base deed he had done. One by one, all higher instincts fell away from him, and the bad habits and vices from which Torfrida had raised him returned. He became a broken man, querulous, peevish, melancholy, at times apathetic; and he quarreled with Alftruda and with his Norman neighbors, who hated him. These neighbors, headed by that Sir Ascelin who had been Torfrida's suitor, and later Alftruda's, took counsel together to slay him; and it fell that one day, when his knights were escorting Alftruda, who had journeyed to Croyland with Countess Judith to the tomb of her husband, Earl Waltheof, the Normans entered Bourne while Hereward slept. When he awoke he saw above him a crowd of fierce faces, and knew that his end was come. There was no time to arm, but he seized his sword and hewed silently, with grinding teeth, till finally they bore him down, and with a last shout of "Torfrida!" he fell dead. And Sir Ascelin cut off the fair, golden head and put it over the hall door.

So perished "the last of the English."

And Torfrida came from Croyland and demanded Hereward's body, and so did she terrify the Normans through their belief in her powers of magic, and by her majesty and eloquence, that they yielded the body to her. She took it to Croyland, and there it was buried in the choir; and in the same tomb was Torfrida laid many years afterward.

TWO YEARS AGO (1857)

Kingsley's son Maurice says of this work: "The only novel, pure and simple, Kingsley ever wrote was *Two Years Ago*." The other works of fiction written by him, his son adds, were avowedly polemical or historical. "Yet, if one cares to read between the lines, there is as strong a purpose in this story as in anything that came from his pen."

TOM THURNALL, born in the village of Whitbury, Berkshire, was a rover from the days of his youth. There was not a stream in all that region which he had not followed to its source, whipping its placid surface with his trouting-line. Clad in velveteen jacket and leather gaiters, with gun on shoulder, he had penetrated to the remotest covert where lay the pheasants preserved and predestined to sate the British desire "to kill something." When arrived at young manhood he went to Paris, and became the best pistol-shot and billiard-player in the Quartier Latin; and then he went to St. Mumpsimus' Hospital in London, and became the best boxer therein, and captain of the eight-oar, besides winning prizes for medical proficiency without end, and becoming in due time the most popular house-surgeon in the hospital. But settle down to steady practise, either in London or at home, he would not. And yet, cost his father a farthing more he would not. So he accepted a professorship of anatomy in a South American republic. When he got there, he found that the annual revolution had just taken place, and the party that had founded the college had all been shot the day before. Whereat he whistled, and went north, where institutions were more stable and professors of anatomy, rather than coroners, were likely to be in demand.

Finally he turned up in the Southern States of the great American Republic, where he found an institution much too stable for his liking, and he proceeded to undermine it. Slavery in the abstract appeared to him as a mere "relic of barbarism," destined to pass away with increasing civilization, and he had for it only the silent contempt of a man of science. But slavery in the concrete, in the appealing person of a beautiful octoroon girl put up on the auction-block in New Orleans, to be sold to whatever libidinous scoundrel could outbid his fellow-debauchees, struck a tingling blow at every sensibility in his emotive system. And he answered it by quietly, daringly, and, from a financial standpoint, economically (for he had accumulated enough money in his wanderings to buy her) stealing and running away with her to Canada.

Then, in order that she might make the most of her natural gifts—beauty, a voice like a mocking-bird's of her own native groves, quick mental perception, and a highly emotional temperament—he pressed upon her the money he had saved by the elopement, that she might go abroad and fit herself for an opera-singer, and was off for California to refill his traveler's belt with virgin gold. But, finding that the first pickings were over and that fortunes were no longer made in a day, he used his first earnings to take ship for the newly discovered Golconda in Australia. And remaining there because opportunity to get away did not offer, in a few years he accumulated fifteen hundred pounds. With this he determined to return to his old home and settle down to the quiet country practise he had formerly contemned. So he traveled to Sydney, converted his fortune into bank-notes, which he buckled in his belt, and took ship to England. His vessel was wrecked on the coast of Devon, near the fishing-village of Aberalva. He alone of all on board escaped with his life, and then only by the exertions of the village schoolmistress, Grace Harvey. Standing in a group of fishermen on shore, watching the breaking vessel in the dim moonlight, she caught sight of the returned miner, with outstretched arms like a polypus, clinging to a rock. Before the next great surge could bear him back, she sprang toward him and seized him about the waist. She was followed by the fishermen, who, forming a human chain, held the miner and the schoolmistress firm through the rush of water that was upon them, and drew them ashore at its recession.

"Saved!" and a cheer broke from all lips, save those of the

girl herself; she was as senseless as he whom she had rescued. Her hands were clenched about his waist so firmly that old Mrs. Harvey, who had run down from her cottage to the water's edge, had much ado, seemingly, in opening them.

The fishermen bore Grace to her own bed and Tom to the house of Dr. Heale, the village physician and apothecary. Kicking open the door, they carried their insensible burden upstairs, where they found the doctor in a drunken stupor on a bed. They pulled him to his feet, and laid Tom in his place, and Gentleman Jan, the leader of the fishermen, said:

"If you won't come to your patients, doctor, your patients shall come to you. Why were you asleep in your liquors, instead of looking out for poor wratches, like a Christian? You look after 'un, and then go and see schoolmistress; she'm worth a dozen of any man, and a thousand of you! If you don't, we'll break every bottle in your shop."

The next day Frank Headley, the village curate, called to see the shipwrecked miner. He found Tom fully recovered, and eager to learn details of his rescue. When informed that it was a young woman who had saved his life, he inquired: "Handsome?"

"Beautiful," said Frank.

"Money?"

"The village schoolmistress."

"Clever?"

"Well—a puzzling intellect," answered the clergyman, who had been fighting, against the schoolmistress and all the village, to supplant her with a good churchwoman, Grace being a dissenter. "In fact, a quite irresponsible and self-willed person."

"Whew! I hope she won't seize upon me as her property and marry me forthwith. Better send for the coast-guard officer and let him claim me for the Admiralty, as flotsam, jetsam, and ligan; for I was all three last night."

"And very thankful to Heaven you ought to be for that," said the curate, reproving his levity.

"And now," said Tom Thurnall to himself as Frank left the room, "to begin life again with an old penknife, a pipe, and a quarter-pound of honeydew. I wonder which of my noble rescuers got my girdle? What a fool I was not to jot down the numbers of those notes. Now I can't stop payment."

Walking into the apothecary shop, Tom looked around upon the dirt and confusion that indicated the inefficiency of the proprietor.

"I see my opening here," he said, and began to put things to rights.

Dr. Heale came in as he was doing so, and Tom tackled him for the job of assistant—wages to be bed and board. On learning the castaway's medical attainments, the old man readily assented to the proposal.

Finding from the doctor that Grace Harvey had fully recovered, and, indeed, had already returned to the beach, caring for the corpses that were coming ashore, Tom set out to find her and thank her for saving him. She was pointed out to him on the shore, gazing seaward. Going up to her, he made a bow of which an ambassador need not be ashamed.

"I am exceedingly grateful that Miss Harvey should have incurred so much danger for anything so worthless as my life."

She looked at him with a far-away gaze, and answered, not him, but her own thoughts: "Strange, is it not, that it was a duty to pray for all these poor things last night, and a sin to pray for them this morning?" Then, as one starting out of a dream, she blushed scarlet at talking thus to a stranger.

"What a beautiful creature!" Tom exclaimed to himself, and an emotion flamed up in his heart which no woman, not even the queenly octoroon, whom he had saved from infamy and who had repaid him with open adoration, had ever before kindled in his breast.

He blushed beneath the bronze of his cheek, and, as they stood looking at each other in silent confusion, a strange, new emotion sprang up in Grace Harvey's heart also, an interest in Tom because she had saved him and so was responsible for him. So little did she understand that this was love, that she put her feelings in words, when Tom had recovered his composure sufficiently to murmur something about "impossibility of ever repaying her."

"You might repay me," she said, in a sad and tender tone.

"Turn to God, now in the day of His mercies—unless you have turned to Him already?"

In the reaction from the emotion that had possessed him, and of which, in true British fashion, he was ashamed, Tom seized upon this appeal as a means of recovering self-mastery. Though in his heart of hearts he recognized its sincerity, he chose to regard it as cant, and became brutal in "putting her in her place," in so far as her control of his spiritual affairs was concerned.

"Madam," he said, "I do not require any spiritual assistance in accepting whatever fate befalls me with resignation. I always make the best of every situation."

Then he hastily and impulsively added, as she turned away under the rebuff: "But you can be of use to me in a material way. I had fifteen hundred pounds about me when I came ashore last night, sewed in a belt round my waist. It is gone. It was all I had in the world. You know better than I who is likely to have taken it. Help me to recover it."

Grace turned from red to white, and to red again.

"Good heavens," thought Tom, "what have I said! She thinks I am accusing her. And what if the poor creature, who, the curate intimates, is not altogether right in her mind, has really taken the money! Tom Thurnall, you are a cad as well as a brute. I'll never set this right, but I'll spend my life in this place trying to do so."

But Tom was mistaken as to the cause of Grace's confusion. This was due to her sense of shame that there must be a thief among her dear friends the fishermen, and that the entire village was disgraced by this indignity toward a stranger. She accepted the responsibility for the honor of Aberalva, and said, relying upon her power over the hearts of the fishermen to persuade that one who had yielded to temptation in a moment of weakness to restore the money:

"Have patience, Mr. Thurnall, and I shall hand you your belt and its contents."

She set about her investigations at once. By inquiring as if from curiosity as to what had occurred at the rescue while she was insensible, she learned that no hand but her mother's had touched her in separating her hold from Thurnall's waist, and that after that there had been no opportunity for one of the fishermen to take the belt unseen by the rest of his comrades. The conclusion was inevitable. Mrs. Harvey had stolen the girdle and its contents.

Grace was a stricken creature whom it was pitiable for Tom to behold when he met her in his round of duties—for he had virtually supplanted Dr. Heale as physician no less than apothecary. At last she summoned up courage and inquired of her mother what she knew of the belt from which she had disengaged her fingers. At once Mrs. Harvey assumed that her daughter was charging her with theft, and cried bitterly:

"Was she the person to accuse a poor widowed mother, struggling to leave her child something to keep her out of the workhouse? A mother that lived for her, would die for her, sell her soul for her?"

Oh, it was hideous! Grace tried not to see the confession of guilt in its attempted avoidance. She even imagined that she herself had been the thief, tempted during her unconsciousness; that she had hidden the belt away somewhere, and that, by setting her mind to it, she might recall the hiding-place, and restore the money.

"He will surely forgive me when he finds that it was not I." And on that thought followed a dream of what might follow, so wild that she hid her blushes in her hands.

In the mean time Tom had put the lost bank-notes out of his mind. Cholera had broken out in a neighboring village, and he was busy night and day with sanitary measures for preventing its spread to Aberalva. But the fishermen were opposed to such innovations as cleaning pigsties and removing dunghills, and Tom, bethinking himself of Grace's influence over the stubborn fellows, appealed to her for aid—by letter, since he felt a delicacy in imposing his presence on her.

She replied that she would do what she could, and in a short time the entire village resigned itself to the new doctor's orders. But obedience came too late. The cholera appeared, and even Grace forgot her troubles in aiding Tom to minister to its victims. They met at bedsides, and on their errands of mercy in the streets, with no thoughts of their personal relations, though all the while love was deepening into that sense of perfect comradeship which is the sign and surety of heaven-ordained union.

Finally, when the plague had been conquered, Tom spoke to Grace:

"I ought long ago to have asked your pardon for something rude which I said to you in most ungenerous requital of the service you had rendered me, and were still seeking to render me. If I had been the man I am to-day, knowing the beauty of your nature, so far above mine, I should not so have responded. I am thoroughly ashamed of myself—"

But she interrupted him, crying wildly:

"Oh, the belt, the belt! Wait a little longer; have patience with me, and I will restore it; and then you will forgive?—forgive?"

And she laid her hands upon his arms, and looked up into his face with a piteous smile of entreaty.

She never had looked so beautiful as at that moment. The devil entered into the heart of Tom Thurnall. He caught her in his arms, and kissed her pleading mouth, kissed her eyes suffused with tears. "Yes! I'll wait—wait forever, if you will! I'll lose another belt for such another look as that!"

She was bewildered for a moment, poor fond wretch! at finding herself where she would gladly have remained forever; but quickly she recovered her reason.

"Let me go!" she cried, struggling wildly. "You know I am a poor, ignorant girl, not fit to be your wife."

Maddened now, Tom followed a foolish deed with a base speech:

"I know nothing but that I shall keep you in pawn for my belt. And I hope you may never find it."

She tore herself free.

"In pawn? Yes, in jail, if you will; but offer no more insults to a defenseless girl. Oh, I had fancied you—" and she left her sentence incomplete.

Tom had come to his senses.

"I beg your pardon, Miss Harvey. I have been mad. If you will look in your glass when you go home, and have a woman's heart in you, you may excuse my impulsive action. Try to forgive me."

"I have forgiven you."

"Will you forget?"

"Your action, but your words I cannot. For it is too true that you hold me in your power."

"No, it is I who am in your power, Miss Harvey, and to prove it I will do anything you ask."

"Then give me one month. Ask no questions; trust me; and I will bring you the belt. If I do not, send me to Bodmin jail."

"It may as well be a year as a month, for I intend to leave England next week for the war in Turkey. If you find the belt, send the money to the bank in Whitbury for my father. But, Grace, whether you recover it or not, I intend to come home with my savings and marry you; and we'll settle down in Whitbury with dear old dad and your mother—"

"My mother!" ejaculated Grace. "Oh, no! it can never be. Do not go to the war, but return to your father. There must be rich girls in Whitbury only too ready to marry you. Choose one of them, and forget the poor schoolmistress of Aberalva."

"No, Grace, it is you who saved my life, and you who shall bring me my fortune. Let me win your respect by going where my services are in greatest need. It is the only thing left for me to do."

Grace hurried home with a great purpose fixed in her mind. It was sinful enough to allow Tom to be kept out of his money while he was in Aberalva, but doubly sinful when he was going to a foreign country, and would need every farthing he could command. She found her mother reading the Bible, vainly endeavoring to find consolation for her crime short of restitution of the money. Grace took the book and turned to the Thirty-second Psalm, and read it, as none in that parish save she could read:

"Blessed is he whose transgression is forgiven, and whose sin is covered."

At the close she threw herself down at her mother's knees and looked up in her face imploringly: "Mother, mother, mother!" was all she could say.

Base terror had hardened Mrs. Harvey's heart.

"Get up! What is this foolery?"

"I will not get up till you have told me."

"Told what?"

"Whether you know where Mr. Thurnall's money is." She forced the words slowly out in a whisper.

"You viper!" shrieked the old woman. "I see your plan! You love that man, and want to share his money!"

Grace rose, looked steadfastly at Mrs. Harvey in silence, and left the room. Thereafter she kept within doors, doing her share of household duties, but refusing to hold any conversation with her mother. She was pressed by the neighbors to reopen her school, but refused. Upbraided by her mother for this, she replied shortly:

"I will do so when I am not ashamed to face the little children."

Even when Tom Thurnall left for the war she did not emerge from her retirement. Finally her mother was brought to desperate straits to meet household expenses. This was the crisis for which Grace was waiting. She kept close watch upon the old woman. One night, discovering that her mother had slipped out of the house with a lantern, Grace, putting a shawl over her night-dress, followed unobserved.

The tide was low; the beach was bright in the western moonlight. Grace glided after her mother like a ghost, and saw her enter a dark sea-cavern, approachable only at low water. Crouched at the entrance, she beheld the old woman holding the lantern up against the side of the cavern, and removing the long-lost belt from a crevice in the rock.

Grace could not restrain a groan of anguish. Mrs. Harvey, perceiving only that she was observed—by whom she knew not—dropped the lantern, clasped her treasure to her bosom, and rushed out of the cavern, thrusting Grace aside in the darkness. The girl threw her shawl aside, and stood revealed in her white night-dress.

"God's angel, come to destroy me!" cried the guilty woman; and she dropped the belt. Running with backward look, she stumbled and fell, striking her head against a sharp rock.

Grace ran to her side, picked up the belt, put it in her bosom where it was to remain till she gave it to its owner, and then lifted her mother in her arms and bore her out of the reach of the incoming tide. Summoning help, she got the insensible woman home. The shock brought out the disease of cholera latent in Mrs. Harvey's system, and in two days she was dead.

Grace sent the contents of the belt to the bank at Whitbury, and then vanished from Aberalva. Taking a place as nurse, she set out to find Tom in the Crimea, to right him, to right herself. Wearing his belt, she followed one false scent after another, but continually missed her lover. At last she realized that God was teaching her patience, and she was content to return to England and bide His own good time. Her heart went out to old Mr. Thurnall, and, going to Whitbury, she obtained a place as kitchen-maid in his house for her keep, and ere a month was past she was to the old gentleman as a daughter. She was cheerful in his presence, but her face, however gentle, was sharpened as if with continual pain. No wonder; for she had worn that belt two years, till it had almost eaten into the heart above which it lay. It gave her perpetual pain, which was to her perpetual joy, for it was a constant reminder of Tom.

And Tom at last came home, bearded to the eyes, in ragged sailor clothes. He found his father seated on the porch, and fell on his knees before him.

"Here is the prodigal, daddy," he cried.

"My son! my son! Let me feel whether thou be my very son Esau or not!" murmured the old man, playfully endeavoring to conceal his feelings.

After recovering from the excess of emotion, he said: "Tom, you must see Grace."

"Grace who?" said Tom in astonishment.

"Oh, just Grace," said the old man, "a girl who has been with me for a year and has become dear to me as my own daughter."

"If she is the Grace I think she is, and whom I looked for in vain at Aberalva, even before I came to Whitbury to see you, she will soon be your daughter too, father."

And Grace Harvey, bearing the belt, came out of the door.

"Take it!" she said. "I have carried it to Varna, and you were not there; to Scutari, to Balaklava, and you had just departed. Cruel, not to wait! At last the snake is unclasped from my waist."

She burst into an agony of tears, and Tom caught her in his arms.

"Dear," he said, "I have been in a Russian prison, and have lost my nerve, there was so much time there to remember. Oh, Grace, I have come home to have you teach me to forget what I have been in the past. Teach me to turn to God, as you once enjoined me. Through poverty and wealth, for better, for worse, I want you by my side. Forgive me, Grace!"

"Oh, Mr. Thurnall, my brave, wise, wonderful Mr. Thurnall! Come home again; come home to God! And to me, Grace Harvey, the poor, ignorant teacher of fishermen's children! Nobody ought to forgive you for that, but I shall."

THE WATER-BABIES (1863)

In the spring of 1858 Charles Kingsley's youngest son was born at Eversley rectory and was named Grenville Arthur, for his godfather, Dean Arthur Stanley, and Sir Richard Grenville, one of the heroes of *Westward Ho!* One spring morning in 1862, Kingsley was reminded of an old promise to the effect that "Rose, Maurice, and Mary have got their books, and baby must have his." Without replying he at once went to his study and a half hour later returned with the story of little Tom, written without a correction. This formed the opening chapter of *The Water-Babies*, and the rest of the tale, which was printed in monthly instalments in *Macmillan's Magazine*, was written as rapidly and with as much ease as the first chapter, the copy going to the printer with hardly a flaw. It appeared in book form the next year, dedicated "To my youngest son, Grenville Arthur, and to all other good little boys." According to Mrs. Kingsley in her biography of her husband, it was "perhaps the last book that he wrote with real ease, and which was purely a labor of love," for his work was now becoming a burden on account of frequent illness.

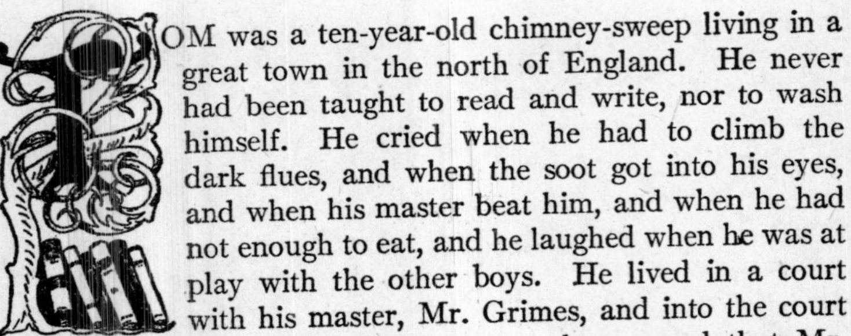

OM was a ten-year-old chimney-sweep living in a great town in the north of England. He never had been taught to read and write, nor to wash himself. He cried when he had to climb the dark flues, and when the soot got into his eyes, and when his master beat him, and when he had not enough to eat, and he laughed when he was at play with the other boys. He lived in a court with his master, Mr. Grimes, and into the court one day came a smart young groom to leave word that Mr. Grimes was to go to Sir John Harthover's mansion, Harthover Place, the next day, as the chimneys there needed sweeping. Tom's master was delighted to hear this, and by four o'clock Tom and he set out for the Place, Grimes in front on his donkey, and Tom behind with the brushes. They presently came up with an Irishwoman trudging along the highway, and as she walked beside Tom she asked him many questions about himself and seemed sad when he told her he had no prayers to say. She told Tom that she lived far away by the sea, and that in summer children bathed and played in the sea, till he longed to behold it and bathe likewise. At last they reached a spring, and while the woman helped the lad to pick flowers, Grimes bathed his head in the spring. He was angry when Tom began to do the same, and while he was beating the boy the woman said:

"Are you not ashamed of yourself, Thomas Grimes?"

Grimes said no, and the woman added:

"True! If you ever had been you would have gone into Vendale long ago."

Grimes now understood that she knew some things to his discredit, and as he was moving off she said:

"I have one more word for both of you, for you will both see me again. Those that wish to be clean, clean they will be; and those that wish to be foul, foul they will be." Thereupon she disappeared.

Sir John's keeper met them at the lodge-gates and went with them to the mansion, a mile farther, and there the grand housekeeper gave Grimes solemn orders, as if he instead of Tom were going up the chimneys. Every now and then Grimes said under his voice, "You'll mind that, you little beggar," and Tom attended as well as he could.

There were so many chimneys to sweep that the lad grew tired and perplexed and, coming down the wrong chimney, at last found himself on the hearth-rug in a strange room. There was a bath there, and towels and other conveniences for washing, and Tom thought that the lady to whom the room belonged must be very dirty to want so much scrubbing as all that came to. Then he perceived a bed in which lay a beautiful little girl asleep, and he wondered whether all persons were as white as she when they were washed. Looking around, he saw his own little black figure in a mirror, and knew for the first time that he was dirty. Bursting into tears of shame and anger, he turned back to the chimney to hide, but upset the fender with a tremendous noise. This woke the little girl, who screamed loudly on seeing Tom, which brought the nurse, who caught him by his jacket. Wrenching himself away, he sprang from the window into a tree close by, down which he slid to the ground and was off across the park, while the nurse continued to scream "murder!" and "fire!" at the window.

And now began an exciting chase; for everyone at the Place

forsook his business of the moment and pursued poor Tom. There were the under-gardener, the dairymaid, the groom, the steward, the plowman, the keeper, Sir John even, and the Irishwoman also. My Lady was the only one that did not join in pursuit of Tom, and that was because her wig fell into the garden and put her out of the running. There was never such a commotion at Hall Place before, for all were shouting "Stop thief!" as if Tom had his pockets filled with stolen jewels. But Tom outwitted them all except the Irishwoman, who kept close behind him, though he did not know it. At last he reached the open moor, but between him and loftier moors lay a deep and narrow green valley, in which he saw a cottage and a garden. He thought he could climb down to the garden in five minutes, but the cottage was more than a mile off, and a thousand feet below him. After a long and dangerous descent, accompanied all the way by the unseen Irishwoman, Tom reached the bottom of the cliff exhausted, and it was some time before he found strength enough to go to the cottage, near as it now was. When he did so he found there a neat little old woman with a dozen neat children before her learning their Criss-cross-row.

"He's sick," said the old dame, "and a bairn's a bairn, sweep or none."

Then she brought him milk and bread, and was amazed to hear that he had come from Harthover Place down Lewthwaite Crag. Putting him to rest on soft hay in an outhouse, she promised to come to him an hour later when school was over. He did not fall asleep at once, but longed to cool himself in the river. After that he drowsed for a time, but did not know that he was saying aloud: "I must be clean, I must be clean."

Suddenly he found himself in a meadow with a stream at hand, and pulling off his ragged clothes he threw himself into the cool water. Just before he came to the stream the Irishwoman had stepped into it and as her clothing slipped from her the fairies of the stream came and bore her away through the water, for she was their queen. She told them she had brought them a new brother, whom she had watched over all the way thither, but he was not to see or know them now because he was a savage and must be taught. Meanwhile, they were to see that he came to no harm.

At noon the old dame went to see Tom in the outhouse. He was gone, and she thought she had been tricked, but she changed her mind next day. After Tom's pursuers had lost sight of him they went home crestfallen, and when it was learned that the little girl and her nurse had only seen a tearful sweep, and that nothing had been missed, Sir John felt much troubled, the more especially as no tidings of him were heard next day. The next day Sir John and his keepers followed Tom's scent with a hound till it stopped at Lewthwaite Crag. They feared he had fallen over the precipice, and going by road down into the valley they saw the old dame, who told them all she knew of Tom. The dog was once more put upon the scent and soon brought them where Tom's clothes lay beside the stream—and that was all they knew of the vanished sweep.

As for Tom, he presently found himself swimming in the stream, and only about four inches long, having also a set of external gills like those of an eft; for the fairies had transformed him into a water-baby. There are land-babies—then why not water-babies? But good Sir John did not understand this, and he took it into his head that Tom was drowned. His shell was buried in the Vendale churchyard, and the old dame placed flowers upon the grave every Sunday. And all the while Tom was swimming about in the river, with a pretty lace collar of gills about his neck, as lively as a grig and as clean as a fresh-run salmon.

Tom was very happy in the water, and life at first seemed an endless holiday to him, but he was mischievous, and presently began to tease the water-animals till they got out of his way and left him without any playmates. At last he made the acquaintance of a dragon-fly, from which he learned so much that he gave up his teasing habits for a while. An otter one day tried to eat him, declaring that Tom was surely an eft, but was presently driven away by seven little terrier dogs, which were really water-fairies sent to protect him.

Tom now concluded to descend the river to the sea, and on the way he met many salmon coming up stream, and these he warned against the wicked otter. One night he saw some men spearing salmon, and these were soon set upon by others. In the fight a man fell into the water whom Tom recognized as his old master, Grimes. He did not turn into a water-baby as Tom expected, but lay still in the pool and never poached salmon any more. After many perils Tom reached the sea, but to his great disappointment saw no water-babies to play with, though he asked concerning them of many strange sea-shapes.

Now, Lady Harthover had taken her daughter Ellie, whom Tom had frightened, to the seaside, and there Ellie often walked on the shore with a famous naturalist who had an unpronounceable Polish name. Ellie was sure there were water-babies, but the naturalist said there were not, and just then he lifted Tom out of the water in his net. He did not like to admit that he had been wrong, so he said:

"Why, this must be a cephalopod."

And Tom called out as loud as he could: "No, I ain't."

Ellie declared it was a water-baby, but the naturalist made light of her belief and poked Tom carelessly with his finger, which Tom at once seized and bit. The naturalist dropped him quickly, and Tom disappeared in the water.

"It was a water-baby, and I heard it speak," Ellie exclaimed, and while trying to catch Tom she slipped and fell on the rocks. She was put to bed, but she lay quite still, only now and then saying something about the water-baby, and the fairies came one moonlight night, bringing with them a pair of wings, with which she flew away in their company.

Tom, when he slipped into the water, wished that Ellie could have been his playmate, but he presently found a friend of his, a lobster, caught in a lobster-pot, and tried to help him out. He never had been helpful before, but he had hardly left the lobster when he saw hundreds of water-babies ready and willing to play with him. In their company he went to St. Brandan's fairy isle, the home of the water-babies. Tom, however, still liked to amuse himself by tormenting the anemones, crabs, and other creatures, although the water-babies said to him:

"Mrs. Bedonebyasyoudid is coming."

He paid no attention, but one morning she came indeed. She was very ugly, Tom thought, but she gave the children sea-candies, though when his turn came she put into his mouth a hard pebble, at which he began to whimper. Then she reminded him of his cruelty in putting pebbles into the anemones' mouths to make them think they had caught a good dinner.

"As you did to them, so I must do to you," she said. She assured him that it was useless to try to hide things from her, and that she could not help punishing those who did wrong. She told him, further, that she was the ugliest fairy in the world, and would always be so till people behaved themselves properly, but then she should grow as beautiful as her sister, Mrs. Doasyouwouldbedoneby.

Mrs. Bedonebyasyoudid then dismissed the other children, but told Tom to see what she was going to do, saying that every Friday she served all who had ill used little children as they served the children. So she called up the doctors who gave children too much physic, and gave them their own mixtures; punished the careless nursemaids, and the cruel schoolmasters, and many more. It was hard work for Mrs. Bedonebyasyoudid, but we cannot always choose our own profession.

On Sunday came the beautiful Mrs. Doasyouwouldbedoneby, and all the children were delighted to see her. She was especially kind to Tom, who told her that no one ever had cuddled him before. Being comfortable does not always make persons good, and Tom became so fond of sea-lollypops and the like that when he found where Mrs. Bedonebyasyoudid kept them he secretly ate all he could discover, and as she watched him she said to herself:

"You poor little dear! You are just like all the rest."

But he had his share at the next distribution, though the fairy looked sadly at him as he took it from her. When Mrs. Doasyouwouldbedoneby came, he wished to be cuddled like the rest; but she said this could not be, for he had become horny and prickly. And so he was, his body had become thus while his soul grew prickly with wrong-doing. Then he confessed to Mrs. Bedonebyasyoudid, and she forgave him, but said she would send a schoolmistress who would teach him how to get rid of the prickles. The schoolmistress proved to be a beautiful little girl; and under her teaching the prickles vanished, and by and by she knew him for the little sweep that came to her bedroom.

They studied together seven years, but Tom always wondered where she went on Sundays, and grew discontented. She was tired of him and wished to be rid of him, he said, and thereupon Ellie vanished. Then Mrs. Bedonebyasyoudid assured him that she had sent Ellie away. She next showed him *The History of the Doasyoulikes*, who came away from the country of Hardwork, and what became of them. Tom now determined to go, if necessary, to the world's end to find Mr. Grimes, who, the fairy said, was at the Other-end-of-Nowhere. To accomplish this, he must first go to Shiny Wall, and through the White Gate that was never opened, thence to Peacepool and Mother Carey's Haven, where the good whales go when they die. There Mother Carey would tell him the way to the Other-end-of-Nowhere and Mr. Grimes.

It was a long journey, and Tom encountered on the way the King of the Herrings, of whom he asked the route to the Shiny Wall, and who directed him to the Allalonestone, where he would find the last of the Gairfowl. She was much like a penguin, and while she spoke to him Mother Carey's chickens came to escort him farther. The Shiny Wall was an iceberg, under which Tom dived, finally reaching Peacepool. In the midst of this sat Mother Carey, like a gigantic marble statue on a throne from the foot of which millions of new-born creatures continually swam away. These were Mother Carey's chickens.

After many strange adventures, Tom reached the Other-end-of-Nowhere, and exhibited a pass that Mother Carey had given him, and was admitted to a kind of castle, where he asked for Grimes, the master sweep. He was informed that Grimes was up chimney No. 345, and that he would have to go up to the roof. When he came to chimney No. 345 he found Grimes with his head and shoulders just showing. In his mouth was a pipe that would not draw, at which he grumbled incessantly. Recognizing Tom, he said he supposed Tom had come to laugh at him. Tom declared he had not, but only wished to help him. He picked up a live coal and touched it to Grimes's pipe, but it went out at once, because the man's heart was so cold that it froze everything that came near him. While Grimes was again complaining, Mrs. Bedonebyasyoudid appeared, reminding him how he had often treated Tom in the same way that he was now treated. Tom implored her not to think of him, but to let him help Mr. Grimes, but though he tugged at the bricks he could not loosen them. Nor could he wipe the soot from Grimes's face. Tom's desire to help him at last softened his old master's heart, and at the thought of the mother whom he had forsaken in his youth Grimes wept, and his tears at length washed the soot from his face and clothes, washed the mortar from the bricks, crumbled the chimney, and allowed him to get out. Grimes promised Mrs. Bedonebyasyoudid that he would do whatever she bade him, and he then recognized her voice as that of the Irishwoman they had met so long ago on the road to Harthover. He was assigned to sweep out the crater of Etna, and off he marched in the custody of a stout truncheon.

And now Tom returned to St. Brandan's isle, where he found Ellie, and as the fairy stood by them they cried out:

"Who are you? You are our dear Mrs. Doasyouwouldbedoneby. No, you are good Mrs. Bedonebyasyoudid, grown quite beautiful."

"To you," the fairy said. "Look again."

"You are Mother Carey," Tom said, "grown young."

"To you. Look again."

"You are the Irishwoman that met me on the road to Harthover."

But when they looked she was neither of them, and yet all of them at once.

HENRY KINGSLEY

(England, 1830–1876)

RECOLLECTIONS OF GEOFFRY HAMLYN (1859)

Henry Kingsley, after leaving college, spent five years in Australia, where he gained the material for this and the following story, published after his return to London.

THOUGH I, Geoffry Hamlyn, have led an uneventful existence, I have been much concerned as a spectator in the love-making and the fighting of sundry persons whose experiences I record; consequently, I shall keep myself in the background as much as possible, and appear personally only when there is no way out of it.

In the little Devonshire village of Drumston about the year 1820 lived John Thornton, the vicar, with his beautiful daughter, Mary, and his sister, a quiet, good old maid, who had been a governess all her life. Though fairly well off, and with the only relatives he cared for in the world to make his old age comfortable, Thornton was unhappy. With all the fine young fellows of the county to choose from, Mary would have nobody but George Hawker, who was handsome and agreeable indeed, but had little education and a character that promised to develop badly. This opinion of mine was shared by Major Buckley and his wife, and by Dr. Mulhaus—all friends and constant visitors at the vicarage.

In the most desolate part of the pass that traverses the rugged country of northern Dartmoor, a man crouched over a smoldering peat fire one rainy winter night, awaiting the arrival of George Hawker. This unkempt, savage-appearing man was William Lee, an escaped convict, who had returned from Australia to Drumston, his old home, only to find that his very name had become obliterated from the memory of men. Since that time, living by the various means forced on him by necessity, he had chanced on Hawker, and in the acquaintanceship that followed the latter had confided to the convict that his affairs were in a ruinous condition. Lee, acting as counsel for a small fee, had advised forging the name of Hawker's father for two hundred pounds, which was done, and that was an end to the matter till this dismal winter night.

When Hawker finally arrived and finished cursing his companion for calling him out in such weather, Lee calmly went over the incidents of their first acquaintance, and concluded:

"Now you are about to marry a young lady with five thousand pounds, so I should be neglecting my own interests if I did not collect three hundred pounds for holding my tongue."

The wretched Hawker cast a hurried glance around, as if considering the chance of mastering his enemy; but a confederate of the latter appeared suddenly from behind a rock, and the young man could only protest hoarsely:

"You know I cannot get three hundred pounds."

"Do as you did before," said Lee promptly. "Your father is half blind, and you manage nearly everything."

Dick, the confederate, strongly advised the same course, and drew a vivid picture of the gallows as the alternative.

"Needs must when the devil drives," George answered. "As you promise to leave the country, I shall give you the money this day week." But during his ride home he took this resolution under different advisement.

George's father was a satyr-like old wretch, who since the death of his wife, years before, had lived with Madge, a gipsy woman. The latter was still handsome, with a shrewd mind that usually dominated her companions, though quarrels were fierce and frequent in the ill-constructed household. As the half-blind old man was constitutionally mistrustful of all, he would have Madge check over his bank-account with him; but apparently she had not detected the former forgery by George, who managed the estate.

As she and George were on friendly terms most of the time, and she sometimes extorted money from the old man to give to him, George, now beset with dangers, considered an appeal to her for assistance. But the natural cowardice of the guilty mind prevented, and he resolved on a more devious course. In the next few days Madge noticed his constant practise with the rifle.

"'Tis folly to wipe out money-scores with blood," she told him, after he had explained that he was going for a deer.

This gave George a scare, but did not change his resolution, and on the night payment was due he stole into the northern pass to settle accounts with William Lee. But the latter and his confederate were too alert, and he was caught in the act of stalking them down. The only outcome of this adventure was that Lee increased his price to five hundred pounds, with an emphatic assurance that George should be hanged if the money wasn't counted down next day. There was no possibility of resistance or evasion; the second forgery was committed, and George saw no more of his enemies for many years.

Another circumstance that rose to vex him at this time was the reappearance of his cousin Ellen. She was an orphan who had formerly lived with them, and had been turned out of the house by old Hawker after the birth of a boy had opened his eyes to George's relations with the girl. But money was given to her, and she was packed off with her baby, and George was left with only one obstacle to overcome before he could claim Mary Thornton and her five thousand pounds. This was the vicar's suddenly aroused opposition.

Notwithstanding the vigorous remonstrances of his intimate friends against permitting Mary to receive Hawker's attentions, John Thornton never had opposed him strenuously. He did not like the young man, and was aware of his father's infamy; but his own wife had long been dead, and Mary, having grown up under a loving, unworldly old man, puzzled by such a responsibility, was to be governed by no will but her own. Not until an old, discharged servant of Hawker's revealed on his death-bed the fact that George was the child of the gipsy woman, Madge, did Thornton take a decided stand against him.

The vicar told his daughter that he had forbidden the house to Hawker, but did not give his reasons for doing so.

"You encouraged him to come, and now, after my love is given, you wish to break my heart," said Mary, and without waiting to hear her lover directly accused, she withdrew, and for several days remained sulkily aloof from her father.

The good old vicar grieved more over her disappointment than over her conduct. "She will soon see her duty," he told Dr. Mulhaus, "and in time will banish the unworthy young man from her thoughts."

But it happened that when they met again Thornton had passed a sleepless night and was ill, and she construed his dull, stupid manner to mean a continuance of his displeasure.

So that night and the next she stole away to meet George Hawker, and he, having explained to her that her father had objected to him only because of his father's relations with the gipsy woman, railed against the injustice of it.

"Marry me now. You don't know what a change it will make when the thing's once done," George urged, and the girl yielded to his persuasion that it was too late to turn back.

John Thornton delivered his farewell sermon the following Sunday. The next morning his sister came into his room with a note left by Mary, revealing her flight with Hawker and asking forgiveness. In her agitation she made no allusion whatever to marriage; so the vicar read her message again and again, each time more mistily, till sense and feeling departed and he lay before the hearth a hopeless paralytic.

It may appear strange that Mary Thornton should marry a man so far beneath her; but until recently her association had been only with the members of her father's church, all good enough in their way, but far inferior to her in social station. Her aunt and the high-bred wife of Major Buckley had lived in Drumston only a year or two, and their refinement and conversation had only made her conscious of their superiority, without improving her own qualities.

So George Hawker and Mary Thornton were married in London a few days later, and went thence to Brighton, where they were very gay. George had induced his wife to withdraw her money from the funds and place it in a bank; but even with five thousand pounds at his disposal, he was uneasy and took to drinking heavily.

The day before the elopement he had thought best to tell Madge of the last forgery, begging her to conceal it until he could deposit to his father's credit five hundred pounds of money he should obtain from Mary, and so cover the deficit. But the night preceding his marriage Major Buckley appeared at his lodgings with news that boded disaster.

"I got your address from Madge, the gipsy woman," said Buckley, "who said that your father, being sent for by the bank, had returned in a terrible rage and turned her out of the house; and that the forgeries were discovered, and the bank intended to prosecute."

Hawker refused to reveal the whereabouts of Mary, knowing that the Major would attempt to dissuade her from the intended marriage, so the real object of the Major's journey was not accomplished, he having given his word of honor not to molest the forger.

"The malignant old fiend, not to protect his own son from the gallows," said George to himself; and as he could not hear a tread behind him without thinking of an officer, he resumed his old habit of drowning trouble, at Brighton, and from drink turned to the excitement of gambling. Then his familiars—greasy, tawdry, bedizened bucks and their flamboyant women came to his house, where the wildest of gaming revels were soon carried on.

For a time Mary was proud to see her husband in such fine company; but as the birds of prey swooped more closely and began to quarrel, she became terribly afraid of them. Then her husband's manner grew sullen and morose, and he resented her timorous advice to quit gambling, and plunged more deeply into dissipation. One day, when in better humor than usual, he took her to the Brighton races, and there he was drawn aside by a veiled woman, who turned out to be Madge.

"I've been following you," she said. "I suppose you are married and have the girl's fortune?"

"Yes," George answered, "but I've been walking into the money."

"Make the most of it," Madge advised. "Your father died in a fit, after turning me out of the house. But he had altered his will the day before, and all the estate goes to your cousin."

This was a stunning blow to George, who could only grind his teeth and curse.

"He got it into his head that you were not his son, though I know you are. George, who but a mother would have done for you what I have?"

"It's enough to drive me mad," said George, as the full significance of the disclosure dawned on him. "How easy it would have been to give me a hint of this years ago, to make me careful—"

Sternly but kindly she interrupted him, and after a few words of advice disappeared in the crowd.

That night he quarreled with his wife for the first time, and sent her to bed crushed and miserable. A few days later he was penniless and ripe for a fall lower than any he had taken yet. Now, having been fleeced, George found his level among the proscribed of society and began to fleece in his turn. Poverty remanded them back to primitive conditions, and they lived a savage life of snarling tyranny and blows, of sulky defiance or abject terror. Still, Mary, knowing herself for a dupe, loved her husband while she dreaded him, and did not speak upbraidingly of the loss of her fortune.

One day a man of lowering evil face came to the house with George and took possession of a room to which Mary never was admitted. There they worked mysteriously day and night, and she became convinced that they were engaged in some great villainy. Such was her resignation to the great catastrophe she felt was impending that when the police took possession of the house and Hawker and his confederate were dragged out in irons, she only clasped her new-born child to her breast and trembled, without crying out. Several days later she sat in court and heard George Hawker sentenced to transportation for life, for coining.

"I must get home for the baby's sake," she thought, and with only a few shillings to keep her she began the long journey afoot to Drumston.

Through rain and wintry winds the unfortunate creature held her way, begging by the roadside, sleeping by night in tramps' lodging-houses, or lying unsheltered in the open fields. One Sunday morning at the vicarage they found Mary sitting on the doorstep, whereat there was rejoicing in the hearts of all her loyal old friends. Her health, broken by hardship, was soon restored, and when their tactful, wholesome kindness had, as it seemed, called her prostrate spirit from the dead, she became the Mary of former days, but with all the selfish qualities swept away by experience.

By this time I had sold out all my property in the neighborhood of Drumston and settled in Australia with James Stockbridge, a friend of my boyhood. We had hardly finished our ranch buildings and begun the business of sheep-raising when we were fairly overrun by an exodus from our native Devon that included nearly every character in this narrative. Of this party Major Buckley became our nearest neighbor, securing a run of sixty thousand acres of well-grassed plain-land, which in three years carried twenty-eight thousand sheep.

Stockbridge and I were delighted at this; for the Major, who had distinguished himself greatly in the Peninsular and Waterloo campaigns, was a splendid type of the high-bred Briton in character, manner, and appearance. No description of him should disparage his wife by comparison, for she equally attracted us, and their son, Sam, was a sturdy little man of six years.

Ten miles from this place, which they named Baroona, was the ranch of Tom Troubridge and Mary Hawker, his cousin. The old vicar had died shortly after Mary's return, and as all her old friends were bound for the new land of promise, she came also, rather than be left alone. With the five thousand pounds left by her father, she entered into partnership with Troubridge; and as her aunt, Miss Thornton, lived with them, and her little boy made up in part for the dreary havoc of the past, they formed another contented, interesting group.

The Buckleys were joined later by Dr. Mulhaus, who was shrewd in counsel and a bold abetter of our enterprises. He had a fine education, and his profound knowledge of politics led me to believe, even at that time, that he had once been a considerable figure in the world, though we knew nothing of his life prior to the day he came to Drumston. He afterward undertook the education of young Sam Buckley.

In this pleasant state of life sixteen long years of peace and plenty rolled over our heads before the first great calamity fell upon us. Then my dear friend and partner was killed in the bush by the blacks. Hardly had the sharpness of this affliction worn away when another trouble appeared in our happy colony. A second generation now began to fill this theater of events, and affairs that blossom when the heart is young soon occupied our attention.

Colonel Brentwood, whose station was several miles from Buckley's, had two children, James and Alice. The latter, with her brilliant Norman style of beauty, soon proved the apple of discord between young Cecil Mayford, another neighbor, and Sam Buckley, now grown to as fine a specimen of manhood as his father. The rivalry was unfriendly, and then bitter for a time, but to my great delight the young lady, after the customary indecision, concluded by accepting Sam. But poor Cecil's character was gloomily affected to the end.

All this time Mary Hawker had lived in comparative happiness, almost oblivious of the rest of the world in her devotion to her son. Charles was now a sturdy, fearless youth, with a high, uncertain temper, and bore a painful likeness to his father. He domineered over his mother, but was rather afraid of Troubridge.

Through William Lee, whom we have heard of before in an evil transaction, but who had now been for many years a faithful servant of Troubridge's, the latter first received word of an event that boded trouble to us all. Lee informed him that George Hawker had escaped from the penal colony and was now prowling about the station.

"And there is no doubt," he concluded, "that Hawker is the leader of the bushrangers who have been raiding up country."

Mary had given so little evidence of her old petulance and temper in these later years that we supposed her character steadied and elevated by experience. But when she heard this news a momentary terror was succeeded by feverish rage. The habit of years was stripped off like a garment, and we had to deal with the same unreasonable person that had formerly caused so much trouble.

She had an indefinable terror of Charles meeting his father, whom the boy supposed to have died in England; but her irrational behavior excited his suspicion that some secret was being kept from him, and she went so far with Troubridge as to urge that he kill her husband if he approached the house. In fact, Hawker did once attempt this, in the dead of night, but found Troubridge on the watch and withdrew.

While the condition of affairs was thus suggestive of calamity, Desborough, the celebrated Inspector of Police, met the bushrangers with a body of his troopers and almost exterminated them in a pitched battle. But our alarm was not abated when we learned further that Hawker had escaped with a young companion, who resembled him so closely in feature and manner that Desborough did not doubt they were father and son. This strange circumstance and two incidents occurring soon after the defeat of the bushrangers should have warned us of the danger tracking us all.

One afternoon the Brentwoods, accompanied by Sam Buckley and Dr. Mulhaus, made an excursion to Cape Chatham, and there the latter, wandering out on a rocky point, came face to face with George Hawker, who disappeared instantly among the rocks. But when, later, the party saw a sailboat put in to shore from the direction of Van Diemen's Land, they surmised readily that it was manned by escaping convicts for whom Hawker was on the watch. A storm broke soon after the boat was sighted, preventing further observation, and next day no trace could be found of its occupants.

Shortly after this, William Lee was murdered in his lonely hut out in the ranges. He was feared by the bushrangers because of his courage and the knowledge his early prison life gave him of their habits. And besides, he knew many of them personally. There was no doubt that his old enemy had committed the crime, as a weapon carved with Hawker's initials was found in the hut.

You will say that we were amply warned of what was to follow, but as a fortnight passed without incident, and some of Desborough's men were in the neighborhood, we were lulled into a sense of security.

I was visiting the Buckleys when the storm broke. The party, including Desborough and Charles Hawker, were on the veranda after luncheon, when suddenly we heard two persons come quickly through the house. For some reason, my heart grew cold when I heard those footsteps, and my strange fear of ill tidings was verified by the appearance of one of Desborough's troopers, pale and silent, and a black boy who clung to him as if for protection. Before I could warn the trooper not to speak before Mrs. Buckley, the brief and terrible story of the black boy was repeated, and we sat staring at one another, dumb and horror-stricken.

That morning, while talking to the black boy, near the stables at the Mayford place, Cecil had turned to watch the swift and silent approach of a body of horsemen. He seemed to have wondered idly who they were, when the kitchen door was thrown open and his old hut-keeper rushed out, crying:

"Save yourself, Master Cecil—the bushrangers!"

Cecil dashed into the house, followed by the hut-keeper, and shut the door. The boy, who had hidden himself in an out-house, saw the bushrangers burst it open, and heard yelling and pistol-shots inside, and then the sound of brutal riot. When the outlaws rode away down the river toward Brentwood's ranch, the boy stole into the house, where he found Cecil and the hut-keeper shot to death, but no trace of Mrs. Mayford and her daughter. We learned afterward that they had escaped while Cecil was conducting his brave defense at the front of the house.

This was a time for quick, determined action, not only to avenge poor Cecil but to save the Brentwoods, who, we knew, would be the next to suffer. Desborough ran to assemble his troopers, and Sam, stunned a moment by the thought of the danger about to fall on Alice, rallied his powers like a man.

Sam's noble horse, Widderin, stood in the stable, and the boy and I spoke not a word as he hastily put on the bridle and saddle; then with a hand-clasp he was off like the wind.

From the Mayfords' place to Captain Brentwood's was about twenty miles; from Buckley's, barely ten; so Sam had a good chance to get there before the bushrangers—and, in short, he did so, after a ride that is famous in the tradition of that region to this day, and bore Alice away to a safe hiding-place as the bushrangers rode up. The house was speedily looted and wrecked, and as the first of Desborough's men appeared over the plain, the outlaws retreated to a rocky defile in the mountains several miles away.

I have remarked that the men of Lucknow don't like to speak

of their experience, and with the same reluctance I speak, however briefly, of the dreadful affair of that next day.

Charles Hawker was with Desborough's party, which included all our friends, and knowing, as we did, that his own father was in command of the outlaws, we urged him to go to the protection of his mother, who was alone at her ranch in this troubled country.

It took Desborough's stern command to send him away; but what was my horror the next morning, as we rode up the defile where the bushrangers had taken position, to see Charles Hawker dash past me. Some fool had met him on the road and taunted him with deserting on the eve of battle. So he had turned back—and toward the close of that desperate fight was consummated the tragedy that no human intervention could stay, when fate had been so long preparing. The father and son met face to face, and the son fell.

In the pleasant home of Sam and Alice, who in our native England have gathered those near and dear around them, I write these lines. But after many years I cannot dwell calmly on the suffering of George Hawker, when he was captured and learned that he had killed his son. Before the expiation of his crimes by sentence of law, he repented them with a sincerity that shook his soul, and I believe he died a better man than he had lived.

The young man who resembled him so closely turned out to be the son that the girl Ellen had borne him, who, brought up in squalor and ignorance, had been transported for some petty crime. He was pardoned after the episode that closes our story, and died an honest man.

Dr. Mulhaus, our faithful old friend, comes occasionally to visit us. My first suspicions of this man have been verified; he is the famous Baron von Landstein, who, withdrawing from his country after a period of political misfortune, has been recalled by the King of Prussia and is now the head of his ministry.

Why should we dwell on the darker side of the life of Mary Thornton, who has suffered so grievously and so often as the whirligig of time brought in his revenges for her great transgression? She is now the happy and contented wife of good Tom

Troubridge. For, though Mary has many noble traits, she is not a woman of enduring impressions, and the first impassioned grief over the death of her son having worn away, this new love entered her heart, and she has learned to look on the past as only a sorrowful picture whose colors are fading out with years.

RAVENSHOE (1862)

Kingsley failed to make a gold fortune in five years of Australia, but found one in novel-writing after returning to England. Beginning with *Geoffry Hamlyn* in 1859, and following that with *Ravenshoe* in 1862, he put forth fourteen tales in all. The plot complications of *Ravenshoe* are concerned, as are so many English novels of the first half of the nineteenth century, with the rivalries of Catholic and Protestant control of wealthy families; while the author's athletic, equestrian, and warlike tastes are as evident here as when he was war-correspondent for his paper, the *Edinburgh Daily Review*, during the Franco-Prussian conflict in 1870.

PETRE RAVENSHOE, ESQ., of Ravenshoe, Ireland, was the scion of one of the oldest "commoner" families in England, one that had for centuries been loyal to the Roman Catholic Church. He married Lady Alicia, daughter of Lord Ascot, a Protestant, and had one son, named Densil, born in 1783. As Lady Alicia had turned Catholic, Ravenshoe retained the kindly Father Clifford as family confessor. That good man had a difficult task, one day, when sent to London to bring back young Densil, who at twenty-one had been loosed in town, "to see the world," but had added to his visions the Flesh and the Devil, the latter personified in the Right Honorable Viscount Saltire, atheistic dandy, gentleman gamester, and general fascinator of men and of women.

Father Clifford found Densil at his rooms, playing *écarté* with Lord Saltire, who with ironical courtesy awaited the outcome, and laughingly offered to bet five to one on the priest. Densil refused to budge; was cut off from funds by his father; was for two months imprisoned for debt; and when in despair was good-naturedly persuaded to go home by Lord Saltire, who brought his mother to him. He yielded, was welcomed at Ravenshoe, and when hunting with James, his faithful servant, who had shared prison-quarters with him, agreed with his remark:

"This is better than the Fleet, sir."

It was. Densil settled down as a good Catholic (the Ravenshoe income was about ten thousand pounds a year); married a Catholic, who died childless; lost his parents shortly afterward; traveled on the Continent, and fell in love with a beautiful young Protestant, whom he brought home as his wife, to the dismay of good Father Clifford and the disgust of astute young Father Mackworth, his coadjutor.

Father Clifford became fond of the heretic mistress, but Mackworth—with whom the interests of Holy Church were paramount—never did. As after two years no children appeared he was about returning to Rome when he overheard a conversation in which Densil and his wife agreed that the first child should be reared as a Catholic, but all after that as Protestants. Father Mackworth remained.

Cuthbert was the eldest son. When he was about five years old, another was born, named Charles; but the mother died, and the baby was given for nursing to James's wife, Nora, who had herself just borne a chubby boy. So little Charles Ravenshoe and little William Horton were foster-brothers, and predestined life-companions. James Horton, the faithful valet of Densil, who as he matured had a look much like his master, had become gamekeeper; and he and Nora had also a little girl, Ellen, about five years older than Baby William.

Father Clifford died, and when Father Mackworth found the only hope of retaining a Catholic head for Ravenshoe was in Cuthbert, he made himself the agreeable companion of the father, the loving instructor of Cuthbert, and the unsympathetic critic of Charles.

But little recked the bonnie Charles of that, or of anything. His was a sunny heart, which won love on all sides. Cuthbert was his idol, but had more interest in his books than in his brother. He preferred the library and Father Mackworth, while Charles became a general outdoor expert.

Charles was once invited to Ranford, Lord Ascot's place, and, as might be expected, charmed everybody, including the lively, witty old Lady Ascot, who kept house for her son, a widower. There, among a throng of riders and hunters (for the chief household interest was in horses), he met a handsome, gray-headed, keen-eyed gentleman, Lord Saltire, who sent friendly messages to his father, and took an amazing fancy to the boy. Welter, a daredevil lad of Charles's age, was Lord Ascot's son; and Adelaide Summers, a beautiful blonde fairy of ten years, granddaughter of an old friend of Lady Ascot's, whom she had adopted, was Charles's bewitching companion.

Amid general regrets, Charles returned to Ravenshoe in a terrible storm, which grew worse and worse. The fine old mansion faced the sea on the north, and about dawn a cannon-shot aroused the household. Family and servants hurried to the beach, finding there the whole village. They watched a dismasted troop-ship, driven helpless upon the outer rocks. She broke and sank, drowning the gallant soldiers aligned on deck, the passengers, and the crew, all but five sailors, the mate, and a child borne in his arms—her mother gone. She was little Mary Corby, warmly welcomed at Ravenshoe. Between her and Charles arose a close friendship; but before he went away to Shrewsbury school he confided to her his passion for Adelaide: so that was arranged.

At two-and-twenty Charles was a student (so to speak) at St. Paul's College, Oxford. His cousin Welter, unfortunately, was also at Oxford, and had led Charles into riotous company. One night there was an outrageous orgy, in which Charles, the only sober one of the crowd, tried to keep Welter straight. But they left his room a wreck, and both Charles and Welter were rusticated for a year.

John Marston, an earnest student, was devoted to Charles, and often tried to wean him from his wild comrades. Before Charles left Marston tried to keep him from going to Ranford with Welter. But Charles told him of Adelaide—who had refused him, by the bye—whom he must see; and he sent home his horses by his foster-brother William (who was as faithful to him as James, his father, had been to Densil), and went to Ranford.

Adelaide had grown into a superb but selfish and ambitious blonde beauty. She and Charles were still comrades, although with many little quarrels. One evening they got into a discussion, and she shed tears, with the result of embraces and kisses on the part of Charles, and her acceptance of his love. This Lady Ascot finally approved.

Charles now returned to Ravenshoe. Mackworth had been

talking much about Charles's ill conduct at Oxford to the father, who finally had silenced him. Cuthbert had defended Charles, and the brothers came to a fine understanding. A new priest had come to the house, Father Tiernay, a jolly Irishman, who did much to mollify the frequent sparrings between Mackworth and Charles, with the latter of whom he took many a stroll.

A few months later Lord Saltire arrived, to visit his old friend Densil. Mary met him, all the others being out, and the old gentleman and she had a long talk, in which he became thoroughly interested in the amiable, intelligent girl. When Charles returned he had a letter from Marston, who, working for a "first" at Oxford, was run down by overreading and feared he would not even get a "second." So they invited Marston down for a rest. Meanwhile Lord Saltire had become almost foolishly fond of Charles, who had taken to study again, for his return to college.

Marston came, and in his visit of weeks endeared himself to everybody. But he fell in love with Mary Corby, and when she gently told him it could not be, he was greatly cast down. Charles and he had been out with some fishermen that day, and in a sudden storm had nearly been drowned, but had been rescued, so that the atmosphere was emotional. Charles greeted Father Mackworth cordially, and the priest said:

"Charles, your nature is frank and noble. I was in terror to-day lest you should go to your account bearing me malice."

"A Ravenshoe never bears malice, Father."

"A Ravenshoe never does, I am aware," replied Mackworth, emphasizing the word "Ravenshoe."

But Charles frankly apologized for his conduct on former occasions, and they concluded a peace — "So long as your father lives, an outward peace, if no more," said Mackworth.

Ellen, who had now grown to great beauty, had suddenly disappeared. William and Charles were deeply distressed, and vainly scoured the country. They suspected that Mackworth knew more than he would tell, for he kept close connection with the Catholic Hortons; but they had no clue. Poor old Nora, her mother, fell ill and sank gradually. Father Mackworth was with her continually. One day, when he was away, Nora sent

William to call Charles to her, instantly; but she died before he reached her.

"She knew something, Master Charles," said William, "and Ellen knows it, too. Some time we shall have to hunt her through the world, to get the scent."

Lord Welter, who had been visiting Charles, was now going; Marston left for Oxford, and Charles also, but with Welter, to take Ranford on the way. The Ascot fortunes were in trouble. Lord Welter's debts were very large, and Lord Ascot, in deep financial embarrassment, was staking all upon a horse he was training, in hopes of winning the Derby.

At Oxford Welter had been expelled for some new impropriety, and Charles, fond of him, because of his generous good-heartedness despite his blackguardly wildness, was sorry. Rowing in the University eight, Charles participated in a great victory over Cambridge, and then was summoned home by his father's illness, but arrived too late to find him alive. This was a sad bereavement to Charles, who had loved his father dearly and companioned much with him. He and Mary found comfort together. She was about to become nursery governess with young Lady Hainault, who had taken her widowed brother's children to care for. Old James had died soon after his master; and they were to be buried side by side under the chapel altar. Cuthbert and Charles had an affectionate and affecting interview, Cuthbert begging Charles to remember how he loved him.

One night, before the funeral, Cuthbert came to Mackworth and said:

"Will nothing induce you to forego your purpose?"

"How can I, Cuthbert, in common honesty?"

And Cuthbert offered him ten thousand pounds, if he would consent. "Think of that, Father. As an English Roman Catholic of fortune, with your talent, you might aspire to a cardinal's chair!" Mackworth did think of it, hesitated, and then furiously refused. And Cuthbert passed out, while Mackworth, dazzled by the temptation, yet resolute to do what he considered his duty to the Church, pondering, went to bed.

Lord Saltire came for the funeral, and after it he departed, asking Charles to come and see him as soon as things were settled. The young man then went, on request, to the library, where he found Cuthbert, Mackworth, and William, on whose shoulder he laid his hand. Cuthbert then, with evident pain, told Charles that when he and William were babies, Nora had exchanged the two, that William was the Ravenshoe child, and Charles the son of James Horton. Then, to account for the strange resemblance of William to both the brothers, Mackworth told how James Horton was an illegitimate son of Petre, the grandfather, a half-brother of their father. As to the exchange of children, Nora had confessed it to Father Mackworth, and he had it in her handwriting. It was an awful moment for all. The paper was examined by Charles, and Cuthbert told him what he had vainly offered Father Mackworth to destroy it—told that, to convince Charles of the priest's sincerity; and further said he should provide three hundred pounds a year for Charles's use.

Charles thanked Cuthbert, declined assistance, said that he should like to have William take his horse, his dog, and his guns, bade them all good-by, begged Father Mackworth's forgiveness for his many rudenesses, shook hands with each one except Cuthbert, whom he kissed on the cheek, and departed. Cuthbert ran after him, knelt, and called him his dear brother. William smilingly went too, saying: "I shall follow him to the world's end, and shall never leave him."

Charles would not go to Lord Saltire in this humiliating condition; he promised Mary to see her at Lord Hainault's in London; he gratefully received William's promise to go with him, and then departed alone, silently, by night. He went first to Ranford, to see his Adelaide, and arrange with her their future, when he should have somehow established himself—and found that that versatile young woman had eloped with Lord Welter. He told his good friend Lady Ascot about his fall, but she loved him none the less, and when he had gone she scolded herself for having kept some other secret for Lady Alicia's sake, but, saying that the boy should yet have his rights, she wrote to Lord Saltire.

Despairing under his accumulated misfortunes, Charles went to London and in a tavern fell into conversation with a genial, horsy man, through whom he obtained a place as groom with

Lieutenant Hornby, of the 140th Hussars, a wealthy, good-natured, gaming young officer. Hornby quickly noticed his gentlemanly qualities, but, scenting mystery, said nothing at first. After a little he told Charles his suspicions, but cheered him up to stand it while it must last, and a sincere liking grew between them.

Lady Ascot was enraged when she found that Charles had gone, for she and Lord Saltire had a plan for him. But he had disappeared, and her expensive hiring of detectives resulted in nothing. Mary found a pleasant home with the amiable young Lady Hainault. She hoped day by day to see Charles; but that young man in livery dreaded to meet any who knew him. One afternoon Charles went to Grosvenor Square, to leave a letter for Hornby's coachman, to a scullery-maid, and in front of Lord Hainault's house he saw Mary with two lively children, and was comforted to see her happy, though she did not dream of his being there.

One day, too, he made acquaintance with a pretty, dirty little shoeblack—indeed, he became great friends with him—which was yet to serve him vitally.

The day before the Derby, Hornby told Charles that Lord Welter was married to Adelaide. Their talk brought out his acquaintance with the couple, and his identity as Charles Ravenshoe; but Hornby agreed not to mention it, and discussed Lord Ascot's folly in betting all he was worth on his horse, Haphazard, although the horse was the favorite. Next day the race was won by Haphazard; but Lord Ascot, although publicly backing his horse, had hedged largely, was ruined, and fell in a fit.

Lord Welter sent Adelaide home from the race to prepare for an evening at cards, at their place in St. John's Wood. For Welter was a gambler, and, with the reckless and beautiful Adelaide as partner, enticed young fellows to his house for gaming.

When Adelaide had gone to this house with Welter, she was welcomed by Ellen, who had run off with Welter before, and now, as a waiting-maid, received the new mistress.

Lieutenant Hornby was one of the expected guests that evening. He had played with Welter in St. John's Wood before, and had fallen in love with Ellen. He came often, not losing much money, for he was Welter's master at play, yet intentionally keeping on the losing side. He took Charles with him that evening, leaving him in the hall, where Charles went to sleep in a chair.

Suddenly Charles woke, and saw the lost Ellen—his sister now—standing in thought. Adelaide came out of a room as Ellen passed, and Charles suddenly grasped the whole situation. No one noticed the groom asleep on the chair, and Charles covered his head with a coat. He presently heard two voices. Lieutenant Hornby was asking Ellen to be his wife; and she acknowledged her love for him, but refused to ruin him by marrying him. She went, and Charles told Hornby the whole story. Then, asking Hornby to wait—for the guests had gone—Charles went into the room. Welter, although a bully, was brave, and, remembering their long friendship, met him frankly, acknowledging his wrong done to Ellen—although he had not known she was Charles's sister—yet saying that he had offered to marry her, but she had refused to learn gaming or to marry him. Adelaide, he said, he had bought with a title. He knew she cared nothing for Charles and would make him miserable; but to him a beautiful, unscrupulous wife was a valuable asset. They agreed that Ellen should go with Charles the next day, and, Welter promising not to mention having seen him, they parted.

All that night Charles lay awake in misery, and the next afternoon went for Ellen—only to find her gone. The poor fellow consoled himself with the belief that she had sought a safe Catholic refuge, but he felt very desolate. Meantime the Ravenshoe household were deeply concerned about him, and—despite Mackworth—Cuthbert and Marston and William decided that William should go forth again to seek him.

One day, being in the park with Hornby, Charles saw Adelaide on horseback with Welter. The wind blew her hat off, and he instinctively ran, picked it up, and handed it to her. She recognized him, and asked him to drop that groom's masquerade, and, if he was desperate, to go to the war. Her words were few and sharp, but gave him an idea. That same day she sought Lady Ascot and Saltire and William, who were together in London, and told them what she had seen. They delightedly thought they had found Charles; but alas! the obstinate fellow had taken his master's horses to stable, left a note for Hornby, and, as Charles Simpson, enlisted in the 140th Hussars for service in the Crimea. He was not in Hornby's company, and felt sure of not being seen.

Lord Saltire and Lady Ascot now had her lawyers advertise one hundred guineas' reward to parish clerks, for the registry of marriage between Petre Ravenshoe and Maria Dawson, supposed to have been solemnized in or about the year 1778. But it was in vain. Lord Ascot, crushed by his troubles, died, and Welter became Lord Ascot. He and Adelaide saw in the *Times* the notice of the death of Cuthbert Ravenshoe, drowned while bathing, and in the very next column the advertisement about the parish register. Then Ascot told his wife of old Petre's first marriage, to a pretty milkmaid, who gave birth to James; and he, consequently, had been really the eldest son, and heir to Ravenshoe, although reckoned as an illegitimate child. Now that Densil and Cuthbert were dead, Lady Ascot and Saltire boldly advertised for proof of Petre's first marriage, the fact of which Lady Ascot had known and concealed. William, who now saw the truth, was about setting out for the Crimea to find Charles, for his own displacement. Adelaide sneered at William as a fool, but Ascot said that, for Charles, he might even be such a fool himself.

So William went to Varna, where the 140th had been encamped. A lying scamp told him that Charles had died of cholera, and even took William to the grave, and the sorrowing brother plucked from it some grass as a memento.

Meantime, Charles's voyage, the new life, the love of horses, and activity had roused him afresh. He outlived the camp pestilence; sat his horse in the reserve through the battle of the Alma; did much march-riding; and at last took part in the desperate charge of the Six Hundred through hell's valley at Balaklava, was severely wounded in his left arm, and was laid up in Scutari hospital. In the fight he had saved the life of a young cornet, and had received the last words from the dying Hornby, who was fatally shot.

Lord Saltire now made his will: legacies to servants; twenty thousand pounds to Mary Corby; ten thousand to John Marston;

fifty thousand to his old friend, Lady Ascot, and the rest, about five hundred thousand pounds, to Lord Ascot, with the provision that if Charles should reappear he was to have eighty thousand pounds.

Charles lay long in hospital; his arm had been penetrated by a bullet, and, while not broken, it was temporarily useless. He was sent home, and on Christmas Eve he found himself in London, with eighteen shillings and ninepence in his pocket. He went to see the cornet whom he had saved, and was joyously received and taken into his service, although he could do but little, being still weak; and he began to be nervous, sleepless, dispirited.

One night Lord Ascot had business with the horsy man that had got Charles his first employment, and sought him at the Servants' Club, which Charles had joined when a groom. Before entering, looking through the glass door, he saw Charles—pale, wan, but undeniably Charles Ravenshoe.

And now—what? A black angel and a white one followed him home, where Adelaide desperately tried to dissuade him from throwing away a fortune. At last he silenced her with curses, sped away to Lord Saltire, and told him that he had seen Charles.

"Of course you know that I shall alter my will?"

"Yes, but I cannot conceal Charles's return. There are some things a fellow can't do, you know."

When he had gone, Lord Saltire said to himself: "He is a noble fellow. He shall have it. Charles will be well provided for." And in the morning Lord Saltire was dead.

The group in the Servants' Club were aroused by the coming of a tawdry, draggled-looking girl, inquiring for Charles Horton. She told him that his little shoeblack friend, her brother, was dying, and wished to see him. Charles went with her, and as they crossed a bridge over the Thames he longed for rest from pain, weariness, sleeplessness, worry, despair. In a distant alley was the foul tenement, and they climbed to the garret. There were the dying boy, a woman asleep, the doctor, and a visiting Scripture-reader who sat in the shadow. The doctor went; the dying child threw his thin arms about Charles's neck, showed him a ball that Charles had given him, and, with his head on his friend's breast, quietly passed away.

Charles sat long with the dead child in his arms, fighting a dull terror when he thought of his homeward journey across the bridge. Someone moved. He looked up, and John Marston, the Scripture-reader, laid an affectionate hand upon his shoulder.

Charles was saved. Marston took him home, on the way telling him of the many changes in their circle. All this, in Charles's enfeebled condition, was too much, and he lay long in brain fever. But he came through, and in the spring was brought to Lord Hainault at Casterton, where the surgeons extracted a splinter from his arm; and by summer he rapidly convalesced.

His friends gathered about him. He and Mary "found a way" to compose their differences; Ascot and he became better friends than ever. Adelaide was living, but crippled for life by a hunting-fall. William joyously welcomed him to Ravenshoe; and one night poor Father Mackworth, enfeebled by a paralytic stroke, summoned Ellen, and she brought the marriage-certificate of old Petre Ravenshoe to Maria Dawson, establishing Charles as the heir of Ravenshoe.

Mackworth acknowledged that he had known it, and all the rest, and had used the exchange of babies to cast out Charles the Protestant and bring in William the Catholic; but he was near death, and must die in charity with all. Charles, of course, freely forgave him.

William and Ellen were handsomely provided for; Charles married the faithful Mary; and William on the same day married a humble but lovely sweetheart of his own. At the wedding-breakfast Lord Ascot made a stumbling, affectionate speech that brought them all to happy tears, and they drank with loving enthusiasm to the health of dear old Lady Ascot, the only remaining one of the elder generation, which had so tangled, but at last so happily untangled and united, the strands of their lives.

RUDYARD KIPLING

(India, 1865)

THE LIGHT THAT FAILED (1890)

This is the first novel by the Anglo-Indian author, and it was distinguished by having two endings; one edition having a happy finale to please the publishers and one with that given here, which the author himself preferred.

DICK HELDAR, an orphan, was placed in charge of Mrs. Jennett, a widow, who, it was erroneously supposed, would take the place of a mother, and who, as guardian of Dick, had for six years visited on his young life such burdens as were not easily borne. Dick's tutorage, under the unpropitious training of Mrs. Jennett, had resulted in inoculating him with justifiable fears, which unconsciously stimulated the habit of prevarication in his relations with his guardian, until, by frequent detection, she was led to regard him as a hopeless liar, which title was not wholly unmerited.

After a dreary period of this solitary life he was joined by an orphan girl, long-haired, gray-eyed, whom Dick was to know as Maisie. A similar course of discipline attempted toward this second charge, by Mrs. Jennett, was met with a coolness that baffled her.

"I have been beaten worse than you can ever beat me," met the threats of the widow from Maisie, who added: "I am not afraid of you." Then, again: "I will write to my lawyer peoples and tell them that you do not give me enough to eat."

Meantime Dick had begun his school-days away from Mrs. Jennett's, and only on vacations and holidays did he return, to find the same treatment awaiting him, and the same little Maisie, self-possessed and fearless.

On one of these occasions Maisie and Dick had purchased a pistol on the sly, and had spent most of the day in firing at a mark. Maisie's goat, which was now her chief companion, swallowed several cartridges, and an explosion was tremblingly anticipated.

The time arrived when Maisie, too, was to be sent away to school; and Dick heard of this with dismay. They were pledged to care for each other in this their double separation, though Maisie protested that, "if she cared, there would be no need of promising."

"You belong to me forever and ever," said Dick; and Maisie confirmed the heroic troth, though with a little mental reservation.

Years passed. Dick Heldar had become a war-correspondent in the Soudan campaign, far away on the Nile. There he was discovered by a black-browed man in a flannel shirt, Torpenhow, who represented the Central Southern Syndicate, organized for furnishing the world with "picturesqueness and abundance of detail." When found, Dick was sitting on the edge of an abandoned redoubt, sketching. Torpenhow examined his sketches, and in the evening had him engaged to the Central Southern Agency.

Torpenhow and Dick became fast friends. They repeatedly fought side by side against Arab attacks, and in one of these skirmishes Dick received a ghastly cut above the eye which resulted in delirium, in the midst of which he called to the restless Nile for "Maisie," and again "Maisie!"

The Soudan campaign and Dick's broken head had been some months ended and mended, when Torpenhow and Dick parted company. Torpenhow went to London; Dick loitered in Ismailia, Alexandria, and Port Said, and began a new campaign in sketching, not omitting the mad dance of the naked Zanzibari girls; from which he was aroused by a telegram from Torpenhow, in England, calling him to "come back quick; you have caught on; come." So to London went Dick, and after much tribulation he found Torpenhow, who had secured quarters for him. Torpenhow apprised him that his sketches were all the rage.

"You are wanted by half a dozen papers; you are wanted to work up your smaller sketches and sell them to dealers."

Dick was found, seven stories up, by a representative of the Central Southern Syndicate, who proved to be the president of the company, and who came to secure Dick's services, at the same time refusing to return to him his own Eastern sketches. Dick's measures were prompt. With a revolver in hand, he blandly ordered the visitor to write a note instructing the office to send, by bearer, the folio of sketches belonging to him, to his rooms. The note was written; Torpenhow was the messenger, and the folio came back with him. Dick had done some meretricious work, and Torpenhow took him to task for trying, for money's sake, to palm it off on the public. One canvas ripped as Torpenhow's booted foot shot through it. Dick responded:

"I've been trying to make myself angry, but I can't, you are so abominably reasonable."

One day he suddenly encountered Maisie.

"Where have you come from?" she asked.

"Over there." He pointed eastward through the fog. "And you?"

"Oh, I'm in the north, across the Parks; I'm very busy."

"What do you do? Why, what's happened? You had three hundred a year."

"I have that still; I'm painting, that's all."

"Are you alone, then?"

"There's a girl living with me. Don't walk so fast, Dick; you are out of step."

A few days later he met Maisie in the Park again. She was greatly absorbed and dissatisfied with her work. Then he spoke to her of his own. He took her to a print shop and showed her some reproductions from his sketches. They stood together and listened to the quaint, graphic comments about these prints by some workmen.

Dick promised to help her, and she eagerly consented. But later, when Dick pleaded his deeper, personal interest in her, saying, "What's the use of worrying? Come to me instead, darling," she replied: "I've work to do, and I must do it."

"Do it with me, then, dear."

"No, I could not; it's my work—mine, mine, mine!"

"I beg your pardon, darling," once more came back from

Dick. But she insisted that there must be nothing between them.

"I don't wish you to go out of my life," she said, "now that you've just come back."

"It's your audacity in proposing to make use of me!" Dick retorted.

"Pooh! You are only Dick—and a print-shop!" said she.

"But, Maisie, you believe, don't you, that I love you?" still pleaded Dick.

"It's absurd, but I believe."

And so they parted once more, to meet the next Sunday at Maisie's rooms.

Torpenhow did not understand Dick's moodiness.

"Liver out of order?" he asked, as they sat smoking.

"Dick, is it a woman?" finally ventured Torpenhow.

Dick neglected work and spent from Sunday to Sunday marking time; for now, each week, he made his regular pilgrimage to Maisie's rooms. The one hindrance on these occasions was the red-haired girl who roomed with Maisie, and who silently watched Dick.

"I'll poison that red-haired girl on my wedding-day; she's unwholesome," he said to himself.

Dick planned to invite Maisie to a day's outing, when they would go to Fort Keeling, over the ground that they had trodden ten years before, when they were subjects of Mrs. Jennett's despotic rule. Maisie, weary and dejected about her work, surrendered, and the excursion was arranged for the next day.

"Where are we going, Dick?" Maisie asked.

"Wait and see."

Torpenhow and the Nilghai speculated, that day, about the absence of Dick.

"It isn't *a* woman, it's *one* woman, and it's a *girl*." Torpenhow was sure of this. The Nilghai conjectured that "perhaps it's only a *married* woman."

Meantime, Dick and Maisie were happy in their day at Fort Keeling. Dick pressed his love-plea again, in this old-time haunt, but Maisie begged him not to.

"I know perfectly well what you want, but I can't give it to you, Dick."

"Is that true, dear?" he asked.

"You've been very good to me, Dickie, and the only way I can pay you back is by speaking the truth. I daren't tell a fib."

All Dick's love-dreams seemed to dissolve in thin air. So now they talked of Maisie's art studies. Dick, in his honesty, could render them only faint praise.

"I used to run about, wondering at my own magnificence and getting ready to astonish the world," he told her. Then he talked of his Egyptian life, of the wonders and loneliness of dead cities, of uninhabited islands, of the stone gods and the deserted palaces. And oh, wouldn't she be his and go there with him? "Because I love you," he said.

"Suppose I said, take me to these places, and in time, perhaps, I might really care for you, what would you do?" said Maisie.

"Send you straight back where you came from, in a cab. No, I wouldn't, I'd let you walk."

When Dick reached home he found the Nilghai with Torpenhow. To these, in answer to their question where he had been, he was evasive. "He had been to the sea, to watch the ships go out, and to get a sniff of real sea air." But not a word of the one who was with him. To Torpenhow's banter about his having done no work for days, he could only answer that he "didn't feel that way."

Suddenly Dick left them for a few moments. Returning, he brought with him his great, clasped sketch-book, in which were fancy sketches of the Nilghai, represented as living a very unseemly career, such as matrimonial alliances with African princesses, betrayal of Arab wives, and various fabulous situations of the star correspondent's, whom the Nilghai did not love too much. Here, indeed, was material for Dick's retaliation on the Nilghai's "honest opinion" about Dick's pictures, published in the papers at the former's dictation.

Dick began to feel an impulse (since his love for Maisie was proving so fruitless) to seek "the old, hot, unregenerate life again; to take ship and know the sea once more."

"What is to hinder?" Torpenhow asked, in the long hush that followed their singing. "After all," Dick said to himself "the Honeymoon will be that tour. I didn't feel it so much when I was with Maisie; these damnable songs did it." When Dick went to Maisie's rooms again, he found she had outlined a fancy head and was going to Paris a month earlier than she had intended, that she might advise with her teacher, Kami. Kami had been Dick's teacher also.

"It will be a waste of time," he said; but Maisie was firm.

In a few days Maisie and the red-haired girl were to leave for Paris with the intention of returning in August (it was now February). As the day came for their departure, Dick went to Dover to bid farewell to Maisie on the pier.

"Only one kiss, Maisie," he pleaded. It was only one kiss, but it was a long one.

"Good-by, darling." But Maisie would not respond to his endearments.

"Will you write to me?"

"Yes, my poor Dick, what can I say?"

"How dared you take a kiss from him when he was nothing to you?" asked the red-haired girl.

When Dick returned, he found that Torpenhow had sheltered in his rooms a young girl who was starving. He had given her Dick's dinner, and she was lying on Torpenhow's sofa asleep. As Dick glanced at her, he remonstrated with his friend. When she awoke Dick looked at her searchingly, saw that her eyes had a peculiar expression that would be of service to him in his sketches, and arranged with her to be at his studio the following day, that he might draw her head and face. He had determined to paint a conception of "Melancholia," the subject that Maisie had gone to Paris to study. Bessie, his new model, sat day after day for him. She ingratiated herself into the good-will of the two men by many little devices, until one day Dick found her pleading with Torpenhow to take her into his service that she might live with him. Torpenhow would have yielded to her solicitations but for Dick, who persuaded him to take a run in the country and regain his tone.

"Never resist the devil; he holds the bank. Fly from him!" said Dick.

And now a strange thing happened to our hero as he sat at his work in his studio. A veil seemed to pass before his eyes. He rubbed them, but the gray haze would not go away. He consulted his physician, who sent him to an oculist, and an examination revealed the fact that the scar from his sword-cut, made years ago, had affected the optic nerve. With desperate courage he put the question: "What is my time-limit, avoiding all strain and worry?"

"Perhaps one year."

"My God! And if I don't take care of myself?"

"I really could not say."

"You have been very good in telling me the truth. Without any warning—without any warning!" said Dick. The blow was hard to bear, for his life-work was before him. "What can I do now, before the light goes?" he cried.

He awoke the next morning, and remembered. He stirred Bessie into unwonted rage, that he might watch the flash of her eyes. He was possessed with the "Melancholia." All other visions faded out of mind. He visited the sideboard frequently, alas! drinking his grief away. Torpenhow had been away six weeks. A brief line announced his early return.

"News! Good news!" he wrote. "Back on Thursday."

The Nilghai was with him. When they came, Bessie met Torpenhow on the stairs and said, in whispers:

"Drinking like a fish. Has been at it nearly a month."

Dick welcomed them to the studio. He was but a shadow of his former self; haggard, nervous, and unshaven.

"I cannot see much, but I can see best when I am drunk," he said to Torpenhow. "I have work to do before I become blind."

In the afternoon of the third day after Torpenhow's return, he heard Dick calling for him.

"All finished!" he shouted. "I've been down to hell to get her; but isn't she worth it?"

Dick had finished the "Melancholia," a full-lipped, haggard-eyed woman.

Torpenhow exclaimed: "What eyes! what insolence!"

When the final touches were given to his canvas, Dick sank to sleep in his easy chair. Bessie was in the room, and now made one last, unsuccessful attempt to capture Torpenhow. Failing in this, she still remained while Torpenhow, as Dick had requested, paid her for her services, and then himself left the studio.

Bessie, remaining there, determined to have revenge on Dick for his interference with her designs on Torpenhow. She emptied the bottle of turpentine on a duster, and began viciously to scrub the face of the "Melancholia." The paint did not smudge quickly enough, so she took a palette-knife and scraped, following each stroke with the wet duster. In five minutes the picture was a formless, scarred muddle of colors. Then she fled.

Dick did not wake until late in the evening. Torpenhow urged him to go to bed, and as he went, his friend raised the cloth on the picture, saw the vandalism, and knew who had done it. Dick could not sleep, with the delirium of drink in his veins; his eyes were afire and his brain was wild. Then came the discovery that he had already become blind. Torpenhow quieted him as best he could, letting him hold his hand until sleep came at last. In the morning he was delirious, and through his ravings Torpenhow was informed of Maisie and of every detail.

Dick realized his loss of sight at every turn. Three letters came from Maisie, but as no replies were returned she at last was silent. Torpenhow coaxed him out, walking with him in the park. The Nilghai and the Keneu, the Great War Eagle, were in Torpenhow's rooms when he returned, to urge him to go with them and leave Dick to his fate. Torpenhow demurred; he would resign and be faithful to his new charge. Then he recounted to them the disclosures by Dick, made in his delirium, concerning his relations with this girl, Maisie. Finally Torpenhow determined to search her out, acquaint her with Dick's misfortune, and advise her to unite her life with her lover's.

He set out at once, and the two war-friends were to make his rooms their headquarters during his absence, where would gather the clan of war-correspondents, preparatory to the new campaign. Dick heard the voice of Cassavetti, an old Soudan comrade, as he mounted the stairs; and he sprang to his feet.

"There's a row somewhere, and I'm not in it!" he exclaimed. He stole to Torpenhow's door and entered. He could feel that it was full of men.

"Where's the trouble?" said he. "In the Balkans at last? Why didn't someone tell me?" Then he sat and listened.

"But what's become of Torpenhow?" he asked.

"Torp's in abeyance just now; he's off love-making somewhere, I suppose," said the Nilghai.

"He said he was going to stay at home," said the Keneu.

"Is he?" said Dick, with an oath. "He won't. He stay behind, indeed! Shall I see Torp before he goes?"

"Oh, yes, you'll see him."

Maisie was gazing from her window at Vitry-sur-Marne, on a moonlight night, and saying to herself: "I think—I think—but he ought to have written."

Torpenhow reached Vitry-sur-Marne, and the next morning Maisie was hurrying across the street when he met her.

"I beg your pardon," said he. "It seems an absurd question to ask, but the fact is that I don't know her by any other name. Is there a young lady here that is called Maisie?"

"I am Maisie."

"My name is Torpenhow. Dick Heldar is my best friend, and—and—the fact is that he has become blind."

"Blind!"

"He has been stone blind for nearly two months."

"No! No! Not blind! I won't have him blind!"

"Would you care to see for yourself?"

"Now—at once?"

"Oh, no! The Paris train doesn't go through the place till eight to-night."

"Did Mr. Heldar send you to me?"

"Certainly not. He sits in his studio, turning over some letters that he can't read because he's blind."

"My Dick blind!"

"What! You going to him?" said the red-haired girl, when Maisie had returned to her room.

"I must think."

"Think! If you don't go, I shall."

Torpenhow hardly spoke to Maisie during the journey to Calais. When on the steamer, however, he told her the story of Dick's blindness. When they went to Dick's apartment, Torpenhow led her up to a closed door, opened it softly, and left her there. Three envelopes were in Dick's hand; he put them aside.

"Hullo, Torp! Is that you? I've been so lonely!"

Maisie entered. She hesitated. Dick stared at her, and then she saw that he was blind.

"Torp, is that you?" he called again.

"No, it's only me," was the hushed answer.

This, then, was Dick! He started from his chair and groped his way to her, guided by her breathing. Reaching her, he sobbed: "It's Maisie!"

"I came—to see you, please."

He went back to his chair, saying: "I am down and done for. Let me alone."

Maisie sank on a chair, with her face in her hands.

"I can't, I can't! Oh, Dickie, I am so sorry! You wouldn't ask me, would you?"

"And now you've come and seen, I'm immensely grateful."

"Perhaps I could come and see you sometimes?" she sobbed.

"It would be kindest not," he replied.

"I'll go, Dick. Oh, I am so miserable!"

"Wait a moment, dear; I have something to give you first, it's my 'Melancholia.' She was a beauty when I last saw her. There she is. What do you think of her?"

Maisie had an insane desire to laugh; and yet her voice was subdued.

"Oh, Dick, it is good!"

"Won't you have it, then? I'll send it over to your house if you will."

"Oh, yes, thank you." And then, trembling, she hastened from the room, called a cab, and went to her house across the parks. She remembered that Dick had not asked her, and she scorned herself!

Dick doubly felt his misery now. "It's all I had, and I've lost it; Torp will think that he has been so infernally clever."

"Hullo," said Torp, entering after Dick had had two hours by himself. "Are you feeling any better?"

"How in the world did you find it all out?" said Dick.

"You shouldn't go off your head if you wish to keep secrets, Dickie."

That night there was a crowd again up-stairs.

"Come out and frolic," said the Nilghai. But no, he could

not. Then he went to bed, and Torpenhow came in the morning and told him he had engaged to go, in two days, to Brindisi.

"Will you get a hundred pounds cashed for me before you leave?" asked Dick.

"That's a slender amount for housekeeping, isn't it?"

"Oh, it's only for marriage expenses," said Dick, who thought he must deceive his old friend.

The next day Torpenhow bade him good-by, leaving him alone in desolation, not knowing.

Torpenhow had been gone for some time, and Dick had settled down to helpless despair. He was speculating on the possibilities of fifty years more of life, when Alf, son of the janitor, entered.

"There's a letter for you," he said. "Perhaps you would like me to read it?"

"Read it, then," Dick said; and Alf began in his school-boy fashion:

> "I could have given you love; I could have given you loyalty such as you never dreamed of. Do you suppose I cared what you were? But you chose to whistle everything down the wind for nothing. My only excuse for you is that you are so young."

"That's all," he said, returning the paper to be dropped into the fire. Dick had forgotten when or how he had put himself in the way of winning these trifles of love and loyalty from the hand of any woman. Later Beeton, the janitor, came to give him some fresh air and exercise. They walked down by the waterside. Beeton was describing the scene to Dick, when suddenly they came face to face with Bessie. She hesitated, and looked at Dick, to whom Beeton had made known her presence, and then they spoke to each other. Dick's welcome was cordial, and she became reassured. Beeton left them, to do his marketing, and Dick, discovering that he had gone, asked Bessie to help him home. They went to his rooms, where Bessie, discovering dust and disorder, began to apply the remedy. Dick called for tea and muffins, and Bessie gave the order to Mrs. Beeton with a flourish. The greetings and good-nature between Dick and Bessie served to establish an intimacy between them. Bessie advised Dick to be shaved, and have a new suit in place of the slovenly one he was wearing. She promised to return the next day and put everything in order. She kept her promise, and had considered whether it would not be advantageous to enter into service with one so helpless as Dick. She finally spoke to him about it, and his extreme loneliness added to his appreciation of her solicitude. A woman's hearty greeting, in the midst of his despair, revived his spirits, and Bessie, not to be outdone, met him with such inviting intimacy that he was led to more than friendly advances. Then she felt impelled to confess to him how, in a paroxysm of anger, she had destroyed his picture.

This produced in Dick a revulsion of feeling that, though partly concealed, led him to abandon the contemplated compact with Bessie, and, in his intensified despondency, to conceive in its place a desperate adventure. He first induced her to go with him to the bank, where he drew out ample funds for the fulfilment of his new plan, and he then procured tickets for an ocean voyage. Returning to his rooms, he dismissed her with the stipulation that she should return again Thursday morning (it was now Tuesday) to pilot him to the steamer at Gallon's Station. When she was gone he sent for Beeton; haggled with him about the worth of the furnishings in his rooms, at last to close a bargain with him for a hundred pounds; drew up his will, leaving all his possessions to Maisie; had it witnessed and sealed; burned all his remaining letters and papers in the studio fire, and then sat down before the stove until the flames died out. Thursday came; Bessie was there, and they hastened to the steamer.

"Good-by, Bess; I promised you fifty; here's a hundred, all that I got for my furniture from Beeton."

Bessie was in Dick's cabin, where he finally bade her farewell with a kiss, and lay down in his berth until the decks were cleared. Before sailing he made free-handed arrangements with the head-steward for the voyage; then, surrendering himself to the rest he needed, he fell asleep and did not awake until the steamer had passed the mouth of the Thames. He made friends with the doctor, smoking with him far into the nights, and so won the latter's good-will that he promised a few hours with him after they should reach Port Said. When they arrived there he induced the doctor to take him to Madame Binat's.

"Whew!" said the doctor, "I suppose you know that there they will rob you to begin with, and knife you later."

"Not they. Take me there, and I will look after myself."

Madame Binat received Dick with unwonted kindness when she discovered his blindness, and treated him with that generous fidelity which even the heart of a hard woman may experience. She, the keeper of one of the most notorious resorts at the Port, claimed the privilege of being his protector.

"Do not think any longer. I know, and it is for me to think. Thou shalt go to see thy friend."

She procured him a guide, and by morning had all arrangements made. She brought him his chocolate before he had risen, kissing him a good-morning between the eyes.

"I shall expect Torp to kiss me next," he protested.

Six days the voyage to Suakim lasted, and thence to the camp at Tanai an iron train conveyed them.

"An armored train; better and better!"

"They begin to shoot not far from the city," the guide explained.

"The dears! they always used to!"

The bullets from the children of the desert rained on the iron cars, and the machine guns answered back.

"Give 'em hell, man! Oh, give 'em hell!" Dick cried.

When they arrived Torpenhow was on the firing-line, far ahead, so a night of peril on a camel, with a treacherous camel-driver, was before Dick. He found George, his guide, and ordered him to take him to make his bargain. The night was dark, the children of the desert in hiding on the route; but go to Torpenhow he must and would; so he conceded the extortion of fifty pounds English money as the price. But the camel must be a Bisharin. The bargain completed, he overheard the sheik talking in low tones to the driver, and the latter's reply: "A little way out only; any baggage-beast will serve. Am I a fool to waste my cattle for a blind man?"

"And though I cannot see," Dick lifted his voice, "yet I carry that which has six eyes, and the driver will sit before me."

Dick felt the cheek of the camel; his hand passed over the

hide, and found the branded half-circle which is the mark of the Bisharin.

"Cut this one loose," he ordered. "Remember, no blessing of God comes on those who try to cheat the blind."

Outside the camp they mounted, driver first.

"Go on!" Dick called out.

The driver turned to see whether there was any chance of procuring the revolver and ending the ride.

"Remember it will be life or death to thee," said Dick.

They rode on until, at last, they noted the change of air.

"I smell the dawn!" Dick whispered.

"It is here; and yonder are the troops. Have I done well?" the driver asked.

Two or three shots were heard.

"It's from the desert," said the driver. "Well it is that the dawn didn't uncover us an hour ago."

The camel hastened forward toward the column; the shots were behind.

"What luck! What stupendous, imperial luck!" said Dick. "Oh, God has been good to me!"

"We are in," said the man, as he drove into the rear-guard, and the camel knelt.

"Torpenhow! Coo-ee, Torp-en-how!"

Torpenhow saw the gray hair on Dick's temples, and that the face was that of an old man.

"Come down, you damn fool of a Dickie! Come off!"

Torpenhow was at his side, and Dick came falling at the feet of his friend. His luck followed him even to the end, with a kindly bullet through the head.

Torpenhow held Dick's body in his arms.

CAPTAINS COURAGEOUS (1897)

This is one of the works that resulted from Kipling's residence in the United States. It is a tale of Gloucester fishermen and the cod-fishing industry under present conditions, for there has been no important change since the author saw these operations for himself in 1896. With his characteristic thoroughness, he went to Gloucester and shipped aboard a schooner bound for the Banks, studying his subject in every detail at close range. The story was designed for boys, but it has found quite as much favor with grown-ups as any of Kipling's longer works.

HERE was one subject on which the smoking-room passengers were substantially agreed: dislike of Harvey Cheyne. Such an annoyance as he was—a boy, not quite sixteen, aping the mannerisms of a man, and not a very likable man at that; taking his first trip to Europe, tyrannizing over his mother, flaunting his father's incalculable wealth in everybody's face; an insolent boy, if ever there was one, who needed a right smart hiding. At all events, such was about the way one unpolished passenger put it, and no voice was raised to mitigate the severity of the boy's hypothetical sentence. His offensiveness was at a climax when the big liner was crossing the Banks, though it may have been that the dreary, wet fog had something to do with making him seem more objectionable than usual; and it probably was with the idea of handing him some sort of punishment that one of the men gave the youngster a particularly black cigar. Harvey took it boldly, and for a minute or two commented favorably on its rich flavor. Then there was that within him which said that he would cut a better figure out of sight of the presumably unsympathetic smoking-room contingent; and he staggered as far aft as he could go. While he was communing with the sea over the rail of the turtle-back, dizzy, unstable as the element he traveled on, a sizable wave reached up a soggy arm and pulled him overboard.

When he awoke, Harvey was lying on the bottom of a small boat in which stood a strange-looking man blowing a conch-shell. The boy had a miserable idea that he was dead, and that this man was his keeper, but he of the conch-shell assured him cheerfully to the contrary.

"Your boat almost catch me," he said, "but I blow my horn and she yaw a little. Then you come dreeft, dreeft, and I take you like big fish. Good job, what?"

"Where are we?" asked Harvey.

"In the dory. My name Manuel. I live to Gloucester. I belong to schooner *We're Here*."

Information enough, according to the Portuguese fisherman's lights, to satisfy the most exacting, but it meant nothing to Harvey who was indifferent, even after he had been lifted aboard a larger boat and lowered into a dark hole where men took off his clothes and gave him hot drink. After that he slept for nearly twenty-four hours. On his next awakening he saw across the tiny cabin a boy of about his own age, dressed in blue sweater and oilskins, who addressed him with cordial familiarity and told him more specifically where he was.

The schooner *We're Here*, Captain Disko Troop, had but recently come to the Banks from Gloucester. Manuel, who had saved Harvey's life, was one of the crew; others were Long Jack, Tom Platt, both seafaring men with long records, Uncle Salters and old Penn, farmers who had been fishing of late years for their health, the cook, a negro from the provinces who spoke Gaelic, and Dan, the captain's son. They expected to stay on the Banks until September, about three months away. "And it's a good job you come aboard," Dan concluded, "for we lost a boy a few days ago, and you can take his place. Dad's waiting to talk to you about it."

"Tell him to come down here," said Harvey shortly.

Dan's eyes opened in astonishment. Then he looked quietly amused and shouted through the forecastle hatch: "Dad, he says you can come down and see him, if you want to. Hear?"

Dan's father heard and replied to the effect that fooling was not to his taste; and Harvey Cheyne, who could not remember when he had taken an order from anybody, heard something in the man's deep voice that advised him to waive ceremony and go on deck. He found Captain Troop ready enough to listen to him, and he told his name, explained who his father was, and demanded to be set ashore at once. "You can put in at New York," he said loftily. "It will be worth your while."

"Haow?" asked Troop thoughtfully.

"In money," Harvey answered. "My father will pay you twice over the worth of this dirty little ship," and, as he spoke, he felt in his pockets for his own money. This was an almost instinctive movement on his part. The habit of commanding whatever he wanted with money was on him, and if he had been given to thinking he would have thought that the display of money at this moment would go a long way toward persuading the Captain to give up cod-fishing for the passenger trade. But Harvey's pockets were empty. "I've been robbed!" he cried.

"Hm," murmured Captain Troop; "haow much did ye have?"

"A hundred and thirty-four dollars," said Harvey. "'Twas part of my monthly allowance."

There were many other influences against the lad, but that remark really settled everything. One hundred and thirty-four dollars! In a boy's pocket! "Part" of his monthly allowance! It was so preposterous, from the Gloucester point of view, and made so unspeakably worse by Harvey's sticking to it, that nothing he said thereafter was thought worthy of the slightest attention. As they were kind-hearted men aboard the *We're Here*, they put him down as more lunatic than liar. They really believed that his experience in the ocean had turned his head. Troop talked patiently with the angry boy, and overlooked many an insulting reference to the schooner; but when for the third or fourth time Harvey accused the crew of robbing him, the Captain gave him one calm blow in the face that sent him, with a bleeding nose, into the scuppers.

"Be gentle with him, Dan," said the skipper, "or I'll give you twicet what I give him. He ain't responsible, poor feller. Help him sluice off that land blood, and he'll feel better."

Dan was full of gentleness and good advice. "It just don't pay to crisscross the old man," he said. "He knocked me down oncet, only oncet though, for that was enough. But Dad's all right. He's a mighty just man; everybody in the fleet says so."

Harvey was tearfully inclined to dispute the skipper's justness, and the boys had a bit of an argument in which Dan, doubtless because he was a boy, was more convincing than his father had been. He was a little inclined to believe Harvey's stories of his father's wealth, but he advised strongly that nothing more be said about it, for the men would certainly be incredulous, which would make things worse for the newcomer; and the end of it was that Harvey, having stanched the flow of shore blood, began to see that he had not acted very considerately toward the men who had saved his life. He did not stop to think this over, but went below at once and apologized to the Captain. The stammering difficulty with which the apology came out was proof of its sincerity; and Troop forgave him with great heartiness, after which Harvey was set to work.

Not only had Harvey never done a stroke of work before, but it never had occurred to him that he could or ought to work; but, somehow, it did not occur to him at this time that he should refuse. You may say that the skipper's blow really did knock the uselessness out of him; but you may also observe that he had as a companion an eager, enthusiastic boy who went at his task, however much he might dislike it, with a vim that could not but arouse emulation. Furthermore, there was no small detail of the schooner, from jib-halyard to keel, that was not new to Harvey, and stimulative to curiosity; things that Dan did as of second nature, Harvey could not do at all, which was stimulative of wholesome shame and desire to learn. And so it came about that when the dories returned fish-laden shortly after peace had been made with the Captain, Harvey went to work, blunderingly but energetically, did what he was told with growing pride as he saw that what he did was effective to the purpose designed, and so came to the plain but bountiful supper-table with such an appetite as he never had known before.

Thus began a long series of fog-drenched days, most of which were all work and no play. Harvey learned to obey orders on the run, not at a walk. When lack of other duties permitted, Long Jack drove him from stem to stern, teaching him the names of things and basting him with a rope's end when he miscalled them. Sometimes the catch was so heavy that he fell asleep at his work, and there was no rope's end for that; seasoned veterans who have harvested the Banks for a lifetime occasionally fall asleep at their work, which means merely that they have worked to the limits of their endurance, and the roughest skipper knows that no man can do more. But there were days when all was idleness; when the winds kicked up the smoking waves to such a fury that the dories could not go out. Then there were hours of music and stories in the tiny cabin; songs that fairly dripped brine, tales that shuddered with the rattle of dead men's bones, and shivered with the rising of misty wraiths from the troubled deep. Again there were days when Dan and Harvey were permitted to go out in a dory by themselves; and on the very first of these days Harvey caught a hundred-pound halibut. Is there any wonder that he did not sorrow much for his mother? Of course he felt sorry for her, but what could he do but work, and play, and revel in this thrilling, venturesome, unexpected life?

From time to time the men made sly remarks about the extravagances of wealth, but Harvey soon learned not to take the bait. He did tell them stories of youngsters who had ponies and carriages of their own, who went to dances where they paid more than a season's wages for flowers, and all that sort of thing; but the hero of these marvelous tales was always somebody he had known slightly, never himself. Thus he escaped derision and gained some measure of credibility. He had learned not only the rudiments of seafaring, but he had learned also to respect these uncouth men who toiled with him. Captain Troop had made him a member of the crew at ten dollars and a half a month, the wages earned by the boy who had been drowned just before his advent to the *We're Here*, and though Harvey at first scorned the wages, simply as wages, and soon regarded the amount with quiet amusement, he eventually discovered that he must work not only hard but skilfully to be worth even the slight cost of his food; and after that wholesome discovery his wages appeared to him as a very respectable matter; and he strove with all the might that was in him to deserve them.

A summer on the Banks could not well pass without its adventures, and Harvey had his share. There was the sailor who died aboard a French schooner. The vessel was sailed to a spot some miles from the ground where the fleet was anchored, and Harvey watched the burial through Troop's telescope. A few days later Harvey and Dan were fishing in a dory, miles, as they believed, from the spot where the burial took place. Harvey thought he had hooked another giant halibut. He drew the dead Frenchman to the surface. The tide may have moved the body, or the boys may have mistaken their bearings in the dense fog that prevailed; but the crew of the *We're Here* would have it that the dead man was following them; and that night the black cook set a lighted candle on a bit of wood and launched it over the rail to keep the uneasy corpse away.

On another occasion Dan and Harvey crept out of their bunks at four in the morning to hook fried pies from the cook's stores. They could have had the pies for the asking at any time; but theft made them taste better, and it also made the cook mad, which was quite as great a consideration. They found Troop ringing the bell incessantly, for, as was usually the case, the sun was rising somewhere behind a fog. The Captain gave the bell to Harvey, told him to keep it going, and went below. Far away the boys heard the dismal, warning note of a liner's whistle, and Harvey's memory went back to the time when he was aboard such a boat, with a room and bath to himself, with breakfast at a late hour in an elegant dining-room where the bill of fare was printed on gilt-edged paper. It hardly seemed to him that he was the same boy now, ringing a bell at sunrise, clad in crackling oilskins, munching fried pies, and, inexplicable fact, enjoying himself. The bass groan of the liner came nearer and nearer. How ghastly it was that comfortable people on board her might eat their breakfast a bit later without consciousness that their vessel had smashed a schooner and massacred its crew! Harvey rang with desperate energy. Was it possible that his little tinkle-tinkle could be heard over this immeasurable expanse of white mist?

"Gorry! she's a big one," said Dan, after one of the booming groans from the steamer, and he went to blowing furiously on a conch-shell. The bell tinkled, the shell wheezed, the liner roared; then, of a sudden, Harvey saw a thirty-foot wall apparently falling on him at the rate of twenty miles an hour; brass-rimmed port-holes hurried past; a puff of steam heated his helpless hands; a stream of water rushed along the rail of the *We're*

Here; and the schooner staggered like a drunken man on screw-tossed waves. There was a faint crash somewhere in the fog, and a voice cried: "Heave to! You've sunk us!"

In that instant Harvey was ready to believe that it was the *We're Here* that had been cut down; but there was Troop scrambling from the cabin and bellowing orders as he had never yet bellowed; there was such a sudden changing of the course of the schooner that Harvey was thrown to the deck; all the crew got away in the dories except old Penn, the cook, and himself. The liner went out of sight as quickly as she came into it, and it was fishermen only who searched the gray sea for survivors. While the three were waiting on the schooner, a blue jersey containing part of a man drifted past.

When the dories came back they brought one man, a Gloucester man, captain of the wrecked schooner. He cursed Troop for saving him, and would have leaped into the sea if they had not forcibly restrained him. His boat, which was his fortune, had gone down, and so had his son, who was his life. Then came the strangest adventure of the whole summer. Old Penn had been a Moravian minister, but since the Johnstown flood, in which he had lost his wife and all his children, he had been demented. He knew nothing of his past, could not tell his real name, and was the helpless but useful ward of Uncle Salter, the farmer, who took to seafaring in the hope that his hapless friend's health might be improved by it. In the presence of this disaster, with its cursing, maddened survivor, Penn's past came back, and he was again the minister of God. He knew not his recent companions, knew not where he was; but he did not ask, for the emergency called for action. With the voice of command that speaks from absolute faith, Penn addressed himself to the stricken captain of the lost schooner.

"The Lord gave, and the Lord hath taken away," said old Penn. "Come! come with me!" And the survivor, bewildered with his sorrow, followed the old man into the cabin.

They were there together for an hour or more, and the men on deck frequently heard old Penn's voice raised in prayer. When at length the former minister came up, his face was covered with perspiration, and there was an anxious look in his eyes.

"How long have I been mad?" he asked. He could now

attend to his own affairs, for the unhappy man below had been brought to view his hard situation calmly; there was no longer danger of suicide. His companions found it difficult to answer Penn's questions; and they were spared any immediate necessity by the approach of another schooner with a hail that demanded all attention; for that schooner had picked up the son whose supposed loss had brought the *We're Here's* survivor to the verge of madness. The father went to join his son on the other boat, and by the time the excitement incident to that episode had subsided, poor old Penn had slipped back to his customary imbecility.

The *We're Here* was the first of the fleet to get a full load that season; and it was a proud crew that sailed into Gloucester one evening in September. Harvey telegraphed the news of his existence and whereabouts to his father in California as soon as he could make land, and on the following day he showed the answer secretly to Dan. It confirmed the wild stories that Harvey had told when he knew no better than to boast of wealth, but the boys would not disclose the facts as yet. They held themselves in until Mr. Cheyne could arrive in his private car that came most of the way across the continent as a special train. Then, when Mr. and Mrs. Cheyne saw their son again, and went to the dock to look over the schooner that had been his home for three months, Gloucester had as fine a surprise as ever visited the ancient town; and the boys felt as if they had put it up.

Mr. Cheyne, as his son had boasted, would willingly have paid Captain Troop twice and more the value of the schooner for bringing Harvey to land, but the millionaire was a keen judge of men, and he saw that an offer of money would be unspeakably offensive to such men as Troop and his crew. Reward he did give, however, in the shape of making a place for Dan on his line of great boats in the Pacific tea-trade; and Mrs. Cheyne, who insisted on giving money to somebody, was persuaded to reward the crew vicariously; that is, she filled the treasuries of orphans' homes, widows' retreats, and placed a large sum in the hands of the priest at whose church Manuel, the Portuguese, attended.

Harvey's father saw that the experience had done for his son what his previous education had failed to do. Further, it brought father and son closer together; and after several intimate talks about it, Harvey consented to forego further seafaring for as long as it would take him to go through college. They struck a bargain about it. The boy was to take a college course in all earnestness, and if he did well his father was to make over to him on his graduation the line of Pacific tea-steamers.

The indications were, just before Harvey was graduated from Leland Stanford, that he would presently be the owner of the line, and that Dan Troop would be one of his captains.

THE JUNGLE BOOK (1894)

Most of the natives of India are nature-worshipers, and they are quite as fond as "Uncle Remus" of putting speech into the mouths of all members of the animal kingdom. Their folk-lore abounds in tales of the relations of the animals to one another regarding the principal interest of the animal kingdom, which is food. One of their favorite characters is a man-child who strayed from his parents and was saved from starvation by the maternal care of a wolf. This incident, and stories based thereon, made its way into the traditions of almost every European nation, beginning, perhaps, with the Roman account of Romulus and Remus.

T was late evening in the Seeonee Hills, in India, and Father Wolf woke from his day-long nap and was about to go out for food for Mother Wolf and their four children, when he heard the angry snarl of a tiger that had missed his prey. Father Wolf knew whose snarl it was, for word had come that the great Shere Khan, a lame tiger whose proper hunting-ground was twenty miles away, had come to the Seeonee Hills in defiance of the ancient rule known to all beasts as The Law of the Jungle. The noises uttered by Shere Khan before and after his snarl told Father Wolf distinctly that the tiger had jumped at something near the fire of a woodcutter's camp, and had burned his feet. Mother Wolf, who also was listening, exclaimed:

"Something is coming up the hill! Get ready!"

Father Wolf crouched, sprang, but paused in mid-air and landed on almost the very spot where he left ground, for in front of him stood a naked brown baby, who could just walk —a soft and dimpled little thing that looked up into Father Wolf's face and laughed.

"Is that a man's cub?" Mother Wolf asked. "I never have seen one. Bring it here. How little, and—how bold!"

The baby pushed his way between the cubs and close to the

mother's warm skin. "Ahai! He is taking his meal with the others!"

Suddenly Shere Khan's great head, thrust into the entrance, blocked the moonlight out of the cave. Father Wolf asked angrily:

"What does Shere Khan need?"

"My quarry! A man's cub went this way. Give it to me!"

"The wolves take orders from the Head of the Pack," said Father Wolf, "and not from any striped cattle-stealer."

Shere Khan could not get his great body through the entrance, but his roar filled the cave with thunder. Mother Wolf sprang forward, her eyes like two green moons in the darkness, and she snarled:

"And it is I, Raksha (the Demon) that answers. The man-cub is mine! He shall not be killed. He shall live to hunt with the Pack. And in the end, look you, hunter of little naked cubs, he shall hunt thee. Go!"

Shere Khan could not stand against Mother Wolf, who had all the advantage of the ground, so he backed away growling and shouted:

"We will see what the Pack will say to this fostering of man-cubs! The cub is mine, and to my teeth he will come in the end, O bush-tailed thieves!"

The Law of the Jungle declares that when wolf-cubs are old enough to stand on their feet their father must bring them to the Pack Council, held at full moon, in order that the other wolves may identify them. After that inspection they are free to run where they please, and until they have killed their first buck no excuse is accepted if a grown wolf kills one of them. The punishment is death, if the murderer can be found.

So when his cubs could run a little Father Wolf took them to the Pack Meeting at the Council Rock, and Mother Wolf went with him, followed by the man-cub, whom she had named Mowgli (The Frog). Akela, the great gray lone wolf who was leader of the Pack, because of his cunning, lay at full length on the Rock, and before him sat wolves of every size and color. The cubs tumbled over one another in the circle formed by their parents, and the grown wolves looked them over carefully, while Akela from his rock cried loud and often:

"Ye know the Law! Ye know the Law! Look well, O Wolves!" And the anxious mothers took up the call: "Look! look well, O Wolves!"

When Father Wolf pushed Mowgli into the circle, Mother Wolf's neck-bristles stiffened, for from behind the rock came the voice of Shere Khan, crying:

"The cub is mine! Give him to me! What have the Free People to do with a man's cub?"

"Look well, O Wolves!" Akela repeated. "What have the Free People to do with the orders of any save the Free People?" But a young wolf asked:

"What have the Free People to do with a man's cub?"

The Law of the Jungle declares that if there is any dispute as to the right of a cub to be accepted by the Pack, he must be spoken for by at least two members of the Pack who are not his mother and father. As no wolf spoke, Mother Wolf got ready for what must be her last fight, if it came to fighting. Suddenly old Baloo, the brown bear that teaches the wolf cubs the Law of the Jungle, said:

"*I* speak for the man's cub. Let him run with the Pack. I will teach him."

"We need yet another," said Akela. "Who speaks besides Baloo?"

Bagheera, the Black Panther, dropped like a shadow into the circle. Everybody knew Bagheera and no one cared to cross his path, although he had a voice as soft as wild honey dropping from a tree, and a skin like down.

"O Akela, and ye the Free People," he purred, "the Law of the Jungle says that if there is a doubt in regard to a new cub he may be bought with a price. Now, to Baloo's word I will add one bull, and a fat one, newly killed, not more than half a mile from here, if ye will accept the man's cub according to the Law."

"Let him run with the Pack! Where is the bull, Bagheera?" clamored scores of voices. Shere Khan roared for rage and disappointment, and Bagheera said, under his whiskers: "Ay, roar well, for the time comes when this naked thing will make thee roar another tune, or I know not Man."

So Mowgli was entered in the Pack, and Father Wolf taught

him his business, and the meaning of many things in the Jungle. Every rustle in the grass, every breath of the warm night air, every note of the owls above his head, every scratch of a bat's claws, every splash of a fish meant as much to him as the work of his office means to a business man. Bagheera taught him to climb, which none of his wolf-brothers could do, and showed him at the Council Rock that, being a man's cub, he could make any wolf drop his eyes by staring at him. Baloo was delighted to have so clever a pupil, for young wolves cared to learn only as much of the Law as applied to their own Pack and tribe; usually they ran away from Baloo as soon as they had learned the Hunting Verse: "Feet that make no noise, eyes that see in the dark, ears that can hear the winds in their lairs, and sharp white teeth." Baloo taught him the Wood and Water Laws: how to tell a rotten branch from a sound one; how to speak politely to the wild bees when he came upon a hive of them fifty feet above ground; what to say to Mang, the Bat, when he chanced to disturb him in the branches at midday; and how to warn the water-snakes in the pools when he splashed down among them. Then, too, Mowgli was taught the Stranger's Hunting Call, which must be repeated aloud until it is answered whenever one hunts outside of his own Pack's grounds; it means, translated, "Give me leave to hunt here, because I am hungry," and the answer is, "Hunt, then, for food, but not for pleasure." Baloo also taught him the Master Words of the Jungle, begging them from Hathi the Elephant, who knows all about these things. So now Mowgli was safe from accidents in the Jungle, because neither beast, bird, nor reptile would hurt him.

But the man's cub chanced upon bad company; he met the Bandar Log, the Monkey People, who do not hunt, and of whom Baloo could teach him nothing, for they had no law, no true language, no sense, no shame; they were mere outcasts. These disreputable creatures promised Mowgli that he should have a tribe of his own and be a leader, and one day they stole him and carried him away, over their own roads through the tree-tops, far above the ground, to their home in the Cold Lairs—the ruins of an ancient city.

Mowgli quickly thought it time to send word to Baloo and Bagheera; so when he saw Rann, the Kite, sailing overhead he gave the Kite Call for "We be of one blood, you and I," which is the password between all creatures that hunt. "Mark my trail!" he shouted. "Tell Baloo of the Seeonee Pack and Bagheera of the Council Rock."

"In whose name, Brother?"

"Mowgli, the Frog. Man-cub, they call me. Mark my trail!"

Baloo and Bagheera had seen the monkeys bear Mowgli away, but as neither could dash across the tree-tops in pursuit they raged until Bagheera bethought him of Kaa, the Rock Python, a mighty hunter, who could climb trees and was so feared by the monkeys that the mere whisper of his name made their wicked tails turn cold. They found him stretched on a warm ledge in the sun, admiring his splendid new coat, for he had just shed his skin. The three greeted one another by name and exchanged salutations. Kaa had heard of a creature known as the man-cub, and when he learned that the monkeys had stolen him and had also used most insulting language regarding himself he was quite willing to join in the chase, especially as he had not eaten for days and his capacity for monkeys was great. But where were the wretches? Suddenly Rann, the Kite, hailed Baloo and told him where the monkeys lived; he had told Mang, the Bat, to watch them in the night and report any change of base.

The Cold Lairs were far away, but Bagheera set out at the rocking panther-canter, and Baloo lumbered heavily behind, and Kaa seemed to pour himself along the ground, finding the shortest way with his never-winking eyes.

The night was not yet half gone, but Mowgli had seen and heard enough of monkey-life. His captors dropped him over a high wall into a family of cobras, who spared him when he assured them in cobra language: "We be of one blood, you and I." He was hungry and sounded the Hunting Call; no one responded, but soon he heard the familiar grunt of his friend Bagheera, who dashed into the circle of monkeys and began slaying right and left. Then he heard the rumbling war-shout of old Baloo, but the monkeys were hundreds to one against each of the big beasts, who soon were lacerated cruelly by myriads of sharp claws. Mang, the Bat, carried the news of the battle throughout the Jungle, and Hathi the Elephant trumpeted, and the noise of the fighting roused all the day-birds for miles around. Bagheera became so exhausted that he sounded the Snake Call for help, and Kaa responded by using his head as a battering-ram against the mass of monkeys. One blow sufficed, for the monkeys shouted:

"Kaa! It is Kaa! Run! Run!"

But none dared to look Kaa in the face; none dared to disobey his commands; so when Kaa hissed, the monkeys stopped running and began to whine. The Python shouted, "Where is the manling?" and Mowgli replied; a blow of Kaa's head knocked down the wall, and Mowgli leaped through the opening and flung himself between Baloo and Bagheera, an arm round each big neck. Baloo said:

"Here is Kaa, to whom we owe the battle and thou owest thy life. Thank him according to our custom, Mowgli."

Mowgli expressed his gratitude so prettily that Kaa was moved to caress him, but said:

"Now go hence quickly with thy friends, for what follows it is not well that thou shouldst see." For Kaa was about to dine.

As the years rolled on, old Akela, the leader of the Pack and always Mowgli's friend, began to weaken. Soon he must miss his kill, after which he must himself be killed. And the Pack had learned to hate Mowgli, for he was wiser than they and he might succeed Akela as leader. Shere Khan never had ceased to demand him, and the wolves that hated him began to side with the tiger. Bagheera, who was old and wise and had been a captive among men before he knew how to strike for liberty, warned Mowgli of the impending danger and advised him to go to the villages and get the Red Flower—fire, of which all animals are afraid.

Mowgli did so, and not a day too soon, for when he returned the wolves were at the Council Rock and old Akela had missed his kill. Shere Khan, too, was there; so was Bagheera, and there was no end of threats until Mowgli defied the entire Pack, declared himself its master, ordered that Akela be unmolested, and enforced his order by tossing a pailful of live coals on the coats of the wolves, when all cringed before him. He swung a blazing brand on Shere Khan's whiskers and called all to witness that when next they should meet he would spread Shere Khan's skin on the Council Rock.

Then he went to the village and became a herder of cattle; for it had been told him that Shere Khan lived in the vicinity and preyed upon the villagers' flocks and herds. He called his oldest brother, the cub of Father Wolf and Mother Wolf, to his assistance, for strategy and concerted action were to take the place of strength in the destruction of the great lame tiger. It was not to be a one-sided battle, for Shere Khan had plans of his own; it was his misfortune that he talked of them to some gossips among the animals, and Mowgli heard and was fore-armed. His plan was to separate the herd of cattle, the cows with their calves to be at the lower end of a ravine in which Shere Khan lay in waiting, while at the upper end were to be the bulls. Shere Khan was a greedy beast; he hunted and drank every day, and after eating he could not climb the steep sides of the ravine. Could the bulls be so frightened by the wolves that they would charge down the ravine, Shere Khan would be obliged to run before them, and whether overtaken by the bulls or driven against the cows, his fate was certain, for a gorged tiger is helpless against the hoofs and horns of a herd of cattle.

When old Akela came to his assistance—Akela, whose life he had saved at the Council Rock, Akela, whose age had not robbed him of his cunning, the success of Mowgli's plan was assured. Shere Khan died the death of a thief and coward; the wolves drove the cattle from his body, Mowgli began work with his hunting-knife, the wolves dragged the skin off as fast as it was loosened, and before night he, accompanied by the two wolves, carried Shere Khan's skin to the Council Rock and called the Pack to witness that he had kept his word. Then he danced on the skin and sang a song without rhymes, and Gray Brother and Akela howled between the verses.

The Pack, who had fared badly since Akela and Mowgli left them, begged Akela to be again their leader; they begged Mowgli to lead them, but Bagheera purred them a scolding full of hard facts, and Mowgli refused to hunt again except with his four wolf-brothers. And Mother Wolf, who was the first of the Pack to be shown the skin of Shere Khan, was as proud of her foster-son as if he had four feet and a coat of gray hair.

ELLEN OLNEY KIRK

(United States, 1842)

THE STORY OF MARGARET KENT (1866)

The questions presented in this novel excited wide discussion and interest at the time it was published. The sympathetic treatment of the subject was new in American letters, and although it has been followed by many more radical, it was considered a daring experiment. The most interesting point about it is that it is all true. Margaret Kent was a real person, and her experiences in the book are narrated from the actual occurrences of her life.

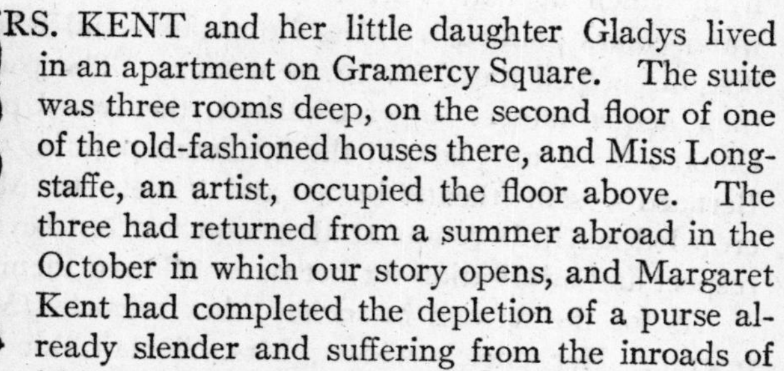

RS. KENT and her little daughter Gladys lived in an apartment on Gramercy Square. The suite was three rooms deep, on the second floor of one of the old-fashioned houses there, and Miss Longstaffe, an artist, occupied the floor above. The three had returned from a summer abroad in the October in which our story opens, and Margaret Kent had completed the depletion of a purse already slender and suffering from the inroads of travel by furnishing her rooms cosily—to the male eye, even luxuriously. A feminine observer would have detected signs of economy and feminine ingenuity, but nevertheless would have admitted a homelike and tasteful effect.

Margaret Kent earned her living and that of her child by her pen, and had done so since Robert Kent, her husband, after spending her inheritance, had taken his departure for Rio Janeiro several years before, leaving her alone and uncared for. She was about twenty-six years old, beautiful, with features both delicate and noble, hair of reddish gold, eyes of dark blue, and skin of an ivory paleness. There was hardly a vestige of color in her face except in her lips, which glowed like a double carnation. She was, besides, one of those fortunately molded women who can do nothing ungracefully; and, whatever was her attitude or occupation at the moment, it was one to be studied. Her little daughter, a child of seven or eight years, looked like her, except that where the mother showed *insouciance,* imperiousness, and dignity, the child was serious and frank. Miss Longstaffe, much older, was of singularly plain appearance and uncompromisingly blunt manners.

Margaret Kent had made many friends during her stay in New York, but they were mostly men. Mr. Bell, the well-known poet, was the most devoted of these, and would gladly have married her, notwithstanding his seventy years, both from love and from a desire to shield her from the many disagreeable chances to which her situation laid her open. She had made his acquaintance through his kindness in accepting her work while he was editor of an important magazine, and she owed much of her literary success to his continued influence in circles from which he had retired. He also adorned his walls with water-colors painted by Miss Longstaffe, and wherever it was possible helped these two brave women. The younger men of their acquaintance, Roger Charlton, the two Updegraffs, and Colonel Weir also bought the mediocre paintings exhibited at Bernard's, sent theater-boxes and violets to Margaret, and crowded her little rooms at afternoon tea; but beyond this their respect and admiration for her never allowed them to go.

As for the women in society, they regarded Margaret with reserve. Her uncle's widow, Mrs. Sinclair, kind-hearted and timid, had given a luncheon for her on her arrival in New York, but her brilliant talk and independent ways had puzzled the leaders of society, and her popularity with men had aroused their jealousy; and where her friend, Lily Townsend, had invitations to all balls, parties, and suppers, tickets to private concerts, exhibitions, and "first nights," Margaret found herself practically shelved and ignored. Even Mrs. Sinclair confined her invitations to family dinners.

Almost every one of us has some friend, or it may be some enemy, against whose prosperity we measure our own, and according to the sum of whose successes we count our individual gains or deficits.

Such a friend to Margaret was Mrs. Townsend. She belonged to society and had a quick wit to win its advantages.

It was perfectly well known that she made a great deal of money by writing social gossip for the Sunday newspapers; yet she never admitted the fact, but posed as a woman of leisure. She retained her friendship for Margaret, as she recognized her value as a sparkling attraction at the little dinners she was so fond of giving in her tiny, well-furnished house on Thirteenth Street; so she took her up or ignored her as seemed advantageous to herself. Margaret recognized her insincerity, but had neither the self-denial nor the ill temper to refuse her attentions when they came.

Mr. Bell had a nephew, Dr. Walton, a man who had won distinction in his profession and who was devoted to study and scientific pursuits. He had recently returned from a prolonged stay abroad, and was renewing his New York affiliations. Rumor said he was to marry Elinor Devereux, a beautiful girl of the conventional type. The Devereux place adjoined Mr. Bell's in the country. They were people of unexceptionable social standing, of the oldest family connections, and serenely satisfied with themselves and their surroundings.

Mrs. Kent, Miss Longstaffe, and Gladys had spent the day with Mr. Bell, a day of perfect happiness wandering about the beautiful grounds and looking at his treasures of art in the big, comfortable library. In walking through the woods they had encountered Dr. Walton and Miss Devereux. Dr. Walton had lifted his hat, and, glancing at Margaret, would have stopped for an introduction, but Miss Devereux had hastened by with but a word of greeting. It was the first time that Walton and Margaret had seen each other. Mr. Bell spoke of his nephew after the walk, telling Margaret that he wished her to know him.

Before this luncheon party Mr. Bell had been thinking much of Margaret and his love for her, and had made up his mind that she should seek a divorce from her husband, when he would offer to marry her and take care of Gladys. He sounded Miss Longstaffe on this subject, and was startled at her emphatic declaration that Margaret's whole duty was to her husband while he lived.

A few days after the luncheon, Mrs. Townsend, having some English notabilities to entertain, invited Margaret to a little dinner given for their benefit. Dr. Walton was invited also, and he and Margaret met, with quick and sympathetic understanding. He told himself that he never had seen so beautiful, so exquisite and attractive a woman. The dinner was a brilliant success. Mrs. Townsend was too good a hostess not to appreciate this fact, but, as a woman, she jealously laid it up against Margaret and determined that she should pay for it later.

An unexpected opportunity came for Margaret to call society together at her own house. The great opera-singer, Mademoiselle Donati, happened to be an old friend of hers, and the operatic manager having just then broken his contract with her, she appealed to Mrs. Kent for help. The latter knew social lines too well not to recognize her chance. Roger Charlton had interested his mother in the beautiful woman he so sincerely admired, and she, an impulsive, independent person, took entire charge of the musicale that Margaret gave for the operatic star. Mrs. Charlton would have liked to have the musicale at her own house, but as Margaret stood firm for having it herself, she threw her whole soul into it, and gathered the best of society in the little rooms at Gramercy Park. All the men Margaret knew sent flowers in profusion, and the small place seemed to be the abode of luxury. All was going well, and Margaret was near the goal she so longed for—the approval and friendship of her own sex—when Mrs. Townsend seized an opening to make insinuations concerning her.

"Who do you suppose paid for all those flowers?" she inquired of someone, laughing. This was enough to set the ball of suspicion and gossip going, and when later Dr. Walton, who had come on from Philadelphia especially for this affair, stood quietly aside with Gladys till the crowd should have dispersed, and he could wait for a cup of tea with Margaret and Miss Longstaffe alone, Mrs. Townsend's quick eye detected his waiting attitude, and her barbed tongue made the most of the simple circumstance.

All Margaret's seeming success, accordingly, counted as nothing; she received no invitations after her affair except to one luncheon at Mrs. Charlton's, at which she was quietly cut and ignored as only women know how to wound one another; and she saw herself left out now with much more intention than before. This was the more galling to her as she saw that Dr.

Walton took it for granted that she was one of the circle in which he was so much at home. During his short call after her musicale their acquaintance progressed by strides. All she could think of, while the conversation flowed so easily, was that soon he would be going away to see Miss Devereux, while he blushed to realize the boyish infatuation that kept him nailed to his chair.

"What are you going to do to-night?" he said, rising at last. "Shall you be at Mrs. Trowbridge's?"

"Oh, no," she said sadly, feeling that her enchanted hour was over. "I never go to parties. We have a box at the theater."

"May I drop in to see you there?" he asked, with a direct gaze into her eyes. She assented with a vivid blush. She could not hold her own against that strong gaze.

Little Gladys thought a great deal about her own father, whom she idealized. One afternoon Colonel Weir happened in when the child was alone, and he encouraged her to talk about him. The Colonel was a true friend to Margaret, and believed himself to be doing her a service when he conspired with her little daughter to write a letter to that far-away parent, and beg him in her own and her mother's name to come home. The letter was written, directed, and posted, and the two conspirators pledged each other to secrecy.

Dr. Walton had talked every minute of the time at the play with Margaret, and had followed this up with a call, at which time, fortunately, Miss Longstaffe and Gladys were out. They arrived at a mutual understanding at this interview. Margaret told him she was poor and was earning her own living. This was an amazing discovery to Walton, and it moved him strangely. His uncle had talked of her literary work, but had not told him it was a necessity. He showed himself more and more indisputably in love with her, and was telling her so unequivocally when Miss Longstaffe came in. She took in the situation at a glance, and began at once to talk, holding the center of the floor, to Margaret's bewilderment and Dr. Walton's disgust, until finally he took his hat and abruptly departed. To Margaret's querying glances Miss Longstaffe vouchsafed a stern reply: "The man was making love to you, and you were permitting it!"

Mr. Bell did not know of his nephew's infatuation, but he felt that Margaret's social situation was daily becoming less secure. His own health was suddenly undermined by what seemed a heavy cold, and he decided to take some decisive measures. He had given up the idea of marrying Margaret himself, and, thinking over the men who were devoted to her, fixed upon Roger Charlton as the one to talk with. He accordingly sent for him, and found the young man ready and willing to seize opportunity of marrying Margaret, could a divorce from the unworthy Robert Kent be secured. Mr. Bell had written to Rio Janeiro, and had procured evidence as to Robert's life which left nothing in doubt as to Margaret's right to separate from him. Mr. Bell then wrote Margaret a long letter, in which he counseled her, as her best friend, to get a separation from her husband and to marry a young man who loved her and who would make her happy. This influenced her very strongly in her thoughts of Dr. Walton, whom she knew now that she loved with the love that can come but once in life. Her former girlish feeling for the man who had so wronged her after marriage was but the pale shadow of the reality.

About the same time Mrs. Sinclair was moved in the same direction. Someone she knew who lived in South America wrote to her of Robert Kent's reckless life there, and she called on Margaret one afternoon, and, overcoming her natural timidity, solemnly advised her to get a divorce from Robert. Poor Margaret's mind was therefore in a whirl of doubt and hope.

Dr. Walton was returning from an interview with Margaret one day, at which the most perfect understanding and communion had existed between their minds. He was in a state of exaltation which received a rude and chilling shock when he saw Mrs. Townsend beckoning to him from her carriage. Most reluctantly he entered the vehicle, and the conversation immediately turned on Margaret.

"It is a pity she is not free to marry," said Mrs. Townsend.

"What do you mean?" he said, looking straight ahead of him.

"She has a husband living, you know. There is no secret in that."

Dr. Walton left the carriage soon, he hardly knew how, and walked away feeling dazed.

"I will find out from herself," he said audibly at last.

That interview with Margaret seemed like a nightmare. He had supposed her to be a widow. She in turn had thought from his uncle's letter that he understood her situation, and feeling almost benumbed she tried to explain it to him. He, thinking he had been deceived, left her in scorn, feeling that his heart was broken and his life a ruin.

Margaret, in her turn, accepted her fate. When Miss Longstaffe tried to comfort her, she looked up, her face drawn into such strange lines of pain and horror that it was hardly recognizable.

"What did he say?" Miss Longstaffe whispered.

"Not much. Not the worst that came into his head; still I knew what he was thinking. I am glad he despises me. I am glad he hates me. I wish he had called me names, stamped on me, spit on me."

"Oh, Margaret!"

"I deserve it. And you don't know how he looked at me! Oh, my God! if ever I forget that again!"

She looked up once more with an agonized face.

"Sarah," she said, "help me to live for Gladys. Help me to be noble. Help me to be good."

Some days after this, Robert Kent came home. Gladys's letter had called him. Margaret accepted his foolish ill-bred demonstrations of affection with calmness, and once the shock was over, made the best of her failure of a husband before the critical eyes of her friends. His health was delicate and she tended him carefully, giving him the place of head of the house. He enjoyed the novelty of the situation for a time, and then began to show the real man, dissipated and hopeless. He took all Margaret's money, driving her to despair, for her mind was running dry in those days, and literary ideas would not come.

He next borrowed all poor little Gladys's savings, and tried to borrow from Miss Longstaffe, who repelled the idea, telling him scornfully what she thought of him. This drove him to a three-days' riot of frightful dissipation, during which time

Margaret thought he had destroyed himself, and chaos seemed to open under her feet.

When he returned, a severe illness followed, through which Margaret nursed him dutifully.

On his convalescence, the family went to live in a little house belonging to Miss Longstaffe in the country. Here, as a situation was open to him, Robert actually worked, and Margaret spent two quiet, almost happy years, busy in caring for her house and the two, Robert and Gladys.

She saw with dismay, however, that returning health brought longings for the old life to her husband, and with a heavy heart she bade him good-by once more, as he set out for his family home in the South.

Soon after this, a letter from his cousin, Robert Cary Kent, told of a yellow-fever epidemic, and of Robert's illness. Margaret reached him on his death-bed, and then followed a final collapse for herself and a long period of nursing.

Dr. Walton, offering himself to help stay the plague, cured her, and for one happy moment thought she was to be his at last, but being informed that Robert Cary Kent was cured, he again fled, and once more left the country.

One bitter January morning, two years after this, Dr. Walton walked off the gangplank of an incoming steamer and ran into Miss Longstaffe. In their greetings, she disclosed the truth to him—that Margaret was indeed a widow, and once more in distress, for Gladys was very ill.

A few hours later, Margaret was sitting by the child's sick-bed when she heard the door shut down-stairs, and she ran to the top of the staircase.

Somebody was ascending.

While Margaret lives, she never will forget that moment. Alexander Walton sprang toward her, held out his arms, and clasped her to him.

"I've come," said he. "Never, never to leave you again, if you will let me stay."

ALEXANDER LANGE KJELLAND

(Norway, 1849)

ELSA (1882)

With malice prepense the author entitled this tale *Elsa: a Christmas Story*, and published it at holiday time with the pretty ornamentation suited to gift-books. Its simple language and unpretentious beginning aided the hoax, and thousands bought it in good faith to present it to friends "with the compliments of the season." It was really a most searching satire of the social and religious life of Norway, and accordingly it created a great sensation and made its author almost instantly famous. His arraignment, however, of the current religious and social canons made him especially unacceptable to the influential persons of that day, and so, a few years later, when a measure was proposed in Parliament to grant Kjelland the "poet's pension," which was the manner then in vogue of recognizing literary merit, it met with such opposition that the Liberal Party of Norway was split into factions, one of which, being adverse to Kjelland, joined with the Conservatives to form a new ministry. This faction was led by a clergyman who, it is understood, had served as the model for the chaplain in *Elsa*.

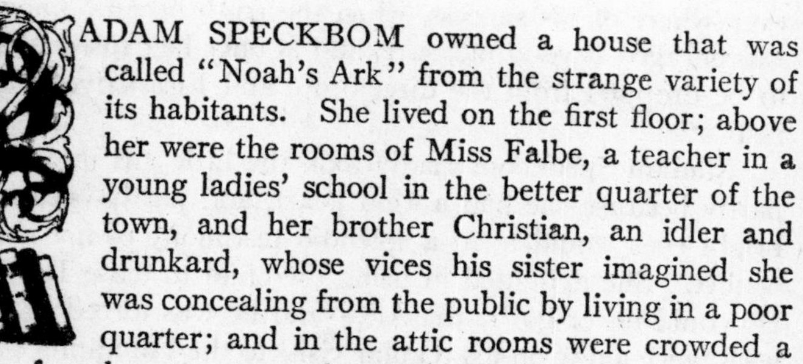

ADAM SPECKBOM owned a house that was called "Noah's Ark" from the strange variety of its habitants. She lived on the first floor; above her were the rooms of Miss Falbe, a teacher in a young ladies' school in the better quarter of the town, and her brother Christian, an idler and drunkard, whose vices his sister imagined she was concealing from the public by living in a poor quarter; and in the attic rooms were crowded a number of unclean creatures that went by the general name of "the gang." Individually these were old Schirrmeister, a besotted German musician, who boasted that once the great Spohr had laid his hand on his head and said, "You will go high"—a prophecy which thus far had been fulfilled only in the fact that Schirrmeister lived in a garret; Lena, or Nymphalena, as the old musician called her, who was housekeeper for "the gang"; her brother, who played the flute, and, having once been a steward in the jail or "jug," was called familiarly, from that fact and from his constant state of intoxication, "Jugsy"; and Jorgen Tambur, a drunken drummer.

Madam Speckbom was a quack doctress. She had a great reputation among the lower classes for cures wrought upon patients who had been given up by the regular physicians. One had only to mention her name before Dr. Bentzen, the district physician, and the old gentleman would grow fiery red, seize his hat, and make off, muttering curses upon her. If, indeed, you mentioned the name of a certain one of his former patients that she had cured, his imprecations would include yourself, and it were well if you did the disappearing. This patient was "Flea Elsa," a foundling, who had been afflicted with a bad disease of the eyes, and with whom Bentzen had trifled for a good half year, during which she lay like a little beast in a dark corner of the Foundling's Home, screaming whenever they turned her to the light. Miss Falbe was at that time a director in the Home, and, taking pity on the poor, neglected child, she placed her under Madam Speckbom's care without informing Dr. Bentzen of the fact. The Madam soon effected a complete cure of the case, for which Dr. Bentzen took the credit. He had boasted everywhere of his success, when the truth became known. He was enraged beyond measure, and at once he caused Miss Falbe to be dropped from the directorate and Elsa driven out of the institution.

Madam Speckbom gladly took the little girl into her home, partly because she had a kind heart, and partly because Elsa's bright eyes would form a splendid testimony of her skill as an oculist. She delighted in using the child to tease Dr. Bentzen. He could never go by the Ark—and he was forced to do so at least twice a day on his regular visits to the Foundling's Home—but Madam Speckbom would place the child in the window and have her bow in mock gratitude to the physician, rewarding her with a stick of candy for doing so.

It must be confessed that Elsa grew up a spoiled child. Her nickname of "Flea" was significant of her unreliable character. One never could put a finger on her when she was wanted. She always disappeared, as if by magic, on washing and scrubbing days. Madam Speckbom ascribed Elsa's indolence to "that accursed, aristocratic blood" of the unknown "gentleman" who had seduced her mother, a servant-girl.

But Madam's patients were fond of the little girl, with her merry laughter and playful antics, to which the old woman wisely and generously gave large credit for her cures. And the disreputable tenants of the attic welcomed the Flea, who came hopping up the stairs oftener than Madam Speckbom would have liked had she known it, for there was the place of the little shirk's mysterious disappearances when work was to be done.

Miss Falbe, however, often heard the Flea whisking by her door, and finally remonstrated with her.

"Dear Elsa," she said, "you are now getting to be a big girl. It will not do for you to be with bad men. Promise me you will never go up to the attic again."

Elsa grew red as blood, and promised with tears that she never would visit "the gang" again. That day she was even industrious, for without being told she actually watered Madam Speckbom's window rose-bush, which had four half-opened blooms. And at night she dreamed of roses, and music, and white satin trimmed with swan's-down. She was seventeen years old.

For a time Elsa kept her promise to Miss Falbe. But she loved music, and she heard old Schirrmeister playing his violin. Surely there could be no harm in stealing up to see whether he was alone. So she softly crept by Miss Falbe's door. Schirrmeister was not alone, but, being once there, she remained anyhow. And little by little all became as before, except that she kept her visits a secret from Miss Falbe.

The ladies had met to establish The Institution for Fallen Women. Consul With, who opened the meeting, and the chaplain, were the only men there. With's wife had compelled him to be present, probably to rehabilitate him in the eyes of the community, for she was not ignorant of his bad reputation in regard to fallen women. Indeed, he was accredited with the fall of several of them. Little pity was felt for Mrs. With, however, for at the time of their marriage he was a handsome young spendthrift, and she a rich old maid.

Consul With was forced to say something, and it is always

safe to take a conservative position. Conservatism in charity? Ah, yes; care should be taken that benefits go only to those for whom they were intended. He had his theme, and he got along swimmingly during his general introduction; but when he came to apply his fundamental principle to the particular charity contemplated, he saw breakers ahead. For logical consistency required him to maintain that no woman who had not already fallen should be cared for in the institution. It suddenly struck him that this was putting a premium on vice. What an ass he was making of himself! But as he was in for it, he made the application and sat down, wiping the perspiration from his brow.

To his great relief, the chaplain and the ladies applauded his wisdom heartily, and they elected him president of the institution by acclamation, while the chaplain was made its secretary.

Miss Falbe was not at the meeting, and did not know of the conservative principle on which the institution was founded. She had learned that Elsa had deceived her and was going with "the gang" again. On the night of the ladies' meeting she had met her on the landing, coming down from the attic in a tipsy condition. She knew that Madam Speckbom would beat the girl if informed of her behavior, and that this would probably cause her to run away to the streets. So she called upon the chaplain to see whether the new institution would take the wayward girl in charge.

Dr. Bentzen was the right hand of the chaplain in all public matters, and he had warned him against Miss Falbe. She was insubordinate and officious; her brother was a drunkard; they lived among low people. Accordingly, the reverend gentleman was very cautious, even suspicious. Was the residence of the girl within the parish limits? His manner indicated that he was sorry to hear it. How old was the girl? Seventeen; h'm! Might he inquire what was Miss Falbe's own age? Thirty-five. No doubt she did take a motherly interest in the girl, he remarked, with a significant emphasis on the adjective that brought the red to her outraged cheek. What! did he—but no, for Elsa's sake, for the chaplain's own sake, she would ignore the insinuation.

When and how and by whom did the unfortunate girl fall?

the pastor then asked. What! she had not yet fallen? Did not Miss Falbe know—and he disclosed the sound principle upon which the new institution was founded, with such open contempt for her obtuseness that the school-teacher retired in confusion.

Miss Falbe returned to the Ark, and so contrived it that Madam Speckbom sent Elsa a few miles into the country for a short holiday, while Miss Falbe planned for her future. Consul With's brick-fields were near the place where Elsa stayed, and in visiting them she met a brick-maker, a handsome, dark-eyed, black-haired, olive-cheeked, red-lipped young fellow, with gipsy blood in his veins. They fell in love at first sight, and when it came time for her to return home he stole a morning off from his work to walk with her back to town. As they passed by a garden wall on which roses were blooming, he climbed up and plucked one for her. They had nothing to say to each other, but after a time they found themselves walking each with an arm around the other's waist.

They sprang apart when a carriage came rapidly over the hill behind them. It was Consul With's, who was returning from his brick-works.

"Get back to your work, Svend, you rascal!" he cried to the young man.

"But I am going with the maiden to town," said Svend.

"Never mind, I'll see to that. Come, jump into the carriage, my girl."

They whisked over the hill, leaving Svend standing aggrieved by the roadside. The Consul put his arm about her waist and attempted to kiss her on the neck. Elsa was used to such things, and to keeping men at a distance, but she could not cuff the elegant Consul With. Besides, his arm had so quickly replaced Svend's that it was as if her young lover were still by her side. Anyway, it was very pleasant.

Consul With stopped at his suburban summer villa on the fjord, helped Elsa to alight, and pressed her to his breast in the act.

"Oh, my rose!" cried Elsa. He had crushed its petals.

"Only come along, and you shall have all the roses you want," he whispered, and drew her within the gate.

A few days afterward Elsa made her appearance at the Ark.

She looked so flushed that Madam Speckbom readily believed her story that she had become overheated walking in from the country.

Miss Falbe was pleased to see that Elsa no longer frequented the attic, and when a fine-looking young laborer whom Elsa had met in the country began calling, she congratulated herself on the happy inspiration of the holiday visit. Then, too, Elsa's character had greatly changed. She appeared modest, even diffident, about meeting her wooer. Indeed, she blushed whenever he came.

Madam Speckbom, however, was too experienced in physical symptoms not to have her suspicions that all was not right with the girl, and she suspected Svend to be the cause of the trouble. Still, Consul With was passing by the Ark with unwonted frequency, and once she caught Elsa nodding to him from the window.

"Where did you meet that old hog?" Madam asked.

"At the brick-yards," said Elsa untruthfully.

"Well, don't you have anything to do with him. He means you no good."

Elsa promised that she would avoid him.

Late one night, however, Madam Speckbom was roused from a light sleep by a scuffle in the entry. She felt of Elsa's bed, and found that Elsa was not in it. Softly going to the door, she suddenly opened it, almost at the same time lighted a gas-jet in the entry, and found Consul With embracing Elsa, who was robed only in her nightgown.

She jerked the girl back into the room, and ordered With to take himself off. Then she turned on Elsa. Such baseness! To fool her with the honest lad from the brick-works—her, Madam Speckbom, who had so sure an eye in such matters—and then, with that old hog Consul With! Now, if it had been Svend with whom she had made her slip, she would not have had a word to say. No one could charge that she was hard on young folks!

That very night she turned Elsa into the street. Whether the Consul had waited for her or not, she found a refuge with a woman who had once been his mistress, and who now acted as his procuress.

When Svend next called at the Ark, Madam Speckbom told him the whole story and advised him to think no more of Elsa. But he hunted her out, told her he knew all, and offered marriage.

"I have saved a hundred crowns. Come, we'll go to my uncle's, away up country where these things never will be known."

Elsa, who was under the fascination of the Consul, refused him. Svend returned repeatedly, each time renewing his offer, and holding out to her his little capital, which, alas, was rapidly wasting away, for the poor fellow in his trouble had taken to drink. But each time she shook her head.

Finally the Consul dropped her for a new mistress, and the procuress ordered her to leave her quarters. The faithful Svend put in his appearance at that moment, and Elsa said:

"Now I will go with you."

But Svend answered despondently: "I haven't a crown left."

"No matter," she said, and, taking his arm, she swept out of the door as if it were the greatest triumph in the world.

Miss Falbe swallowed her pride and returned to the chaplain.

"The girl of whom I spoke to you has now qualified for entrance to the institution," she said. "She is about to give birth to an illegitimate child."

"My dear woman, you really ought to have known better. Take her to the hospital."

Miss Falbe did not take Elsa to the hospital, for Madam Speckbom relented, and received her in her old home, where the child was still-born. Elsa gradually recovered, and Svend called almost every day. At last, one day in summer, he came to the Ark in a fuddled condition, and Madam Speckbom refused him entrance.

"Give Elsa this," he said, handing the Madam a rose, and staggered away.

Elsa kissed the rose, and looked daggers at Madam Speckbom when the bluff woman curtly informed her that Svend was drunk and she had turned him from the door. That night Elsa ran away to Svend.

The next winter was a hard one for the poor. There were so many of these that charity had to draw the line. To the vicious help might be a curse. It were a shame to take bread for them from the worthy poor.

The Flea, in particular, deserved no assistance. When she found that Svend could not support her, she had deserted him for another ne'er-do-well, and this for another, turning in the intervals from one charitable person to another for aid. All the ladies were tired of her. At last she took refuge in a bar-room by the wharf, where she earned her keep by tempting sailors to drink with her.

Miss Falbe met Elsa in the street the day before Christmas, and invited her to dinner that evening. Elsa came early to the Ark, and cautiously crept up to Miss Falbe's door to escape meeting Madam Speckbom. Miss Falbe was not in. There was music and merriment in the attic, and she succumbed to the temptation to run in for a moment to see "the gang." The old story was repeated; she remained all that evening drinking with her old cronies, and went out with them after midnight on a raid upon the cellar of a liquor-store into which "Jugsy" had tunneled an entrance. There they remained carousing till morning, when they were found by the proprietor lying in a drunken stupor.

Svend came to the prison to see Elsa as soon as he heard of her arrest, and when they refused him admittance, his gipsy blood flamed out in a wild struggle with the jailer to force his way to her; so they arrested and imprisoned him also. An iron wall separated the two.

Elsa did not know that Svend was near; and she had subsided again into a drunken sleep. Yet into her disordered dreams came the suggestion of a rose—the rose that Svend had stolen for her. His arm seemed to encircle her waist. And then sweet music sounded. She awakened. Oh, misery!

All the church-bells were chiming. And the good people were going to service dressed in their fine clothes, with happiness and good-will beaming on every face.

"Merry Christmas, doctor!" cried Consul With, meeting Dr. Bentzen hurrying by with his medicine-case. "What is the matter?"

"Madam Speckbom's gang—I almost said Miss Falbe's—have been rounded up at last. All are in prison. Burglary of a liquor-store. One girl, the Flea, is in a bad way, and is pretty certain to die. In hysterics; keeps calling on her lover."

"Did she—did she mention any name?" asked With anxiously.

"Yes, a certain Svend. He also is locked up."

"A worthless scamp—one of my workmen; I hope they'll put him through," said Consul With righteously. He bowed, and went onward to church.

The chaplain delivered a beautiful sermon on the lowly birth of the Christ-child. How consoling it was that the true nobility of the world lay in the humble and despised. Therefore no one, however poor, had a right to complain of his station in life. Certainly the preacher's words went home with a blessed effect. Not one member of the congregation complained of his station in life. Miss Falbe was not present. She was holding the hand of the dying Elsa.

ÉDOUARD RENÉ DE LEFÈBRE-LABOULAYE

(France, 1811–1883)

ABDALLAH: OR, THE FOUR-LEAVED SHAMROCK

(1859)

This classic, like the same author's fairy tales, *Les Contes Bleus*, was the diversion of a powerful mind occupied mainly with great questions that concern human progress.

T Djiddah the Rich, on the Red Sea, once lived a wealthy Egyptian merchant, Hadji Mansour, whose great grief was that he had no heir. He was therefore transported with joy when one of his wives, an Abyssinian, presented him with the coveted son and heir, although the baby was almost as black as herself. Hadji called him Omar, which in Arabic means "Ass," to avert the evil eye by a lowly name. For if he had scant faith in God, he had a wholesome fear of the devil.

As another caution, he called in a dervish to read his son's horoscope. "His best friend will be his worst enemy," said the diviner. Then at Mansour's request, backed by five purses of gold, the accomplished dervish evoked Eblis, as the Arabs call Satan, who accorded to this devoted father three wishes for his son. The first two were: that he should always be rich, and that he should ever enjoy good health. Hesitating as to what the third wish should be, Mansour recalled the dervish's prediction that Omar's best friend would be his worst enemy, and craftily asked that his son might never love anyone but himself.

When Omar was but a few hours old, a Bedouin woman,

named Halima, with a child in her arms, called on Mansour. Her husband had fallen in his service, and he said to her:

"Admitted into your family and nurtured with your son, my beloved Omar will learn a purer speech than mine and will find friends among your kindred, who will protect him in after years. Let the friendship of our children begin from this day; let them sleep in the same cradle. Omar shall be your son, as Abdallah shall be mine."

Halima sought the supposedly pious dervish's aid for her offspring. "He will be honest, of course, like his father," said the proud mother; "but I would have him also happy."

"Virtuous and happy?" asked the dervish grimly. "And you address yourself to me! My good woman, what you want is the four-leaved shamrock, which none has seen since Adam. Let your son seek it. If he finds it, be sure that he will lack for nothing."

With that the dervish vanished, never to be seen again.

"Child of my soul," said Halima, bending over her infant, "I know not what this talisman is, but something tells me you shall find it. Satan is cunning, man is weak, but God rules His faithful and does what He will."

Halima reared the two children until Omar was fifteen years of age, and everyone supposed he had been adopted by her, for his blood was not as pure as Abdallah's. Omar acquired the name of the "little merchant," by his tricks of barter and selfish desire of gain; while the other tall, noble boy was generous, brave, agile, and eager to be as heroic as his dead father, Yusuf. He was supple, clear-eyed, ran between the legs of the mares, wrestled with the colts, and climbed the camels without making them kneel. Although he was only six months older, it was his greatest pleasure to amuse, serve, and defend the swarthy, indolent, thick-necked, and paunchy Omar. The two were reared alike by Halima. At ten, Abdallah's education was finished; he knew all that a Beni Amur needed to know. Omar had learned that the best use of a rosary was for counting. Abdallah was instructed also by his maternal uncle, Hafiz, a one-eyed and crippled shepherd, but a brave soldier, pious Mussulman, and good counselor. Abdallah, when Hafiz talked to him of battle, was like a young war-horse that paws and snuffs the wind at the sound of the trumpet.

"O God," he sighed, "grant that it soon may be my time, and make me worthy of those from whom I have sprung."

"He is as handsome as his father, and he will be as brave," his people said when they saw him pass, or demonstrate his strength, far beyond his years.

When Mansour came to take Omar back to Djiddah he also took Abdallah, that he might see how far wealth placed a merchant above the shepherds of the desert. Omar broke into transports of joy over the marts, and commerce, and dealers. He had learned already from his father, on their journey, how to rate the integrity of a cadi, the scruples of a sheik, and even the conscience of a pasha. He reveled in the richness and luxury of his father's house.

But Abdallah was grave and weary of it all, and when Mansour invited him to stay and become a merchant, he replied proudly: "With God's aid, I will live like my ancestors. In the desert, an ounce of honor is worth more than a hundredweight of gold."

He parted from Omar almost with tears.

"Farewell, Abdallah," said Omar tranquilly. "We follow our destinies. You will dwell in tents. I shall be a merchant. If ever I need a stout arm, be sure I shall have recourse to you."

When Abdallah had gone, Omar reproached his father for leaving him so long with "that Bedouin," and pleaded to be taken to the bazaars at once. Mansour was delighted to find in his son more shrewdness, covetousness, and avarice than he possessed himself, forgetting that gold is a blessing to him that gives, and a poison to him that hoards it.

Nothing was wanting to Mansour's content for the five remaining years of his life. Never had anyone combined as Omar did what constitute genius in business—love of gold and contempt of men. He was completely resigned when his father died. He began to draw the wealth of the world into his invisible net, dressed poorly, cringed toward those who could help him, had no friends, and received no visits.

Meanwhile Abdallah grew in piety and wisdom. He became a guide to the caravans and won a name for valor. To live and die like a brave man was his ambition. But he had a keen desire to learn more about the four-leaved shamrock, with which his destiny was linked. He inquired about it of a Persian dervish, pious, old, and poor, who told him it did not exist on earth, and was only a symbol. Once he rescued from persecution a poor old Jew, who in gratitude told him of the four-leaved shamrock. When Eve was driven from Paradise, she snatched one of its plants, the four-leaved shamrock, the most brilliant of its flowers. One leaf was red, like copper; another white, like silver; the third yellow, like gold, and the fourth glittering like a diamond. The fiery sword touched her as she looked, and as she started, the diamond leaf fell within the gates of Paradise, while the wind scattered the other three over the earth, God alone knew whither.

"It may be an allegory; but if you would find it, follow God's law, execute His commands, and create a heaven in your soul. This is all science can tell you," said the aged Jew.

He inspired Abdallah with a desire to find in the desert a well like that dug by Haroun Al-Raschid on his pilgrimage to Mecca, and then he departed, declining the guidance of Abdallah and Hafiz.

"He has nothing to fear who has poverty for his baggage, old age for his escort, and God for his companion," he said. Abdallah bought the spot to which the Jew had drawn his attention, with twenty douros given to Halima by Mansour, and dug until a spring of pure, sweet water welled up in the hot sands.

He gave to his people to drink from it, and when he, the last to taste it, drank the jug dry, a bit of metal struck his lips. It was a copper shamrock-leaf.

"Praise God, my son," cried Hafiz. "The earth brings you from its depths this flower of Paradise."

In a few years Abdallah had a garden spot in the desert like unto the Gardens of Irem, by which Sheddad, King of Ad, had sought to rival that of Paradise. Halima wished Abdallah to place a wife in this garden, and not suffer his father's name to perish. But Abdallah thought only of what would bring him the shamrock. One day a caravan set down at his tent a fat young man. This was Omar, who needed his foster-brother after these ten years.

"Without you, I shall fail in an adventure in which my head is at stake. The Pasha of Egypt designs to send a radiant woman slave to the Grand Sherif at Tait. With you to conduct the caravan, she will go through the desert to him in safety."

That very evening they set forth—Hafiz, Abdullah, Omar, and twelve selected young companions. In the midst of the line of camels marched a magnificent dromedary of the Oman breed, with a superbly decorated litter. Next to this was Abdallah's beautiful mare, the glory of the tribe, Hamama ("the Dove"), snowy, gentle, and fleet as the wind. On the evening of the ninth day they arrived at Yambo. The brig that brought the Sultana had arrived the night before. Shrouded in a bourko whose white muslin folds concealed her face, she was placed in the palanquin. Her companion advanced with like gravity, but suddenly, snatching off her veil, wound it around Omar's head. Then she put one foot on a camel's neck, leaped like a cat to its back, and grimaced like an ape at the Bedouins, shrieking with laughter.

"Cafour, you shall be whipped," cried the Sultana.

Cafour was a hideous negro girl of twelve. The whites of her small eyes were hardly visible, her flat nose was sunk below the cheeks, and a silver ring hung from the wide nostrils to her tattooed chin. She was loaded with jewels, and a plume of parrot's feathers was on her head.

Full license is given to fools, whose souls are in heaven while their bodies drag on the earth. The whole caravan liked Cafour except Omar, whom she called a Jew, and warned her mistress against. Then she taunted the superb Abdallah, who, in his war-dress, mounted on the lightly dancing Hamama, was a vision of beauty.

"Pretty bird, look at us!" cried Cafour. "Oh, it is the virgin of the tribe in disguise. Come up here with us. You are handsome, and so am I, but my mistress is handsomer. Look!"

She mischievously tore away Leila's veil, who covered her face with one hand and boxed Cafour's ears with the other.

"How beautiful she is!" thought Omar, the son of Mansour. "I must have her for myself."

"Glory to him who created her, and created her so perfect!"

murmured Abdallah, son of Yusuf. He felt his heart escaping him, buried his face in his hands, and burst into tears. When the caravan halted he told Hafiz how utterly he was won.

"All women are false—above all, the one that loves thee! No good woman can come out of Egypt. Think of God, and pity thy mother and me," said Hafiz.

For the first time, Abdallah paid no heed to his uncle's words, and he even forgot the four-leaved shamrock. He only longed to fight and to die, for he could hardly breathe. The next day they were attacked by armed Arnauts from Djiddah. A savage conflict ensued, and in the confusion Leila was carried off by a superb chief. Abdallah darted after him, dragged him from his horse, and stabbed him. This decided the fight, and the Arnauts fled.

Then, to Abdallah's delight, Leila revealed herself. Cafour had put on her mistress's mantle, and it was she the Arnauts were carrying off. Everybody wished to go on and leave her to her fate. But Abdallah, though Leila pleaded with him not to abandon her, could not desert the poor negress.

"A Bedouin does not forfeit his word. If a sack of coffee were entrusted to me I would not leave it in the hands of these robbers, and shall I abandon to them one of God's creatures? Who will come with me?"

Hafiz was the only one that would accompany him. Omar was glad to see them disappear. The two overtook the robbers' camp by night, approached a tent, and heard a discussion among three chiefs as to which should possess the captive. When the victor discovered the negress in place of Leila, he drew his pistol and shot her. The next instant he himself reeled and fell, as Abdallah sprang into the tent. Cafour overturned the table, and the lamp went out. Her little hand reached for him in the dark, and, taking the child in his arms, Abdallah fled. He mounted Hamama and hastened to the spot where he had agreed to meet Hafiz, if they were separated. He arrived before dawn, and they prepared to set out for Taif to rejoin the caravan.

"Abdallah, you are my god," said Cafour, falling on her knees. "You saved me. My god was with me, but did not help me. Take it, and break it in pieces." She handed him the tuft of feathers from her hair. "My mother gave it to me. See?" She plucked it asunder, and drew forth a thin piece of silver.

"Uncle, glory to God! Behold the silver shamrock-leaf!" cried Abdallah.

Intoxicated with joy, they embraced the poor child, who was astonished but happy to feel herself beloved. When they reached the caravan, Cafour threw herself into his arms, and Abdallah was forced to command her harshly to return to Leila. When they arrived, Omar bribed Cafour to deliver this message secretly to the Sultana: "Moon of May, a new moon is approaching. If you would know peace, importune, urge, and command. Love is like madness: everything is forgiven to it."

"I am rid of Abdallah," he said to himself, as Cafour repeated the words and departed. "The Sultana's jealousy must force Leila from the harem. Once outside it, she shall be mine."

Cafour found Leila pale and tearful, and soon learned that she loved Abdallah.

"Would to God that I had been born amid the tents, with this beautiful Bedouin for my brother, that I might cast myself into his strong arms with none to despise me."

Cafour musingly repeated to herself Omar's message. Then she said: "Mistress, should you become Abdallah's wife, would you keep me with you? Should I be your slave and Abdallah's all my life? Swear it, and do not question me. Swear by the God of Abdallah."

Leila complied with simple earnestness, and when the strange child bounded away, retired to weep.

"He who is intoxicated with wine," says the sage of Shiraz, "awakens during the night; he who is intoxicated with love awakens only on the morning of the resurrection."

Omar and Abdallah vied before the Sherif in claiming Leila, whom the Commander of the Faithful would not receive when he learned that she had been looked upon unveiled by Omar and Abdallah. Thanks to the diplomacy of Cafour, who had found a powerful ally in the Sultana Fatima, the Sherif declared that Leila should choose her spouse. The beautiful creature bowed, took the trembling hand of Abdallah, and placed it upon her head.

"Thou art my father, my mother, my brother," she said. "Oh, my beloved, I am thine."

Omar, mute, but betraying his rage and despair in his features and actions, departed, refusing to take the hand which Abdallah extended to him.

At dawn, the eager Abdallah returned with Leila, who had arrayed herself in the blue cotton robe and red woolen burnous of a Bedouin. Halima, won by her loving devotion to Abdallah, tenderly embraced her.

Omar's despair and rage were soon known. One morning an Arnaut presented himself before him.

"I am Kara Shitan," he said bluntly. "Your brother killed my friend Mohammed. Give me five thousand douros, and I will rid you forever of Abdallah. Then Leila can easily be made yours. Money can do all things. We can strike at the same time. I will entice away Abdallah, and you can abduct the woman."

"While Abdallah lives there is no security for me," said Omar. "It was predicted at my birth. Deliver me from this enemy, but I never wish to see your face again."

One hot, misty morning a solitary stranger presented himself at Abdallah's tent.

"I am pursued and shall be lost if I cannot reach Medina. You alone can guide me there. My fate is in your hands," he said.

Abdallah prepared to accompany him. The modest board was spread but the stranger would not eat. Cafour suddenly thrust a handful of salt into his mouth, crying impishly: "Salt is good for the appetite." She had detected the Arnaut, and she urged Abdallah to take his gun with him.

"A guest is above suspicion. It would be an insult to him. Alone, with only my lance, I will guide him. Fear nothing. Whom God guards, harm cannot touch," said Abdallah, and the twain set forth.

When they were well on their way, Abdallah said to the other: "Kara Shitan, ere you entered my tent, I knew you. My enemy, under a false name you have accepted my hospitality. God gave you into my keeping. I have accompanied you alone and unarmed. If you meditate evil to me, may God protect me. If you do not, give me your hand."

"May hell be my inheritance if I harm him who has spared me!" said the soldier, offering his hand. "You need go no farther. I will join yonder caravan. Accept this talisman, which my dying mother gave me twenty years ago. I could not show my gratitude in a stronger way."

He rode off, and as Abdallah was about to fasten the little roll of parchment to his arm, he noticed something like a golden bee attached to it. He looked, and uttered a cry of joy. It was the third leaf—the shamrock was complete. The son of Yusuf had nothing more to seek for on earth; the diamond leaf awaited him in heaven.

When he arrived at his tent, he found it a scene of confusion —things overturned and broken, the women gone, and Hafiz, with a shred of Leila's cotton gown clenched in his hand, dead on the ground, his features still contracted with rage. Abdallah fell upon his knees and closed his uncle's eyes, then fired his pistol and cursed the Bedouins, who hastened to the spot, for not protecting his home in his absence. They were stupefied. Bending his head, the sheik said:

"Your brother and six companions came last evening, and Hafiz killed a sheep for their supper. What Bedouin would have dreamed your family needed protection with them there? Come! All that remains is vengeance."

The ardent band followed the traces of the murderers' camels, and at last descried the caravan, which had taken refuge against the desert storm that was threatening. Omar saw them, feigned a defense, left Halima at her command, and hastened onward with some followers.

"Do not pause, my son," cried Halima. "Pursue the negro with the red jacket, who killed Hafiz and stole Leila."

Hamama flew like the wind, and rapidly gained on the negro. Suddenly Leila was thrown from the negro's horse upon the desert sand. Abdallah stopped, gathered up her loved form, and with a last look she died in his arms. Her throat had been savagely cut. The Bedouins hastily returned. They had slain the murderer of Hafiz, but Omar had escaped.

"But the simoom is rising," they said, "and in less than an hour the sand will be his winding-sheet."

Abdallah placed Leila in his mother's arms.

"Peace be to thee, daughter of my soul! If it please God, I shall soon join thee," he said tenderly. Then he sprang to the saddle, and Hamama bore him, as swiftly as an arrow flies, straight toward the advancing fiery cloud. Onward she panted for an hour before Abdallah found the son of Mansour prone in the hot sand, delirious with thirst.

He revived Omar with water, and announced to him his impending death. The wretch asked time for a prayer, as Abdallah drew his saber. Then pity seized his heart, because the nobler in him was always master. He recalled their infancy at Halima's breast, their years of devoted union as brothers. Even Omar's dead victims seemed to cry: "Spare thy brother!" The crafty Omar noted the change.

"My brother, do not add thy iniquity to mine," he wailed. "Pardon me, that the God of Mercy may love thee."

"Rise!" said Abdallah. "Vengeance is God's, not mine. Thou art my brother."

He signed to Omar to mount Hamama. He did so, and suddenly driving the spurs into her flanks, disappeared.

"Abdallah is a fool," he thought, "to remain in the simoom thus; but his folly be on his own head. I will forget him, and live only for myself henceforth."

Abdallah dragged himself through the sand and fiery whirlwind, praying for resignation to the sorrows that had befallen him, until he fell exhausted. Suddenly everything about him bloomed like Paradise. He heard the melodious chant of Israfel, while Gabriel, messenger of celestial favors, descended toward him. In his hand he held a tiny diamond leaf, whose soft but sunlike radiance illumined the whole desert. Abdallah ran to meet him, when suddenly a vast, fiery gulf opened at his feet, bridged only by an immense arch of steel, thin as a hair and sharper than a razor. Despair filled Abdallah. But behold! He felt Leila and Hafiz supporting him.

"In the name of the clement and merciful God!" he cried, and instantly was transported to the other side, where an angel extended to him the mysterious four-leaved shamrock. His recompense had come. The breathless beauty of the eternal splendor poured upon his eyes, and he uttered a loud cry of rapture. Then silence fell, and the whirlwind regained dominion of the desert.

Cafour had been brought to Omar's house at Djiddim. One day, when he was craving peace of soul, she gave him a draught of haschish, in order to wring from him the miseries he had wrought on the household of Abdallah.

"It had to be. My best friend was destined to be my worst enemy," he said.

"What friend have you?" cried Cafour. "Stay! Behold the friend who will cause your death," and she thrust a mirror before his eyes.

"Child of perdition!" he snarled. "I will send you to join your Abdallah."

He fell in reaching toward her, dragged the lamp with him, and in a moment was wrapped in flames.

"Wretch! Die like a dog!" hissed Cafour, setting her foot upon his convulsed face, as she sprang to the door and disappeared. "Abdallah is avenged."

Hamama bore her to the desert, nor paused until she reached the spot where Abdallah lay, cold in death, but his smiling face was radiant. She threw herself upon him and covered him with kisses. "Abdallah, I loved thee!" she whispered, and rendered up her soul to God.

Under the palm-trees near the Well of the Benediction, beneath two mounds, which the trailing jessamine surrounds with odorous blossoms all the year, the Bedouin, the Egyptian, and the negress await together the Day of Judgment.

ALPHONSE MARIE LOUIS DE LAMARTINE

(France, 1790–1869)

GRAZIELLA (1849)

This story is an episode in the life of its illustrious author, a leaf from his memoirs. In 1843 Lamartine had retired to the island of Ischia to write his *History of the Girondists*. There he was within sight of the isle of Procida, where in his youth Graziella had come into his life. Inspired by this environment, he devoted his leisure hours to recording his recollections. He was so engaged one day when his intimate friend, Eugène Pelletan, came to him, and on the impulse from several inquiries his friend made, Lamartine read him a part of the manuscript. Some time later Pelletan, when in Paris, told a publisher of Lamartine's story, and when Lamartine returned home in the autumn he received a letter from the publisher offering to buy the manuscript at any price. On receiving a second and more urgent letter he accepted, and the story that he had written in response to memories awakened by a return to the scene of this episode was published.

ON the first of April I arrived in Naples with my comrade of college days, Aymond de Vivien. Here we tarried, wandering along the seashore or boating in the Gulf of Naples. In summer the fishermen of Pasilippo go several leagues out into the sea to fish. Watching the flare of their torches at night, and talking with them when they returned in the morning, we became impressed with the picturesqueness of their lives, and a longing came over us to join them. My friend was twenty, I was only eighteen—ages when youth is full of dreams and fancies.

While strolling along the shores of Margellina one evening, we came across a robust old man and a boy of twelve, who were repairing a boat. We entered into conversation with them, and before we parted had arranged with the old man that he should take us fishing. For two months we lived the lives of the fishermen, dressed as they, eating their food, toiling with them, still alive to the beauties of the sea and the moonlight nights.

September came, with its equinoctial storms, but in spite of the increased danger and hardship, we continued in our adopted vocation. One morning we set out across a smooth sea to the fishing-grounds. The catch was abundant, and we lingered until suddenly a fierce wind arose, which rapidly developed into a storm. For three hours we fought against the rolling waters, throwing everything overboard to lighten our craft. We were trying to reach the island of Procida, where the family of the old man lived, and finally, weak from exhaustion, we landed under the shelter of a point of land, and crawled ashore to our friend's hut.

A girl opened the door, the granddaughter of our old comrade. I was keenly impressed by her beauty—her black hair, encircling a face of rich complexion, her eyes, of that undecided color between black and dark-blue which expresses both gentleness and passion; a celestial color, borrowed from the brilliant light of the southern skies.

We spent the night on a bed of ferns, and next morning we found that our boat had been dashed to pieces in the surf. Our comrades were in sore distress over the loss of their craft, and heartrending were their lamentations.

That afternoon my friend and I tramped to a neighboring village, where we bought a new boat, which we sailed back and presented to our hosts. How they wept from joy when we gave it to them, and how keen was our own pleasure! Never was there such a happy day.

The storm continued at intervals, and we remained nine days with our simple friends. In the evenings I read to them from that sweet and simple tale of love, *Paul and Virginia,* and they listened with bated breath. As the reading advanced I often noticed Graziella's eyes grow moist, while she drew nearer and nearer, till her hair brushed my forehead and I could hear the spasmodic breathing that betrayed her awakening emotions. Once a tear rolled down her lowered cheek and splashed on the page of my book.

On the ninth day we helped the family pack their few belongings to remove to their winter quarters in Margellina. We would have continued our humble life, but my friend received an urgent letter from his mother, which recalled him to France, and he went, promising to return as soon as possible.

The loneliness of my room in the town weighed on me, and I fell ill. I sent for old Andrea, but he was away, and Graziella came in his stead. How tenderly she reproached me for having absented myself from them so long. Her presence, the sound of her voice, the sweet innocence of her face were so pleasant to me that I detained her as long as I could. Next morning I could no longer bear my loneliness, and I went to Andrea's hut. I found them just setting out to visit me, each bringing a small present. How glad they were to see me again! Henceforth I became a constant visitor in their home.

Graziella was learning to work in coral, and earned a weekly income thus from an uncle, a man of some means. His son, Cecco, frequently came to teach Graziella reading and writing.

Finally I took lodgings with Andrea and his family. While Graziella worked, I helped her, or else read my books beside her. I was happy, without quite definitely knowing why.

Graziella's beauty developed as she grew into womanhood. On Sunday I accompanied her to church, and very proud I was to notice the admiring glances of the people we passed. I can analyze now my feeling toward her; it was affection, but not love. She gave me a delicious repose of the soul; she did not ignite the flames of passion. With constant companionship a gentle intimacy grew between us. The purity of our thoughts removed that reserve which itself often causes love between man and woman.

I also gave her lessons, and under my tutorship she made rapid progress. With Cecco she played; while his devotion to her was unmistakable.

One evening, on my return from an all-day absence, I observed that the faces of my friends were troubled and that Graziella's cheeks were tear-stained. After supper she soon retired, and Andrea told me that Cecco's uncle had made a proposal of marriage to Graziella in Cecco's behalf. The old people were delighted, for such a marriage would mean an end to their poverty. But Graziella had refused to give a definite answer.

A sudden realization came over me that I loved Graziella. The thought that I should lose her dear companionship, that I must give her up to another, was painful. She had been the attraction, not the sea. In vain I sought sleep that night, for Graziella's sweet face haunted me.

I determined to seek relief in a change of scene. I would absent myself till the nuptials had been celebrated. But neither the dead streets of Pompeii nor the glowing crater of Vesuvius could relieve my depressing melancholy and again I drifted back to Naples.

Sad news greeted my return. After my departure Graziella had continued in her undecided state of mind; she wept and remained locked in her room most of the time. Cecco came often, and his father pressed for an answer, but she would see neither. On the evening of my return she had finally consented. That was to me a sleepless night.

In the morning Graziella was gone. I picked up from the table a note in which she bade us all good-by, saying she had promised too much, and had determined to seek repose in a nunnery. Everybody wept. The note dropped from my hands, and in stooping to recover it I noticed a pomegranate flower and her devotional medal lying by my door. She had been kneeling there in the night.

We scattered in all directions to seek traces of her. A vague instinct led me to cross over to the island of Procida, where the summer hut was. It was evening when I landed, and I noticed that a light glimmered from a window in the hut. I ascended to the door, and opened it.

"My God! It is he!" cried Graziella—for she was there. She made one step toward me, then dropped half-swooning to the floor. I threw myself beside her, and clasped her cold hands in mine. An expression of delirious joy spread over her face, and she whispered her love to me.

"You are mine," she murmured. "You are already the husband of my soul. I can give myself to no other, for I have already given myself to you in secret. You on earth, God in heaven!"

She had made an offering of her long, beautiful tresses to the Madonna, and I kissed them passionately. The whole night passed in this artless, innocent communion between our souls. But mine were not the emotions of a passionate love. Fatal error! She was the fire, I only the mirror.

In the morning her people found us there, and in great joy we returned to Naples. None suspected what had passed between us. We two were happy for a while, until the prospect of my approaching return to France saddened Graziella. To seem nearer to me, she borrowed a silk Parisian gown and dressed herself in it. The result was distressing. In Parisian costume Graziella lost her native grace; she was awkward, ill at ease, her hair badly dressed; false flowers ill became her. My lack of enthusiasm brought tears to her eyes.

Meanwhile my mother's letters became more urgent, and at last my friend V—— appeared and took me away. I packed in haste and left a passionate letter to Graziella, promising to return soon. As I departed she opened her door and saw me going. She stretched out her arms, and with a cry fell fainting to the floor. An hour later V—— and I were on our way to Rome.

In Milan I received a letter from her. She was well, but depressed in spirit. In Lyons a second letter reached me, enclosing a carnation. She had been ill, but was recovering.

For three months I heard nothing, but her face haunted me continually. Alas! change of environment brought a change of feeling; I felt ashamed of my love. How I have since reproached myself. Fool that I was, not to have appreciated the worth of that lovely flower!

In November a traveler from Naples brought me a letter and a package. In it were the tresses she had cut as an offering to the Virgin Mary on the night of her flight. She was dying, and she sent me her last farewell.

The shadow of her death has ever since haunted me, and her image has never been effaced from my heart. I never could find her grave, but her real sepulcher is in my breast.

I wrote a poem, inspired by that first youthful love, "The First Regret," of which I need give only the opening lines—

"Near the sounding shore of Sorrento's sea,
Where the blue waves roll to the orange-tree,
In a narrow way by the blossoming hedge,
Stands a little stone by the water's edge—
A tomb it can hardly be"—

to remember all, to hate myself. But souls above forgive, and hers has forgiven me. Forgive me, too, reader, for I have wept!

ANDREW LANG

(Scotland, 1844)

A MONK OF FIFE (1895)

This story professes to be that of a Scotch monk who had fled to France, and now "done into English from the manuscript in the Scots College of Ratisbon." The romance was, in fact, suggested to the author by various records he came upon during his research work in connection with some of his historical writings on Scotland.

NOT for my own glory do I, Norman Leslie, sometime of Pitcullo, and in religion called Brother Norman, of the Order of Benedictines, of Dunfermline, indite this book. But on coming out of France, in the year of our Lord 1459, it was laid on me by my Superior that I should tell of that glorious Maid of France, Jeanne la Pucelle, in whose company I was from beginning to end.

My father minded to make me a churchman, but I took more pleasure in games than in divine learning. Good Father Peter instructed me in the grinding of colors; and he taught me also in the French language, which did serve me well later.

I was playing at that accursed game, golf, one day, when in quarrel I smote a lad of high spirit, and, fearing the wrath of the law, I fled on board a merchant vessel, and thus I came to Bordeaux.

On landing I heard that Orléans was beleaguered by the English, so I pushed on for France, thinking to take service with the Dauphin against the English.

I was nearing Poictiers, well on my road to Chinon, where, as I heard, the Dauphin lay, when I came to a place where the road should have crossed a stream, not wide, but strong and deep. The bridge was broken, and there was neither ford nor ferry. There was another traveler, a huge, dark man, belonging to the Church, who had the foulest and most murderous visage that I ever beheld. On his back he carried, what I never saw on a cordelier's back before, an arbalest and many bolts.

"Your name?" he cried suddenly, and I told him.

"And yours?" I asked.

"My name is Noiroufle, in religion Brother Thomas, brother of the order of the mad Saint Francis of Assisi."

"Do you swim, Brother Thomas?"

"Like a cannon-ball," he snarled.

I would have left him, but he leveled his arbalest at me and ordered me to ferry him across. Being young and afraid, I obeyed.

We jogged on, and his talk was of slaying men. As we drew nearer to Chinon and the Court, we picked up strange companions. Among them was a woman violin-player with her jackanapes and her husband, a hangdog ruffian.

We had to tighten our belts as we neared Chinon, the court of the beggar Dauphin who borrowed money from his cook. Night was falling, and not a white coin among us.

"Horses," suddenly said Brother Thomas, and he gave an order to the men. I had seen evil things done, and held my peace, but in sudden anger I opened my mouth to cry "*Au sécours!*" Brother Thomas caught me behind, and they all fell on me; they gagged and bound me, and sent me flying to the bottom of a ditch.

The horses drew nigh, when a woman's voice rang out:

"We have already arrived, thanks to my brothers in God."

A soft, golden light passed over us, and Brother Thomas bade his crew scatter.

There I lay bound, in fear of wolves. In the night some beast came nestling under my breast, and I knew it to be the woman's jackanapes. Soon the gray stole into the sky, and I heard horses' hoofs coming from Chinon. The jackanapes awoke, and ran out on the road, and thus discovered me to them. A man came and slit my bands. With him was his daughter, and thus did I meet the fair maid Elliot, and we set out toward town together.

"My maid Elliot hath set all her heart on seeing the famed

Pucelle, the Lorraine peasant lass," said the father, "who is to drive the English into the sea."

Then I said that to my thinking the Maid rode after nightfall into Chinon, and I told them of the bushment laid by my late companions.

For many days I was with Elliot, and she spoke ever of the Pucelle, and with us the jackanapes grew fat.

One day the father of maid Elliot and I had gone to a certain lord in the castle with his wares, for he painted banners and inscribed on vellum. He went in, while I waited on the drawbridge beside a French sentinel. Suddenly I started as in a dream, for I heard a rare woman's voice that I had heard before. On turning, I saw the Maid of Lorraine. The sentinel barred the road, but on seeing the Dauphin's pass let her go, though with foul words. She looked at him gently and predicted his instant death. The soldier turned in wrath on me. We fought and swayed, then fell with a crash into the moat below. When I showed my head an arbalest bolt splashed in the water, but I escaped into the laundry of the castle.

I reached home safe, and there met the Maid, and great was her mirth and Elliot's when I related how I had escaped from the laundry in woman's garb.

Elliot's father went to Sir Hugh Kennedy, chief of the King's Scotch archers, who laughed and smote his thigh when he heard my story. But he interceded with the King and obtained for me a free pardon, saying that I must in return take service with him.

Proud, yet with heavy heart, I repaired to the castle, for I loved fair Elliot. One day she brought my fine new uniform, a joy to my eyes.

"Oh, Elliot," I said, ere I wist, and caught her hand in mine, "I love thee."

She seemed at first in anger, but her arms folded about my neck, and we spent happy hours together.

It was said that the Maid won the ear of the King. Learned men were now examining into her holy life, and were amazed at the wisdom of her answers. So now she was to raise her standard.

Among the archers it was said we were to set forth to Orléans, for now the Maid had won all hearts. One day Elliot's sire called me to his house, and within was Elliot embracing a young knight in shining armor. My heart stood still, when lo! the knight came forth unhelmeted, and it was the Maid herself. And she had chosen me for her escort.

Next day, mounted on a good horse and in good company, I departed to Blois, whence the Maid was to set forth to Orléans. The English had encompassed the city; but the word ran that the Maid knew we should pass unharmed, and so it proved.

One night the French captains ordered an attack on St. Loup, and had not told the Maid. But she saw them in a vision and came to them in time to turn the fray. Many priests were captured, and among them was Brother Thomas. I drew my sword to slay the traitor.

"Knave of a Scot," cried the Maid, "wouldst thou strike a holy man and my prisoner? Begone home!"

I spoke to the Maid's squire of this priest's perfidy, and he made my peace with the Maid. But next morning they found Brother Thomas had escaped.

The bridge of Orléans, across the river, was broken, and near to it, on the farther shore, the English had built a fort, St. Jean le Blanc, which the Maid ordered us to attack. But the English had retreated to the Bastile of Les Augustins, and now sallied forth against us. The Maid, in front with her banner, led the men, till the English gave ground and a knight and I forced the palisade. The fight was fierce, but at last the English fled. The Maid spoke to me in a most gracious manner; also, I had an English prisoner, whose ransom was paid in no long time.

The captains held counsel and sent a messenger to the Maid to say that enough was done. But she was wroth, and ordered an attack on Les Tourelles. And so strong was her will that she did as the saints bade her, and the captains were fain to follow. The palisade was soon broken, and the men swarmed up with shields to fend off the stones. And ever was the Maid at their head. Then the Maid, with banner in hand, lightly leaped on a ladder, and the Scots followed her, I being foremost. Then I saw the evil face of Brother Thomas as he aimed a bolt at La Pucelle. Reeling, she fell in my arms, and we laid her in a vineyard near by. The fight waned faint, and then suddenly the Maid came forth and, ever leading the way, ordered a charge. The English were driven back and fled over the drawbridge. We set fire to the bridge and the great English captain, Glasdale, crashed down with it and the last of his men.

"Saints! Will no man save him?" shrieked the Maid, whose heart was ever tender. I thought of the Maid's desire and the large ransom for so great a knight, and plunged into the water. A mailed hand was thrown up, and I seized it. I reached the shore and looked at the man; it was no Glasdale, but the evil face of Brother Thomas.

Men carried me to our lodging, weak and bleeding. The Maid came with words of praise, but my throat was wounded and I could not speak. Then she said she would leave me under the care of the holy man I saved. In vain I tried to speak, and she withdrew.

Brother Thomas drew a bolt and promised me a speedy death. Then, giving me paper and ink, he being no clerk, bade me write that I had accused him unjustly. But I wrote not so, and when he bade me read, I read as he had dictated, and not as I had written. My blood choked me as I read. As he was about to slay me the Maid's squire entered and said it had been revealed that he was the traitor of St. Loup. Brother Thomas showed his confession as written by me, but when he heard what it really was he fled, and none could catch him, the devil ever aiding him.

I lay long in sore fever at Orléans and knew naught of the fighting. It was early June, and the town was full of joy, because the Maid was to visit the city, and fair Elliot came with her.

I saw the Maid and Elliot, who met me with much delight. Then, as she was going to Tours, I joined her in my litter. At Tours, with an old kinswoman, was my old friend jackanapes; and there we found great sorrow, for jackanapes had been missing for three days.

On June 13th the Maid took Jargean, whence the famed Bastard of Orléans had been driven some weeks before. Then messengers followed, saying the Maid had seized the bridge of Meun and driven the English into the castle. She marched against Beaugency, and the English yielded on terms and departed into Normandy without swords. Thus in one week the Maid delivered three strong towns from the English.

I have many a time thought with sorrow that it needed only that the King should obey the Maid, ride straight to Rheims, and thence to Paris, and every city would have opened its gates to him. The Maid kept praying him to do this, but he was residing at Sully, where La Trémouille kept him under governance.

When I had recovered, the Maid bade me follow her to the taking of Paris. After the coronation they should have set out for Paris, but a messenger came from the Duke of Burgundy, and a truce of a fortnight was made. And yet, ere a fortnight had passed, new troops from England came to garrison Paris. The Maid said openly that she loved not this truce.

At dawn I set forth, bidding Elliot farewell. Many years afterward a learned knight, deep in the counsels of the Duke of Burgundy, said to me:

"You were all betrayed when you marched against Paris. On the twenty-third the Maid left Compiègne, but on the twenty-eighth the Archbishop of Rheims met the ambassador of the Duke of Burgundy, and they made a compact. The King knew the Maid was marching against Paris, and manifestly he never meant to put forth the strength of his army in helping her. There was a truce between France and Burgundy, but none between Burgundy and England and the Maid."

There were skirmishes around Paris, but we all camped at St. Denis, where the archers bade me right good welcome. That evening our chaplain bade us all come together in secret, and read to us a paper that was sent to him by a friend in Paris, in which it said that within the walls there was a strong party of Armagnacs who had a long score to settle with them of Burgundy. They had banded together and taken an oath to take our part, if we but won a gate. Said the letter:

"The purpose of the English is to send forth a party to take the Maid before dawn. The craft is to destroy this company; then we shall put on armor like the Englishmen, and some few in our own coats, and you will hale us with you as prisoners. One will attire himself as the Maid. You will lay hid near the Bordeles Gate, where are our good Armagnacs. At a signal, make for the gates with cries of 'Saint George for England!' and thus take possession of the gate."

We did as he advised. Me they clad as the Maid, and our company hid beside the Bordeles Gate. We heard the tramp of the English company as they passed, the signal was given, and we set off for the gate, crying: "Saint George for England! The witch is taken!"

We entered, the drawbridge flew up, and we were surrounded. It was a treacherous snare. A harsh voice caused me to turn; I saw the wolfish face of Brother Thomas, and I then knew that the stratagem had been laid by that devil, and my heart turned to water within me.

I ran my eyes over the vile faces of the crowd and beheld that of the violin woman and on her wrist the lost jackanapes. Then was I led to a cell in the outer-gate tower and put in fetters. As I lay, all hope left me. But at nightfall I heard the din of battle and the Maid's clear, strong voice: *Tirez en avant! en avant!*

As darkness fell, the fighting ceased. I slept, but was awakened by something that leaped on my breast. It was the jackanapes, thin and meager. He put something into my hand, which I found was a wallet containing a file and a long rope. I lost no time. With the jackanapes hugged to my breast, I dropped to the ground and sped on to St. Denis. There I learned that the Maid had been wounded.

Concerning the times of those shameful treasons of the King I have no joy to write. We marched hopelessly to Pierre le Monstier, where we lay, plying the town with our artillery. We made an assault, and were driven back; but at last the town was taken. I had two prisoners, and with their ransoms I deemed myself wealthy enough. From La Charité, which we beset, we had perforce to give back, for the King sent us no munitions.

Much honor was done to the Maid, but she was sad. I had tidings of Elliot. In January the Maid went to Orleans and gave us holiday. I rode to Tours with a gift from the Maid to Elliot, and the jackanapes, who had waxed fat again.

My holidays sped merrily. Eastertide came, the Duke of Burgundy began marching, and manifestly it was his purpose to take the town of Compiègne, the key to Paris, which had yielded to the Maid. She drew all her company and set out northward to Pont l'Evèque on the Oise, so that she might cut off them of Burgundy from all the country eastward of Oise and put them out of power to besiege Compiègne. In Pont l'Evèque there was a garrison of English. Fierce was the fighting, and the Maid entered within the walls. But the English of Noyon attacked in the rear, and she was forced to retreat.

I knew naught of this; for while I was scaling a wall the ladder was overthrown, and I remember only a flight through the air. My right leg was broken, and my head was like to be burst open. While I lay in the Monastery of the Augustines the Maid was not idle and had many a fight. Then the Duke of Burgundy and the English crossed the water and swore to slay us all!

On a day in May it was said the Maid would make a sally, and I was borne in a litter to see her banner move.

She came with her troops and marched on Marguy. The drawbridge was choked with flying men. Now I saw the Maid and two knights gripping her horses' reins. Great was the press. Then I saw the hood of a cordelier. Suddenly came a voice, "Up drawbridge! down portcullis!" and in a flash the order was executed.

Swords and axes fell. The Maid was torn from her saddle, and they were all upon her. Thus was she taken, while we looked on helpless. Now in the throng I saw that accursed Brother Thomas.

"Seize him!" I cried. "Seize that Franciscan!" His had been the voice that gave the order, aided by the devil's craft.

But I was taken for mad. He had come four days since, and was deep in the confidence of our captain.

My only thought now was to free the Maid from the hands of the English at Rouen. I saw Elliot, and she was in deep sorrow. Her intention was to withdraw into a convent, for she would not marry me unless it was the Maid's desire.

I rode to court, and found no promise of help. In secret I left the town, clad myself as an Englishman, and crossed over to

England. There I found service, and by good fortune was sent to Rouen.

I lodged near the castle where lay the Maid. I won the favor of Sir Thomas Grey, who gave me his confidence, and so it was that I saw the Maid again and would have helped her to escape; but the saints had revealed to her that she must accept martyrdom, thus to enter Paradise. I saw it was of no avail to pray to her in the name of France, so I spoke in my own name and told her of Elliot's vow. Then, smiling sweetly, she said: "This is an easy thing and joyous. Hast thou wherewithal to write?"

"Yes, Madam, here is my wallet."

Then she bade me write, requesting her best friend, Elliot Hume, to wed him who loves her.

"And so farewell! farewell!" she said, as I kissed her wasted hand and left the castle.

When Elliot's grief had abated in a measure we were married and for a year we were happy. But God took from me both her and my child.

Then I withdrew to my country, where I have since lived in religion.

EDMOND LEPELLETIER

(France, 1845)

MADAME SANS-GÊNE (1895)

Victorien Sardou's play of this name was a masterpiece of historic and dramatic interest, and met with an immediate success in Paris. Madame Réjane took the leading rôle, which she played later in England and the United States. In reversal of the usual order, Lepelletier founded his story on the play.

N July, 1792, Louis XVI was still nominally King; but his head, though adorned with the Cap of Liberty, was clamored for by the revolutionary mob of Paris. The people were only waiting for the arrival of the battalions from Marseilles to give the signal for the attack on the monarchy, intrenched in the Tuileries. Yet, throughout all the terror and confusion, light-hearted Paris did not abate a jot of its gaiety. The immense ballroom, known as the Vauxhall, was especially crowded on this particular evening, and among the merry throng none was merrier than Catherine Upscher, a laundress living in the Rue Royale. Catherine was notable among her companions, who, because of her plain speaking and blunt but honest ways, had named her Madame Sans-Gêne. She was as virtuous as she was beautiful. She met many partners at the ball, some of whom were to become famous; but none pleased her so well as Sergeant François Lefèbvre, who, like herself, was a native of Alsace, and, indeed, from the parish next to her own. He had all the qualities likely to attract the fair laundress, for he was brave and loyal and a true republican. A few days afterward he made her an offer of marriage, which she accepted joyfully, especially after he had shown her two crossed swords freshly tattooed on his right arm, surmounted by a bursting shell, and beneath the swords the inscription: "Death to all tyrants!" He promised that in a few days he would show her something better than even this masterpiece; and when Catherine eagerly asked what it was, he answered mysteriously: "My wedding-present!" He pressed her to become his wife immediately; but she declared she would remain single until the tyrant had fallen.

So the dread notes of the tocsin that floated out upon the night air on the memorable 10th of August were ringing at once the knell of the monarchy and a wedding-peal for the laundress in the Rue Royale. While she was eagerly watching at her door and waiting for tidings, Lefèbvre appeared at the corner of the street, fully armed and equipped, and running rapidly. After a hasty embrace, he showed Catherine his promised wedding-present. This was a fresh tattoo mark on his arm, representing two hearts in flames, and underneath them the legend: "True to Catherine till death." Then the sound of distant shots broke the silence of the night, and the cannon thundered a reply.

"Good-by, Catherine," Lefèbvre exclaimed, "I go where duty calls me. Don't be afraid; we shall return victorious," and the sergeant was off at once in the direction of the Tuileries.

About noon next day Catherine heard a few shots fired in the immediate neighborhood of her shop. Then there was a noise of hurried steps at the back door of the laundry, which opened on the Rue St. Honoré. She ran and unbolted it, and saw staggering toward her a young man, hardly more than a boy, pale and bleeding, his hand pressed to his breast to stop the blood that was streaming from his wounds.

"In Heaven's name, save me, Madame," he murmured. "I am one of the beaten, and I am wounded. I am Count de Neipperg, an Austrian officer."

He could say no more. He fell across the threshold, and Catherine, with a cry of mingled pity and terror, knelt beside him and drew him in. Then, after securely bolting the door, she made a compress by tearing up the first piece of linen at hand, and when it was too late she perceived she had in her hurry destroyed a man's shirt. "Great Heavens!" she thought, "this is a nice how-do-you-do! And a shirt of that little artillery officer, Napoleon Bonaparte, too! The poor fellow has not too many of them, and he owes me a pretty big bill. Never mind—I'll take him a new one, and pretend that the old one was spoiled in the ironing."

Meanwhile, the wounded man was beginning to recover consciousness, thanks to the influence of the cold water on his face and the bandages that stopped the flow of blood. He was making an effort to thank his preserver when a knock was heard at the door. Catherine started, and turned as pale as her patient. "Who can it be?" she asked herself. "And surely no one will be troubling me about washing on such a day as this."

The clang of arms on the pavement soon told the laundress that her visitors were soldiers. By dint of pulling and pushing the half-fainting officer, she got him into her bedroom and locked him in. Then she opened the door. The shop was soon filled with a squad of National Guards, one of whom was Lefèbvre. After kissing her on both cheeks, he told her that they were in pursuit of an aristocrat who had escaped from the Tuileries and whom they had traced to the alley leading to her shop. Of course, he said, she could not have seen him. He persuaded his comrades, though not without some difficulty, to leave him alone with his sweetheart. Then, as he took Catherine in his arms, he noticed that her eyes were fixed anxiously on the bedroom door, and his suspicions were aroused. He plunged his hand into the wide pocket of her apron, seized a key, unlocked the door and entered the bedroom.

Again there was a knock at the shop-door, which Catherine opened. Outside was a squad of the National Guard, who had come to inform Lefèbvre that he was wanted at the section, as he was about to be elected lieutenant. At that moment Lefèbvre reappeared, carefully locked the door, and returned the key to his betrothed, saying:

"You didn't tell me your bedroom was a hospital, darling. A wounded man is sacred, and a true soldier never fires on the ambulance. Take care of the poor devil, and save him. But don't tell anyone; it might do me harm."

"You are a noble fellow," Catherine answered, and, in a whisper, just as he was departing: "We'll be married whenever you like."

As soon as her patient was somewhat recovered, Catherine

decided to leave him for a while and run off to one of her favorite customers with a basket of linen. This customer was a certain Corsican, named Napoleon Bonaparte, destined one day to shake the world, but now in temporary disgrace and in a state of poverty. Yet this rather shabby-looking young captain was indulging in dreams of Oriental splendor in which he saw himself, another Alexander, with his feet upon the necks of kings, when the face of a woman, fair, young, and energetic, came between him and his visions of glory.

"I've brought you your washing, Captain," said Catherine, somewhat timidly, for this man always frightened her, although she liked him.

"Washing? Oh, all right; put it on the bed."

"And," she continued, more boldly, "I came to tell you I am giving up the laundry. Business is very bad at present. Besides, I am going to marry, and, as my future husband is a soldier, I intend to be the *vivandière* of his regiment."

"*Au revoir*, my child," returned Napoleon. "I hope to see you at your canteen, some day or other."

As she went down-stairs Catherine muttered: "I've got his bill in my pocket—thirty francs, no less!—but I hadn't the courage to present it. Bah! he'll pay me some day."

But it was not until a good many years afterward that Napoleon was suddenly and unexpectedly reminded of his unpaid washing-bill.

Meanwhile Madame Lefèbvre, now *vivandière* of the Thirteenth Regiment of Light Infantry, followed her husband from Verdun to Jemappes, from Jemappes to Toulon. Neither her manners nor her language was much improved by her contact with the citizen soldiery; indeed, it must be confessed that she soon learned to swear like a trooper. But she was always good-hearted and good-natured, and as tender as a mother to all who needed her help, particularly to the wounded. She was a central figure in many critical incidents, was exposed to many perils, but never lost her cheerfulness and courage. At last she had to abandon the canteen (which she did regretfully) and rise to a higher station in society with her husband, who had made his way in the world entirely by his own bravery and perseverance. From the captaincy which he had won at Verdun, he had been promoted step by step until he held the chief command of the army of Paris, and until the capture of Dantzic, one of the most brilliant events in the annals of Napoleonic warfare, made him a duke. He had already been created a marshal in 1804.

So, for the ex-washerwoman and the ex-sergeant, the world they were living in nineteen years after that assembly at Vauxhall was a new world, and, at least to the devoted wife, not altogether a pleasant world. She was now moving, with a somewhat awkward gait, through the gilded halls of the Tuileries, but she was not happy. She could not accustom herself to courtly manners, and her language was still the language of the camp and barracks; all her efforts to forget it and adopt the polite style of those around her were in vain. Then she was, to the great disgust of the Emperor, eternally at loggerheads with the Emperor's sisters, so that he said, truthfully enough, that, with the rows of these women, his court was like the courtyard of an inn. The Emperor had just divorced Josephine and was awaiting the arrival of his new bride, Marie Louise. Why should not Lefèbvre follow his example? The Duchess of Dantzic was no doubt an excellent woman; but her manners made her the laughing-stock of the court, and her language was only too often suggestive of the washtub. He would find a wife for him, a woman with a title, an aristocratic name, ancestors. All his arguments, however, had not the slightest effect on the honest ex-sergeant, who for the first time in his life retired from the presence of the hero he worshiped indignant and disgusted.

When he returned home, he found Catherine trying on a court dress she had ordered for the imperial wedding. The expression of his face told her that something serious had happened. He informed her of his quarrel with Napoleon and its cause, and the hearty embrace of the loyal-hearted couple that followed was a sufficient answer to the ill-advised suggestion.

"Why," exclaimed Catherine, "you could not marry another woman if you would!"

"Why not?"

"Look at this," she said, turning up the sleeve of his coat, and showing on the marshal's arm two hearts in flames, beneath which stood out, as fresh as on the day it was tattooed, the motto: "True to Catherine till death!" "Could you marry an archduchess with a thing like that on your arm?" Catherine asked triumphantly.

Marie Louise, Empress of the French, was holding her first drawing-room after her coronation. One of the last to arrive was the Duchess of Dantzic, and her appearance was the signal for a buzz of malicious comment and envious satire, though many of the women who could not forgive the ex-laundress her rise in the world were themselves of humble extraction. Even the purity of her life and the fidelity of her husband were subjects of mockery among these by no means squeamish ladies. Unfortunately, Catherine often appeared at her worst at such scenes, and the rippling laughter that arose because of a breach of etiquette on the present occasion could not be stifled even by the presence of the Empress.

"Ah!" muttered the Maréchale angrily, "if only the Emperor were here, I'd give them a stroke of the rough side of my tongue."

As soon as the general hum of conversation had been resumed, a pert, soft-spoken, clean-shaven little man approached her, and made her a respectful bow: it was Fouché, the terrible Minister of Police, now out of favor and out of office.

"Madame la Duchesse," he said, "you have many enemies here, and you must not give them the chance of ridiculing you because of a trifling slip that might easily be avoided."

"Well, you know, Monsieur Fouché," Catherine answered, "I forget when my tongue is on the wag, and then I don't care a — There, I was going to do it again!"

Fouché well knew that, although the Emperor might laugh at the Lefèbvres, he respected them in his heart, and their opinion on many subjects had more influence with him than that of all the rest of his court. So the astute ex-minister was making no mistake in trying to lay Madame Sans-Gêne under an obligation.

"Look here, my dear Duchess," said he. "When I see you approaching a snare that may be laid for you, I shall tap my snuff-box."

"Right you are, Monsieur Fouché; I'll keep my eye on you and your snuff-box."

And the pair followed the Empress into the adjoining room, in which supper had been served for the more distinguished guests.

A plan had been formed by the Queen of Naples and her sister Eliza to turn Catherine into further ridicule by getting her to relate, in the presence of Marie Louise, one of her adventures that was more racy than refined. She was nothing loath; but a glance in the direction of Fouché's snuff-box checked her in time. Then she saw the trap into which she had nearly fallen, and a sneer uttered by Caroline still further inflamed her. All Fouché's tapping was of no avail. With heightened color and flashing eyes, she rose from her chair and poured out a torrent of scathing words, each of which cut like a knife into the Emperor's two sisters.

The Princess Eliza rose, saying: "We cannot stoop to bandy words with a washerwoman and a *vivandière*, of whom our brother has made a duchess."

Then, after they and Marie Louise had retired with their suites, Fouché approached the Duchess, and, with a look of mild reproach, said: "I'm afraid you have let your tongue get the better of you this time, my dear Duchess."

"Don't be afraid, Monsieur Fouché," Catherine answered serenely. "I'll see the Emperor, and I bet you he'll say I was right."

At the palace of Compiègne a hunting-party was organized by the Emperor for the following day, and there the Duchess of Dantzic was awaiting a new outfit she had ordered for the occasion. What was her dismay to recognize in the disguise of the tradesman's assistant who had brought her riding-habit the Count de Neipperg, the fugitive she had saved in the Rue Royale! He had accompanied Marie Louise to France, but had been banished by Napoleon, who suspected him of being the lover of his wife. He said he must see the Empress and return her a ring she had given him. The Emperor had found out that she had no longer this jewel in her possession, and his suspicions were increased in consequence. He entreated Catherine, whose husband was Grand Master of the Palace, to aid him in procuring an interview with Marie Louise. The Duchess rebuked him indignantly for a course of conduct that must be fatal to the Empress as well as to himself. She did her best to persuade him to entrust her with the ring, which she would return to Marie Louise, and to promise to leave France immediately. He refused at first, saying that the Emperor Francis had commissioned him to find out whether his daughter was really happy, because it was known at Vienna that Savary, the new Minister of Police, had all her letters opened, so that it was impossible to learn her real sentiments. Therefore he must have an interview with her and a letter from her to her father. But Catherine finally obtained his promise to abandon his wild and fatal purpose. At this point there was a knock at the door, and one of the Emperor's chamberlains informed her that her presence was commanded in his Majesty's study. With a significant nod to Neipperg, the Duchess intimated that their interview was at an end.

Having some idea of the scolding that awaited her, she summoned her best courage, and also provided herself with a weapon that might be useful as a last resource. This was only a small piece of paper, all crumpled and yellow with age.

"Ah, so here you are, Madame la Maréchale!" said Napoleon with a frown. "I have had fine accounts of you. What is all this I hear about your conduct at the Tuileries? You are making my court the laughing-stock of the world! Why can't you keep your tongue between your teeth?"

Then, becoming a little calmer, he told her that her presence at court had become impossible; and that she should consent to a divorce, which he had already proposed to her husband. She would retain her rank and all her privileges. Catherine told him that, while all they possessed, and even their lives, were at his disposal, he had no power to interfere between a soldier and his wife, and if he attempted that kind of battle he would be defeated. As to her having insulted the Queen of Naples and the Grand Duchess of Piombino, she had only defended herself and defended the army, outraged by his two sisters. They had reproached her with being the comrade of the heroic soldiers of Sambre and Meuse. Then for the first time Napoleon discovered that Catherine had served in eighteen campaigns, had been wounded at Fleurus, and was mentioned in the Order of the Day for conspicuous bravery after Altenkirchen. Catherine took care that he should discover something further, that in the year of the memorable 10th of August, 1792, she used often to come to his room.

"And what the deuce used you to come to my room for?" inquired Bonaparte, becoming more and more interested in her story.

"To bring you your clean linen, Sire. You were often in need of it, I can assure you, and I was your laundress. Why, there is a man in this very palace who owes me a bill since those days! And he can't deny the debt, for I have here a note from him asking for time."

And she handed the note and the bill to the Emperor. He was deeply moved when he read them. All traces of his former displeasure vanished, and as his gaze rested on the paper he held in his hand his mind was busy with the memories it awakened.

"Let me see," he said, "what was your name before you married?"

"Catherine Upscher."

"No, I don't remember it. Hadn't you a nickname?"

"Yes; Madame Sans-Gêne."

"Now I remember. And it has stuck to you at court."

"It has stuck to me everywhere, and on the battle-field, too," she answered proudly.

"Well, I suppose the Emperor should pay the debts contracted by the Captain. How much do I owe you?" said Napoleon gaily.

"Three napoleons," the Duchess answered, holding out her hand.

"Aren't you a bit dear?" remarked Napoleon, whose parsimony in little matters was often comical.

"There was some mending with the washing."

The Emperor found he had no money in his pockets, after a vain search for the three gold pieces, and she consented to give him further time. Then he ordered Roustan, his famous mameluke, to conduct her to her apartments.

But just when Napoleon had escorted her to the door of his study a noise was heard at the other extremity of the gallery, near the apartments of the Empress. A woman appeared, who was making a sign to someone to approach, and a shadow advanced. It was Count de Neipperg. "So the unhappy man has not kept his promise," said Catherine to herself. "He is bent on seeing the Empress, and it will cost him his life. What can I do?" Then the Emperor, rushing past Madame de Montebello, the Empress's confidential maid of honor, seized the rash intruder and dragged him into the study.

"Neipperg! I thought so!" he cried, with rage.

Turning to an aide-de-camp who had reached the scene, he said: "Keep him in your waiting-room and send for the Minister of Police. Then let a court-martial be summoned and sentence pronounced. I expect all to be over by daybreak."

Catherine knew it would be sheer folly to seek mercy for the culprit. But she had her plan. Meeting her husband, she asked him to walk heavily and drag his sword on the boards close to the bedroom of the Empress, then to say, at the top of his voice, that no one must enter the apartments of the Empress, and that all letters coming from her must be intercepted. Marie Louise would surely then understand the kind of letter she should give to Neipperg for her father.

Meanwhile, Savary did not arrive, and the Emperor was in a rage. Why was he not there? He had evidently no notion of what was going on.

"The present Minister of Police never knows what is going on—even in his own family," said a piping, sarcastic voice, that of Fouché, who had arrived on the scene.

When Savary did appear, he infuriated Napoleon by insisting that Neipperg never had left Vienna. Then Catherine and Fouché concocted a plan for Neipperg's escape, which was successful.

Napoleon summoned Madame de Montebello and Catherine into his study, and commanded them sternly to conceal nothing from him, no matter how painful it might be. Madame de Montebello assured him that her services were required solely for the purpose of entrusting a confidential letter from the Empress for her father to the Count.

"I am certain," said the Duchess, "that this is the truth. You can convince yourself, Sire, by sending Madame de Montebello for the letter. Let her perform her mission under your very eyes, and then you will know whether you have been deceived or not."

To the maid of honor's request for the letter, Marie Louise answered angrily: "Why does not my father send an ambassador who will fulfil his mission in a rational manner?" Then she arose, wrote the letter, and handed it to Madame de Montebello. Napoleon snatched at the letter, as soon as the door of his wife's bedroom was shut, read it eagerly, and then pressed it to his lips.

"Dear Louise!" he murmured; "how she loves me! You were right, ladies," and he gave Catherine's ear a vigorous pinch, as was his habit when highly pleased with anyone. Thanks to the cleverness of Fouché, Neipperg escaped death, although Savary had assured the Emperor that he had himself given the order for the soldiers to shoot him. Fouché was again restored to favor. As for the Lefèbvres, Napoleon now gave up all thought of divorcing them.

"If all wives were like yours," he said to the ex-sergeant, with a smile, "divorce would be unknown."

ALAIN RENÉ LE SAGE

(France, 1668–1747)

GIL BLAS (1735)

Le Sage spent more than twelve years in the writing of this gigantic novel. It purports to picture the life of Spain, from the point of view of a thoroughly worldly man, from the close of the sixteenth century to about 1645. Much of the material was taken from Spanish romances and other books in the Spanish language current in the author's day. Le Sage incorporated many stories besides the history of Gil Blas in his work, by setting forth the complete life-histories of several subordinate persons, so that it may be said that the book comprises several novels. It has been translated into every European language.

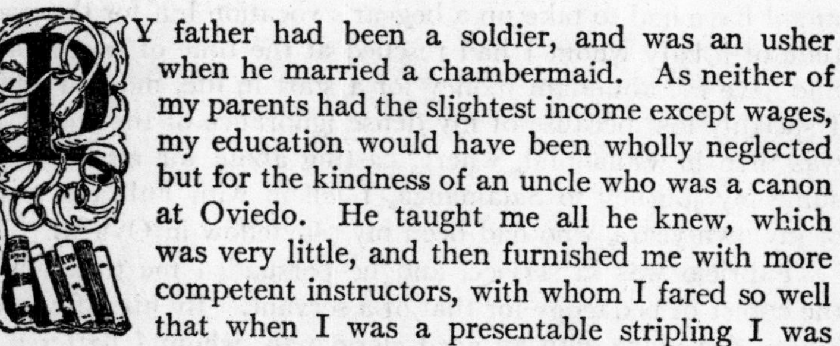

MY father had been a soldier, and was an usher when he married a chambermaid. As neither of my parents had the slightest income except wages, my education would have been wholly neglected but for the kindness of an uncle who was a canon at Oviedo. He taught me all he knew, which was very little, and then furnished me with more competent instructors, with whom I fared so well that when I was a presentable stripling I was despatched to Salamanca, where it was thought I could earn an honorable living by tutoring the students at the university. I was in high feather upon this journey; steeped in learning, as I thought, but knowing as little of life as the veriest chicken peeping from its coop. Fortune has brought me many a hard rap in spite of my early perception of that great factor of success which consists in studying one's employer, or superior in office, with a view to doing all things in his way. Although I have seen Salamanca, I did not arrive at that city of learning on my first journey.

We were not far on the way when a series of minor adventures ended in my capture by robbers, who took me to an underground resort where they kept their horses, accouterments, and spoils. They made me their servitor, and it was their intention to keep me below ground for the rest of my life. Indeed, I dwelt without sight of the sun for six months, and that I escaped at last was due in some degree to my cleverness at the critical moment, but more to the application of that flattering principle by which, after perceiving the uselessness of repining, I undertook to please my captors by ordering my life exactly according to their own mode. This gave them confidence in me, so that when my trick was ready I could play it without much danger of detection. All the money that I took from the robbers' cave, a very pretty sum, was lost shortly afterward when I was arrested at the complaint of a gentleman who recognized the clothes I wore as his property; for he had indeed been despoiled by my freebooting companions. I was wholly innocent of the crime imputed to me, and eventually my innocence was established, but I was freed from prison as ill provided as any beggar, and might have had to take up a beggar's vocation but for the gratitude of a lady whom I had rescued at the time of my escape. She gave me abundant money for a start in life, most of which I speedily lost because of my dense ignorance of the world. I was then in Valladolid, where, casting about for means to resume my journey to Salamanca, I fell in with Fabricio, a lad of my own years, who had been my playfellow in Oviedo.

Fabricio was in service, and he persuaded me to abandon the career of pedagogy for that of a servant. By his influence I obtained a place with an aged clergyman, whom I flattered so successfully that I made certain of being remembered in his will, as in truth I was; but my legacy, when he died, proved to be his library, and that proved to consist of two or three worthless books and a few less valuable manuscripts. Not so much as a real in ready money did I come by for my pains and industry, but I stepped quickly to another place; for Dr. Sangrado, who had finished the aged prelate with rare skill, had been attracted by my demeanor, and engaged me as his assistant. Dr. Sangrado, who was the most eminent executioner in Valladolid, not only made it clear that there was fortune in his profession, but inducted me into it with the idea that I should become his successor. He taught me his methods, which consisted, for all ailments, of taking away from the patient as much blood as possible, and putting into him as much water as he could hold. Phlebotomy and drenching; drenching and phlebotomy—such was the beginning and the end, and sturdy was that physique that succeeded in recovering. So we killed industriously, for it was an unwholesome season that saw my beginning as a practitioner, and invalids were plentiful. I say we, for I was set to work independently, my province being to administer a speedy exit to the lower classes, while Sangrado devoted himself to extinguishing those of the quality who were so unfortunate as to call him.

I remember well the immediate result of my first professional visit. The patient did not die at once, and the head of the family gave me twelve reals. I was so exhilarated by this success that I ran to Fabricio, hurried him to a tavern, and spent four reals in wine. Later I reported to Dr. Sangrado, described the case, and handed him eight reals.

"Very good," quoth he, taking six, "that shall be the proportion of our returns for the present—three fourths for me and one fourth for you."

I was well content, for I perceived that one third of the whole fee added to one fourth of the remainder, equaled one half; and that I made consistently the basis of our business relations thereafter. My prosperity enabled me to enjoy many a bottle of wine, and an occasional adventure with Fabricio, and all went very well until I succeeded in expediting the release of her spirit from the body of a woman who was much esteemed by a certain swaggering bully among the fops of the town. It came to my ears that he had sworn savagely that he would run me through with his sword. This persuaded me that medicine was not my proper calling, and, with many compunctions of conscience for the graves I had helped to fill, I made haste to put as much distance between me and Valladolid as possible.

Then followed a long series of employments in various capacities and places. Sometimes I was a *valet de chambre,* sometimes a secretary, and in all places I studiously adhered to my principle of catering to my master's desires, whatever they might be. Death often robbed me of my employer, but, truth to say, it was now and again my very devotion that brought about a separation, whereby I was somewhat puzzled to reconcile my principles with facts. For example, my experience with the Archbishop of Grenada, who made me his secretary. He was at heart an author, with all the foibles of that craft, and when I had gained his absolute confidence he assured me that it was his ambition to go down to posterity on the strength of his homilies, which he wrote with great enthusiasm and care, and which it was my duty to copy for preservation. He was an old man, and professed to have a horror of preaching after advancing years should sap his strength and render him comparatively ineffective.

"Better stop in my prime," said he, "rather than keep on until men remark that my eloquence is not what it used to be."

So he bade me, by my faith, my sense of duty, my respect for him, ever to watch his utterances, and give him a warning when he should show signs of falling off.

That time came after the Archbishop had a severe illness, from which he recovered miraculously—for a celebrated physician was in attendance. Thus far I had found all things excellent in his commonplaces, and he valued my critical acumen most highly. I was in some doubt as to my proper course, but when I perceived that the people were actually beginning to notice that he did not preach so well as formerly, I believed it to be my duty to advise him, and I did so in the most subtle, respectful and sympathetic, ay, apologetic manner. His aged cheek took on a slight flush, but he heard me through. Then he said, in effect, Go to! you are a fellow of no taste, and I have no further use for you! Like most masters who dismissed me, he gave me a substantial present, and I parted from him with sufficient store of cash to spare me any immediate anxiety about my future.

Thus matters ran for a long time, fortune frequently taking the ground from under me in the most unexpected way, but on the whole leaving me materially advanced, until the accidents of a journey brought me in contact with Don Alfonso de Leyva. Certain misadventures had put him in peril of his life, and at the moment he was as needy as I. By my warning he spoiled the plans of a man who was bent on murdering him. He was duly grateful, and we became fellow-travelers. A storm drove us for shelter to the lodge of a pair of hermits, who, after we had exchanged confidences, proved to be robbers in disguise. They suggested that we join with them in gallant exploits, and we were in just the mood to do so.

Our first adventure was gallant indeed; for we discovered a gentleman and a lady tied to a tree, and four ruffians drenching themselves with wine taken from the gentleman's coach. With no more than pause enough to make certain of our aim, we shot the ruffians dead at the first fusillade. Then we unbound the captives, who were by no means rejoiced at first, for they imagined that we were more bloodthirsty than their captors, but it tickled the fancy of our "hermits," as much as Don Alfonso's and mine, to play heroes for once, and we conducted the lady and gentleman to safety. We did not overlook the booty that was stowed in the robbers' clothes, but took it all, three thousand ducats, which we divided equally among ourselves. The gentleman whom we had saved, Count de Polan, was lavish in his promises to reward us if ever we should call at his castle.

The next exploit to which we gave our attention was a very witty imposition on Simon, a Jewish merchant of Xelva, who was ostensibly a Catholic. One of our "hermits" procured costumes in which we dressed after the style of members of the Inquisition. Thus arrayed, we visited Master Simon, who was mortally frightened at our appearance and made no effort whatever to resist our demands. We told him we were authorized to search for evidence that he was practising the religion of his fathers in secret, and bade him open his closet for our inspection. He did so, and we barred him from it while we hurriedly opened his treasure-chests and took therefrom all the coin we could possibly stuff into our capacious pockets. This done, we gravely sealed the door to the closet and bade Simon not to venture to open it until we came again the next day. Then we departed solemnly until we were well out of his sight, when we made all speed to the place where we had concealed our horses and galloped as far as possible from Xelva before dawn.

Then it was that Don Alfonso's conscience turned upon the dangerous business we had undertaken, and mine was readily persuaded that highway robbery was not the career in which I was best fitted to shine. Therefore, keeping what we had taken from the robbers, but leaving Simon's loot with the "hermits," we bade them farewell. Shortly after this, Don Alfonso had the good fortune to be relieved of all his difficulties and perils, and found himself in the most agreeable relation to the world. His friendship for me stood the test of prosperity, and he heaped me with benefits. He was now in possession of his own large property, and one of his first acts was to send me to Xelva for the purpose of restoring to Simon the whole amount that our rascally crew had taken from him. Later, with the influence of the still grateful Count de Polan, Don Alfonso obtained for me a minor office at court, which swelled my vanity beyond all reason. It was some such post as under-secretary to an under-secretary; but as it brought me into touch with the Prime Minister, I believed that my fortune was made, and I behaved accordingly.

The benefactions of my recent employers had enabled me to accumulate a store of ready cash that would have been considerable if I had chosen to regard myself as a servitor; but no, I was now, if you please, connected with the ministry, and must dress and live accordingly. Behold me, then, buying the most expensive garments, engaging an expensive suite of apartments, and casting about for a servant worthy of my distinguished needs. I am still grateful to that season of folly, in that it brought me to acquaintance with Scipio, a young fellow who attached himself to me as my servant and secretary. After I had been several weeks in the ministerial service, it appeared that the emoluments of office were not forthcoming with any sort of regularity, if at all. One of my colleagues confessed, with a hungry air, that he had not been paid for four months, which was better than the condition of another, who had been six months without pay, and this was luxury compared to still another, who had drudged for fifteen months since he had had an order on the exchequer. These unhappy devils existed each on a little income of his own, not daring to resign and seek other employment because he knew so many state secrets that resignation would have meant imprisonment.

I took quick counsel with myself when I perceived the reality of under-official life, and acquainted Scipio with the mortifying fact that we were flying too high. He chose to stand by me, and we scampered from my expensive apartments to humble back-stairs lodgings, where, with the most painful economy, we contrived to exist while I still toiled at state papers with a single aim to win the confidence and esteem of the Prime Minister. There were two parties at court. My minister was engaged in an intrigue that had for one of its immediate objects the placing of his nephew on terms of the closest intimacy with the Crown Prince, then a very young fellow. It occurred to the Prime Minister and his precious nephew that it would be a good stroke to provide the Prince with a mistress, and I was commissioned to search Madrid for a lovely young person who should be fit for the royal favor. I turned the matter over to Scipio, who presently reported that he had found a beautiful girl, who lived with her aunt, and who might be induced to become the mistress of Spain's future king. I took every pains to discover whether it would be safe to recommend this young person, and in company with the Prime Minister's nephew I visited her. We were so delighted that we opened negotiations, which proceeded with such delicate difficulty that we were the more certain that we had come upon a rare prize. In brief, the Prince himself was abundantly satisfied, and many were the nocturnal excursions I made with his Royal Highness, it being my duty to guard the secrecy of his visits. Money for costly presents to the girl came from the Prime Minister, but none of it stuck in my hands.

One day necessity compelled me to make my poverty known to the Minister. He seemed at first much offended, but the next day he gave me a substantial acknowledgment of past services, and informed me that thereafter I might feel free to recommend applicants for places to him. I had been in court life long enough to know what that meant, and I straightway became a broker in offices. My first candidate paid me three hundred pistoles, and several satisfactory sums of this sort had been taken in, when a man who wanted an office of considerable importance handed me a thousand. My giddy joy was momentarily dampened when the Prime Minister demanded half the fee for himself; but a little reflection made me rejoice the more, for that showed that my efforts to promote candidacies would ever be welcome, and from that time I ceased to wait for applicants to approach me. I approached them, sometimes directly, oftener through the intervention of the subtle Scipio, who conveyed the advisability of bribing me to the candidate by way of the candidate's servant.

My fortune grew by leaps and bounds. I moved back to my former expensive apartments and led a most extravagant life, which nevertheless could not check the steady growth of my cash. My pride grew with my fortune; I was insolent to old friends, and deaf to appeals of charity. That is, I snubbed my good Fabricio, who had wandered to Madrid and was busy there as an author; and when a worthy soldier without means applied for a post, I promised to get it for him, and then sold it to the highest bidder. One thing only I did without material reward, but I confess that it was done from vanity rather than from gratitude: I obtained the governorship of Valencia for Don Alfonso. To cap the climax of my prosperity, I engaged myself to marry the daughter of a rich merchant. All arrangements had been made for the wedding, the dowry of a hundred thousand ducats was to be paid in ready money on the morrow, and I was on my way home to spend my last night as a bachelor when I was arrested and hurried to the prison at Segovia.

I learned after a time that my downfall was again due to my rigorous regard for the wishes of my superior. The King had learned that I had provided a mistress for the Crown Prince, and that I had accompanied him on his excursions to a questionable house. But this, though the worst of it, was not all. It proved that the pretty girl whom I had supplied, as a result of Scipio's discovery, to his Royal Highness, was far more worldly than she and her gracious aunt had appeared to be. There was an underground passage connecting her aunt's house with the one adjoining. In the latter house lived an equally pretty girl with her pious grandmother, and this second girl was the mistress of Calderona, the Prime Minister's hated rival. Well, what then? Why, the two girls were one and the same person! She who served for the cautious aunt in the one case was the pious grandmother in the other; and a perilous time they had of it to contrive to live in one house for the sake of Calderona, and yet always be at home for the Prince in the other.

CHARLES JAMES LEVER

(Ireland, 1806–1872)

CHARLES O'MALLEY, THE IRISH DRAGOON

(1841)

This is the second of this popular author's novels, published just before he became editor of *The Dublin University Magazine*. It has been reissued in numerous editions, both in Great Britain and the United States. The first uniform collection of Lever's novels was that published by Chapman and Hall (London, 1856), with illustrations by "Phiz" (H. K. Browne).

WHEN a mere child I was left an orphan in the care of my worthy uncle, Godfrey O'Malley, of O'Malley Castle, in Galway, hard by the river Shannon. He had lost his wife just before that time, and never remarried, rearing me as his heir, and training me, as he thought, to be a country gentleman. At eighteen I was six feet tall, and could shoot, fish, ride, and swim with the best, though I knew little of books. As for my future estates, they were saddled with debts, and my worthy uncle was often hard put to it to avoid the process-servers.

When my uncle became a candidate for reëlection to the Irish Parliament, he sent me to the house of a distant cousin, Mr. Blake, to solicit his aid. Here I met three persons who were to have a great influence on my life—General Sir George Dashwood, his lovely daughter Lucy—with whom I fell in love at first sight—and an Englishman, Captain Hammersley. To the Captain I took a dislike, and my efforts to lead him into danger on the hunting-field resulted in laying us both up with sundry cuts and bruises. This prevented Blake from explaining to me, as he had intended, that Sir George was to contest the county with my uncle, and that all those present were his supporters. The visit ended by my fighting a duel with one of them and leaving him for dead on the field. Luckily he recovered, but this event I count as the turning-point between my boyhood and my manhood.

The election was marked by much roughness; my uncle won, but ere its close I had the fortune to save Lucy Dashwood's life in a runaway. Just after this I was sent down to Dublin to begin my studies in Trinity College. It was my uncle's wish to make a lawyer of me, though his friends were all sure that I was cut out for a soldier. With me I took as my servant Mickey Free, a boy from my uncle's estate, who was destined to stick by me through my whole career.

As a roommate I was assigned to Frank Webber, the greatest daredevil in college at that time, and under his auspices I was soon consorting with a genial crew of students and of officers from the Dublin garrison, spending my time in carousing and in playing all sorts of pranks.

The Dashwoods had received me kindly and had invited me to a grand ball at their house. Seeing Lucy in the Park, my chum Webber became greatly taken with her, and to my rage he bet Captain Power, one of our friends from the garrison, that he would not only attend the ball uninvited but would kiss the fair Lucy without being kicked down-stairs for his pains.

The night of the ball arrived, and when it was half over, without any sign of Master Frank's boast, we concluded that he had failed and lost his wager. Not long after this a messenger handed to the General a note from his late wife's sister, Judy Macan, informing him that she was on her way to visit him and would arrive that evening. The General had not seen his sister-in-law for years; he had no wish to do so, as she was a queer old lady and an unmitigated bore. And here she was, arriving when the house was full of guests! There was barely time for a hurried consultation before the old lady made her appearance. She sailed in, a figure of the last half-century, and, embracing her niece, Lucy, sat down in a conspicuous place, where she was soon the center of a crowd of curious admirers. Before the evening was over, her oddities and her Irish wit had set the room in a roar of laughter. When the time came for going, the elderly belle, Miss Macan, who had been flirting violently with Fred Power, left with him a slip of paper, on which she said she had written her address. When he unrolled it, however, he found that it bore these words:

"DEAR POWER: You have lost your bet; I have enjoyed the ball, kissed the lady, and quizzed her papa.

"Yours,
"FRANK WEBBER."

Power paid his bet the next day and never heard the last of this jest, which the Dashwoods took in good part.

Not long after this, by the influence of General Dashwood, and with my uncle's consent, I received a commission in the Fourteenth Dragoons—Fred Power's regiment. My departure from college was signalized by a more than usually riotous supper, at which Webber and the rest of us narrowly escaped expulsion. Before I left Dublin I succeeded in obtaining an interview with Lucy Dashwood, in which I declared my love, but asked for no expression in return, and took my leave. I was to join a detachment that was *en route* to the seat of war on the Peninsula, under command of Captain Fred Power. After a sojourn of some time at Cork, where we had various adventures while awaiting our transport, we embarked for Lisbon. Our voyage passed uneventfully and in due time we dropped anchor in the Tagus. What a contrast to the dull monotony of our life at sea! The quay was crowded with hundreds of people, and boats plied unceasingly to and fro, while the din of a great city mingled with far-off sounds of military music.

When I awoke next morning on shore I heard Power's voice calling to me from outside the window. He had been hastily summoned to headquarters and wished me to execute some commissions for him. First, there was a package for Hammersley; secondly, a letter to take from a midshipman to a Portuguese senhora. I breakfasted with a heavy heart, for well I knew that the packet for Hammersley was from Lucy; I could feel a picture within it—doubtless her portrait. "This is the end of my dream of happiness," I sighed. The call of a cavalry trumpet roused me. I leaped impetuously into the saddle and nearly rode down a young girl who stood directly in the road, only escaping by leaping my horse over a mule-cart—a Galway feat for which I received the plaudits of the street and the card of the girl's father, who proved to be one of the richest contractors in Portugal.

That evening I called to pay my respects and made the acquaintance, not only of the charming daughter, Donna Inez, but also of a Captain Trevyllian—a scoundrelly-looking fellow, whom I detested at first sight. When I took up the midshipman's packet next day, what was my astonishment to find that it was addressed to Donna Inez! And, indeed, she had broken the heart of more than one middy.

That evening Power told me of the expected arrival from England of our new commander-in-chief, Sir Arthur Wellesley. The news put life into all of us, for we knew that the ball was about to begin. The roll of the drums beating to arms was the next thing we heard. Preparations for the march occupied me until nearly morning, when I snatched a few moments to bid Donna Inez what I fear was a somewhat too affectionate farewell. Then we set off—horse, foot, baggage, and artillery—what a spectacle did the road to Oliveira present on that 7th of May! We soon began to hear tidings of the French, and that night we bivouacked by the broad Douro. Next morning I received a despatch from General Murray to deliver to Sir Arthur Wellesley and in carrying it I was for the first time under fire, my horse being killed. I heard Sir Arthur order the passage of the river, though we had no boats fit for the task, and then, rejoining my brigade, I took part in the attack on the French on the farther side. It was like the excitement of a fox-hunt—I knew nothing till we had driven the enemy from the guns and had them in full retreat. I did not escape without a wound or two, and Fred Power, too, was injured.

Next morning our regiment was reviewed by Sir Arthur and mentioned with high praise in general orders. I was called upon to stand forth and was promoted to a lieutenancy. A little later, just after we had received orders to pursue the French on the Terracinthe Road, Captain Hammersley came in to congratulate me on my promotion. After fumbling in my portmanteau I handed him the packet entrusted to me by Power. He broke the seal and the morocco case of a miniature fell out. As he saw it he grew pale and trampled it on the ground, while he began to taunt me—why, I did not understand. In spite of his sneering allusions to my "good fortune" it was only too evident that he wished to pick a quarrel with me. Shortly after he left me I was waited on by Trevyllian as his friend. In short, I found myself engaged to fight duels with both of them, and with no clear idea of what had happened!

I was examining my pistols, when an orderly handed me an order to proceed at once on a particular service—to reconnoiter with a troop of cavalry and join the Lusitanian Legion. What should I do? I must decline the appointment or fail on the field of honor. While I was in this dilemma, Power rode past, calling out hastily: "All right, Charley; I've fixed it with Hammersley; you can go."

How happy was I, as I set forth with my first command! That night, as we were in bivouac, I ran across an escaped French prisoner; a young man named St. Croix, who interested me so much that I let him go his way. In return he gave me a portrait of the Empress Josephine that he wore about his neck—he had evidently been a favorite at court. We were destined to meet again. When we finally did fall in with our Portuguese allies we mistook each other for French troops; and had I not heard my friend Major Monsoon, their English commander, urging them on, there might have been a disaster.

After this we were soon ordered to rejoin Sir Arthur, then with the Spanish army. Here I was thrown into consternation by a letter telling me that Trevyllian had been accusing me of cowardice. I had forgotten that what Power said to me related only to my quarrel with Hammersley. I lost no time in seeking out the writer. "Trevyllian now refuses to fight," he said. "He says it's too late; you had your chance and ran away." In spite of this, however, his friends persuaded him to meet me. At the first shot he fell dead, yet they found a full shirt of mail under his clothes. No bullet had pierced him; some tremendous conflict of the spirit had snapped the cords of life.

Not long after this I took part in the victorious battle of Talavera, and later in an affair of outposts whence I was lucky to escape with my life. For several months after this our good fortune seemed to have deserted us. Hard pressed by the enemy, we saw Ciudad Roderigo and Almeida fall successively into their hands. While the former fortress still held out, some of us, seeing through our telescopes some French engineers placing tape lines to mark the position of future entrenchments, conceived the daring plan of moving the lines and so bringing them within our zone of fire. We ran into the French pickets before we expected and had a hard chase homeward. My arm was broken by a pistol-ball, and I saved myself only by jumping my horse into the river. I received a mild reprimand for my rashness, with a promise of an appointment on General Cranfurd's personal staff.

While I lay wounded within my quarters, the movements began that ended in the battle of the Coa. Sappers took possession of my little hut, which soon became an active part of the battleground. I was forced to vacate it, wounded as I was, and by night was in full retreat, with our forces, lying on some straw in a jolting wagon. This did not improve my wound, and the surgeons soon ordered me back to Lisbon. Here I fell in again with the Dashwoods and was warmly greeted by Sir George, who, however, sent the blood back to my heart by congratulating me on what he called my "special reasons for wanting to be in Lisbon." No doubt Lucy, too, had heard of my silly flirtation with Inez. I fell into a brown study, and after leaving Sir George continued to walk, hardly realizing whither I went, until I found myself in the well-known villa. I know not how long I had waited, when I heard Inez's voice and another, which I did not recognize. "*Fi donc!*" I heard Inez say, "I am really very fond of him, though I can't remember his name. Still, you will see how haughtily I shall greet him."

"Maybe I'll spoil that plan," thought I, and as soon as she entered, I clasped her in my arms and kissed her! She laughed and blushed, but just then the glass doors parted and I saw her companion for the first time. Heavens! it was Lucy Dashwood! The blood rushed to my face; then I grew pale, as, with a half smile of recognition she passed me and went to the window. A little later she took leave and the Senhora almost killed herself with mirth over the coldness with which, she said, the English are accustomed to greet each other.

That evening I dined with Sir George. If flattery and champagne could have turned my head they would have done so;

but I did not dare face Lucy and excused myself early. At home I found a letter from Frank Webber, from which I learned that Hammersley had been refused by Lucy. "I wonder what he did," wrote Frank, "when Power gave him back his letters and picture." Here, then, was the solution of my mystery! This explained poor Hammersley's intemperate passion. And Lucy cared for me!

I remember little after this, save that I was very ill. I found myself in the villa where Inez and her family cared for me tenderly for several weeks. After my recovery I attended a masked ball given on the night when the news reached us that the French under Masséna were in full retreat and that we were to go in pursuit. I sought out Inez—having learned from her maid what dress she was to wear—and was taking an affectionate leave when I learned, to my astonishment, that she had taken me for Fred Power, which revelation eased my mind not a little.

The French retreated slowly, and we followed them into Spain, overtaking them at Fuentes d'Oro, where I took part in the hotly contested battle of that name, after which I was appointed extra aide-de-camp to General Cranfurd. At the General's table, with the rest of his staff, I came near being involved in a quarrel. Sir George Dashwood's name being mentioned, one of my brother officers took occasion to discuss the family, including Lucy, in a way that did not please me, and I told him so. General Cranfurd promptly averted trouble by threatening us with the guard-house if we should carry the matter further, and having thus set his house in order said to me, as he rose: "O'Malley, have you forwarded the returns to the Adjutant-General?"

"Yes, sir; this morning."

"Good; irregularities on this score have called forth a heavy reprimand at headquarters."

I remembered that I had given Mike the papers to post, but I did not know until later what trouble this was to cause me.

Shortly afterward I was sent out, in command of a troop of cavalry, on a three days' reconnaissance along the river Azava. On the first evening I had gone out by myself to explore, when I fell in with two escaped French prisoners. There seemed to be doubt whether I had captured them or they me, but the proximity of my troop induced them to be cautious and they invited me to supper. While we ate four Spanish guerrillas rode up. They would not believe that I was an English officer and were preparing to hang me as a spy when a shrill whistle from me brought my men down upon them pell-mell, and in the mêlée I managed to let my French friends go. Next day, to my surprise, I received a curt order to report myself at headquarters under arrest, and, turning over my command to my second, I set out in some bewilderment. A line from Fred Power cleared things up. My man, Mickey Free, had exchanged my despatch to the Adjutant-General's office with a letter of his own to his sweetheart in Ireland, and the Adjutant-General, who had no sense of humor, had threatened me with a court-martial! On my arrival, however, a kind note from General Cranfurd put all to rights.

I was slightly wounded again before San Pietro, and a little later letters from home gave me a sad account of the state of my poor uncle's health and finances. I decided to apply for leave at once, that I might give him what aid I could before the end. But before my request could be acted upon came the storming of Ciudad Roderigo, and as my regiment was to take no part, and I could not keep out of the fight, I disguised myself as a common soldier and in that capacity led a party through the breach. For doing this without leave I was ordered under arrest by Lord Wellesley, and escaped only by favor of General Picton, who had witnessed our exploit. By his favor, too, I found my leave shortly granted and myself entrusted with despatches to be carried to the Commander-in-Chief in London. By his Royal Highness I was received with most flattering attentions, so that I presently found myself a hero. But my heart turned to my old uncle in Galway; and Mickey and I shortly found ourselves on our way to Ireland. What joy filled my heart as I saw once more the dear old isle! We hastened toward home as fast as horses and carriage could take us, and when I broke down a mile or so from the castle I continued my way on foot by a short cut through the woods. Sitting down to rest but a little distance from the house, I was thrilled by a long-drawn sound that I knew only too well; it was the death-wail! How I made my way home I hardly knew; I reached it to find my worst fears realized, and my poor Uncle Godfrey lying in his coffin.

It was evident that my first duty lay toward the property and the tenants that now had become mine, and, selling my commission, I resolved to settle down as an Irish country gentleman. By diligence and economy, and the sacrifice of some acres, I succeeded in once more putting the estate on a good footing; the neighbors began to talk of me as my uncle's successor in Parliament, and more than one young lady cast melting eyes at me. Lucy, alas, seemed lost to me forever; my uncle had quarreled bitterly with General Dashwood shortly before his death, and Sir George let me know, very civilly, that there could be nothing more between us. But I never was cut out for a civilian, and when the great news of Bonaparte's escape from Elba and his triumphant progress through France reached us I could not contain myself. Falling in with the officers of a regiment on its way to the seat of war, I accompanied them to Cork, and while there I was fortunate enough to fall in with the Commander-in-Chief, who recognized me as the officer who had brought despatches to him in London. The result was my appointment as an extra aide on the staff of Sir Thomas Picton, and I was soon with him in Brussels. At the Duchess of Richmond's ball I beheld Lucy once again, though she seemed farther away than ever. Summoned hastily from that scene of revelry, I was plunged at once into active operations, and just before Quatre-Bras was so unfortunate as to be taken prisoner.

My captors took me before no less a person than the Emperor, and my possession of the miniature of the Empress given me in Spain by my French prisoner, St. Croix, insured me a large share of his attention. After vainly trying to wring information from me, he sent me back with the other prisoners, where I was shortly afterward found by St. Croix himself. My French friend, intent on repaying me for my good deeds on the Peninsula, told me at once of a plan for bringing me a French uniform in which I could escape. Our conversation was overheard by a fellow-prisoner, who begged in a broken voice that I should take a few lines of farewell to his daughter. He had been captured, he said, with despatches of General Bourmont upon him, and could hardly escape death as a spy. I recognized him as soon as he spoke; it was Sir George Dashwood! I insisted at once that he should take the uniform and go, instead of me, and after much persuasion he did so. I was thus still a prisoner at the opening of Waterloo, but ere long Lord Uxbridge's force made an attack on our captors, releasing us for service during the rest of that glorious engagement. Near the end of it poor Hammersley and I charged the enemy side by side. I saw by his face that he hoped we should perish together. It was his last charge, but I, though left on the field for dead, lived to tell the tale.

I lived, too, to be reconciled to Sir George, whose life I had saved, and to call his lovely daughter at last my own.

When we were receiving the welcomes of the tenantry on our entry to O'Malley Castle, after the wedding, we were greeted, among others, by a certain Father Peter Nolan, whose quips and cranks of verse, delivered from a barrel-top, seemed strangely familiar in style. So when, after an outrageously absurd peroration, the good father pulled off his wig, disclosing the poll of Frank Webber, I was not greatly surprised. Lucy looked at him in astonishment. "Why!" she cried, "it is surely not—not—" "Yes, my dear," I interrupted, "it is indeed your aunt, Miss Judy Macan!"

TOM BURKE OF OURS (1844)

This story has always been a great favorite with younger readers, because of the glorious adventures enjoyed by the dashing young Irish patriot. It may fairly be called one of Ireland's permanent "best sellers."

WHEN Tom Burke came to himself in an officer's quarters, in the St. George's Barracks of Dublin, he felt very sore and bruised and wondered how he came to be there. Though not yet sixteen, he was a tall, strapping Irish lad with an iron constitution and a stout frame. A wandering life had given him robust health, and the life had been pleasanter to him than the drudgery of a lawyer's clerk to which his father's agent, Mr. Basset, had tried to condemn him after the death of "the old squire." Basset had an eye on the five hundred pounds that was all Tom's father had left him, his brother inheriting the estate.

Lying there, Tom remembered that he had been looking on at the people coming out of Parliament House when a riot broke out and he was carried away and borne down in the rush. That was all, except that he had been a companion of Darby M'Keowan, better known as Darby the Blast, on whose head a price was set by the Government. Before Tom could marshal his scattered wits a rotund officer, dressed in a faded dressing-gown, came into the room.

"And how are we this morning, Tom Burke? How are we? Alive and kicking again, I see. Been pretty bad, Tom Burke; pretty bad. But all right now. Did nobly in the riots; nobly. The Lord Lieutenant is delighted. All the officers of 'Ours' delighted, too. Call you Tom Burke of Ours now. Glad I found you. Son of my old school friend, Burke of Burke Castle."

Feebly but frankly Tom told his host his true story, how he had been taken by Darby the Blast after the death of his father; how Basset was still looking for him; how he had associated with the members of those secret societies that honeycombed Ireland after the disastrous uprising that had recently taken place, and how he happened to be caught in the mob. But the eccentric Captain Bubbleton would have none of his story. He had invented a better one and would not have it spoiled by mere facts.

The truth was that he had found the boy lying bleeding and unconscious after the riot and had taken him into his barracks out of sheer kindness of heart, inventing a tale to go along with his act. Then he had learned Tom's name through his ravings.

Youth recovers rapidly, and it was not many days before Bubbleton introduced Tom into the mess as a hero who had done wonderful things in the royal cause. The officers did not inquire too closely. Bubbleton was a joke, and so was all that pertained to him.

"Tom Burke of Ours we call him," said Bubbleton. "Not a more popular young fellow in the mess. His commission is about to be made out. Should not wonder if he got a knighthood out of it."

Mr. Basset, however, soon found Tom and threatened him with arrest.

"Mr. Basset," said Tom, "you have five hundred pounds which my father left me. Give me one hundred of it, and I will leave Ireland at once. You may keep the rest."

The arrangement was "agreeable," the lawyer said, and Tom prepared to flee to France, then to enroll under the banner of Napoleon, of whose glory his brain was full. Before coming to Dublin he had spent many months with a young French officer, Charles de Meudon. They had been like brothers. The young Frenchman was one of those who had come over to Ireland when the uprising of 1798 gave promise of success. When the attempt had failed and the other officers had "accepted the amnesty" and returned home, De Meudon had remained in the vain hope that something might yet be done for Irish independence. He and Tom had been placed in a remote part of the country to wait, and there De Meudon died.

In the months that Tom spent with him he had filled the boy's mind full of the splendid vision of Marengo and Lodi, of Arcola and the Egyptian campaign.

Before he died Charles told Tom of his sister, Marie, and

asked him, if he ever got to France, to be a brother to her as he had been to the exile.

"Go to France when I am no more," said De Meudon. "Here is a letter that will procure you admittance to the Polytechnique—the military school. And here is a French bank-note for two thousand livres—it is all I have, but it is yours."

One officer of "Ours" looked coldly on Tom. He knew something, and suspected more. This was Captain Montague Crofts, a cousin of his, though Tom did not know it, and in line to the Burke estates if Tom and his brother were out of the way. With Basset he concocted a plan to have the lad arrested for treason.

Darby the Blast got wind of the plot and came disguised as an old woman to warn Tom. Just before Tom was called out to the hall to see the "old woman," Bubbleton, Crofts and some other officers were at cards. Bubbleton, though always talking about millions, was notoriously poor, and lost a bet to Crofts. Tom, who had some money, quickly slipped him what he thought was a twenty-pound note to make good his bet. While Tom and Darby were in the hallway, Bubbleton threw the note on the table, and at that instant a bugle call summoned all the officers except Crofts, who was not on duty, to the evening formation. Out they rushed, leaving Crofts alone. Looking through the door, he called to Tom:

"Young man, how comes it that you have in your possession a French bank-note? I saw you slip this to Bubbleton. Are you, young as you are, an emissary of France as you are a rebel to your King? I know more about you than is well for you."

Tom made a hot reply, acknowledged that the French note was his, demanded it back, and tendered Crofts twenty pounds.

The Captain waxed more insolent and threatening, and at last losing his temper he drew his sword in a frenzy and rushed on the boy. The sharp steel penetrated Tom's side, and the Captain shortened his blade to run him through, when Darby rushed into the room and felled Crofts to the floor, where he lay apparently dead.

"It's life or death now!" said Darby. "Wipe the blood from your face, and try to be calm as we pass the sentry. Can you walk?"

By a great effort—for the blood was pouring from his wounded side—Tom managed to walk down to the river-front. As in a dream he felt himself taken to a house by the water. Then he fainted.

However, he was not badly wounded, after all; and before daybreak he was taken to a smuggler's vessel lying in a cove down the coast.

Thus Tom left his native land and found himself at last in France, and a student in the Polytechnique. There he became as much a Frenchman as any foreigner ever can be; and he filled his young soul with military aspirations and a blind devotion to Napoleon, which he shared with millions. He finished his course, became an officer, and was really "Tom Burke of Ours" at last.

One day, in a mimic battle of the students, he was stunned while leading a desperate charge. General d'Auvergne had come to review the cadets that day and brought with him two ladies. As Tom opened his eyes, the younger of the ladies was stooping over him holding a cup of water to his lips. She was of about his own age, delicately formed, her complexion and her dark-fringed eyes bespeaking the Provençal.

While Tom still gazed at her he heard the roll of drums, the clash of arms and cries of *"C'est lui! C'est lui! Vive Bonaparte! Vive le Premier Consul!"* He looked up. Surrounded by a brilliant staff stood a short man looking down upon him, with a pale but handsome face on which command was tempered by an almost womanly softness as he smiled upon the fallen youth.

"It was well done, my child," said Napoleon. "Very well done, and as you have lost a coat in the struggle we must give you another to replace it. Monsieur Legrange, what is the character of this boy?"

Thus Tom Burke became an officer of the Twenty-first Regiment of Foot, stationed in Paris. He found himself quartered with Lieutenant Tascher, a nephew of Madame Bonaparte, from Guadeloupe.

"And on my word," said Tascher, "the only favor I have received from my distinguished uncle was a sharp reprimand on one occasion for a boyish freak when all the other delinquents

"Adopt, General?" cried the Emperor when the old general told him of his plan. "No, no! You must marry. Come, it is my command. The young lady has no objection to you. The Empress has sounded her. Thus and thus only can you give her your protection and your wealth." Before General d'Auvergne left the palace he was the husband of Marie de Meudon. Josephine had applied the same force to the bride that Napoleon had to the groom; and, pale as a ghost and with trembling hand, Marie signed the marriage contract.

"I have obeyed my Emperor," said D'Auvergne, kissing the hand of Marie, "and now I will obey the dictates of my conscience and take an immediate leave of you. It is the only reparation I can make."

Tom, who had been a witness of this strange scene, followed his chief to the army, sad at heart. But the old General said:

"Cheer up, Burke. You have the girl's heart, and when I am dead, which will be soon, you shall have her hand. Such was my compact with the Emperor."

In the campaign that followed Tom won great honors and regained the Emperor's good-will, which he had lost through the Chouan business. The "Sun of Austerlitz" shone brightly upon him. He was one of the officers selected to carry to Paris the captured Austrian standards.

One of his brother officers who accompanied him was the Chevalier Duchesne, who betrayed Bourbonist and Bonapartist secrets alike, as the fancy took him; but this Tom did not know.

The two young men frequented the salon of Madame de Lacostellerie, a relative of Josephine, and there saw much of her beautiful daughter Pauline. A bitter thought came into the head of Tom. He would pay his court to this wonderful creole beauty. Perhaps Marie would hear of it, and it might make her jealous. Perhaps then she would give some sign that she remembered his existence.

But Duchesne had resolved to marry the creole, and, surprising Tom and Pauline one night as they conversed together alone in the picture-gallery, he interrupted them with well-bred insolence, and as Tom took leave hummed the fragment of a popular song:

"To-day for me, to-morrow for thee:
But will that to-morrow ever be?"

Tom expected a challenge the next morning, but instead he got orders to leave Paris within two hours and rejoin the army. Then came the great campaign that ended at Jena, and in this Tom so distinguished himself that he was recommended for a colonelcy and was gazetted for the cross of the Legion of Honor.

Napoleon was in Berlin. The nations, silent and subdued, lay around him, and kings bowed before him. It was the summit of his greatness. One day Tom was summoned to the palace at Potsdam, where Marshal Berthier handed him a letter that had been seized in the mails. The letter was from Duchesne and was addressed to him. It was written as if the two had been in frequent correspondence, and was full of ridicule of the Emperor.

Duchesne had left the army in disgrace, his duplicity had been found out, and now he wrote to Tom as a fellow-conspirator might write.

The Marshal, after reprimanding Tom severely, said: "I shall return to his Majesty the cross you were to have had; and as to the rest, his orders concerning you are—"

"One moment," said Tom. "I am a foreigner, little versed in the habits and usages of the land for which I have shed my blood. I know nothing of this letter, which is a trick to ruin me. You know the man who wrote it and of what he is capable. I have always been true to the Emperor and to his cause. Have I the privilege of resigning the commission I hold?"

"Certainly," answered the Marshal.

Tom's passports were made out for Paris, and thither he returned.

General d'Auvergne was with the army; young Tascher was there, too—his only friends in all France. Of Marie de Meudon he dared not even think.

After several adventures Tom crossed the channel and stepped once more upon Irish soil. He could have embraced the very ground at first, but then again came over him the thought: "Here, also, even here, I have not a friend." He had left Ireland a boy; he came back a man, war-worn and weary, but bringing no sheaves with him.

And then fortune gave another turn to her wheel. Tom's elder brother died, and he became the heir to a large estate—a country squire of the first magnitude.

But soon he felt how dull and stale the life was after Austerlitz and Jena! While he hunted by day and brooded by night there came the news of the Russian campaign, the retreat from Moscow and the peril of the Emperor. Tom's heart leaped into fire again. He had deserted Napoleon at the height of his power. Now that he was in adversity his sword was again the Emperor's.

Hastily crossing over to Belgium, he made his way to the remnants of the Grand Army and was eagerly welcomed by the general commanding at one of the frontier towns. All France was in arms, and every step was turned eastward. Immense crowds of conscripts crowded the highways. Every town and village was a garrison. The heavy rumbling of the ammunition-wagons and the tramp of horses sounded through the long nights. But no longer did Tom witness the wild enthusiasm he so well remembered among the soldiers of the army. They marched like men going to death, but with the step and bearing of heroes.

Again Tom saw the pale face of the Emperor, as immobile as of old, but with the light of destiny fading from it. Again he heard dying men shout with their last breath: *Vive l'Empereur!* as Napoleon passed by. For a time the tide of battle turned in favor of the Emperor, and in the battles of the "Week of Glory" Tom won his cross of the Legion, the Emperor pinning it on his breast with his own hand on a field of victory.

He was badly wounded, and was invalided and by the Emperor's orders assigned to quarters in the ancient palace of Fontainebleau.

One evening in the latter part of March came the sound of horses' hoofs and he caught the clank of dragoons as their sabers rattled and their sabertasches jingled against their horses' flanks. The escort drew up, not at the main entrance to the palace, but at a side door in a remote wing. There was a traveling carriage in the midst of the escort, but he could not see who alighted from it.

That night, unable to sleep, he was walking in the garden

when he was attracted by a light shining from a room on the ground floor. A man in Turkish dress was sleeping across the door that led into the lighted apartment. Even by the faint light Tom recognized Roustan, the favorite mameluke of the Emperor. Tom attempted to retire noiselessly, but the Turk, awakening suddenly, called out for the guard, seized Tom by the collar, and flashed his simitar above his head. A man came from the lighted room.

"Hold!" said he. "What means this? Who are you?"

In a few words Tom explained his presence and regretted that he should have disturbed his Majesty. "I thought, Sire," he added, "that your Majesty was many leagues away with the army."

"There is no army," Napoleon replied, "and to-morrow there will be no emperor. Go, sir—go while there is yet time, and offer your sword where so many, more exalted than yourself, have offered theirs. This is the day of desertion—take advantage of it."

"Had my name and rank been less humble they would have assured your Majesty how little I merited this reproach," Tom answered.

"I am sorry to have offended you," replied Napoleon. "I remember you. Yes, I remember you. I should have made you a general of brigade had I—" Here he stopped suddenly, while an expression of suffering passed across his face, and then resumed. "I should have known you earlier. It is now too late. Adieu." He extended his hand as he turned to go, and Tom pressed it fervently to his lips.

Tom saw his Emperor once again. It was the next day, when he witnessed that historic scene in the courtyard of Fontainebleau—the farewell of Napoleon to his Old Guard, when that most splendid of earthly swords was sheathed, to leap but once again from its scabbard—on the field of Waterloo.

Tom, being recovered from his wounds, now prepared to return to Ireland. A note was brought to his hotel. It read: "May I request the honor of a visit from you this evening at the Hotel de Grammont?" and was signed "Marie d'Auvergne, *nee* De Meudon." Tom was promptly at the Hotel de Grammont. Waiting patiently in an anteroom, he heard his name called in a low voice, and turning saw Marie standing before him. As their eyes met she cast down hers and blushed. She was dressed in deep mourning, for General d'Auvergne had been killed in one of the last battles of the Empire.

"I was about to leave France, Colonel," she said, "when I heard that you were here, and delayed my departure to have an opportunity of seeing you. His Royal Highness has offered you a command, I hear."

"Even so, Madame," replied Tom—"and I have refused it."

"You loved the Emperor," she exclaimed hastily, with almost passionate eagerness, "even as I loved my dear, kind mistress, the Empress. And you feel that allegiance is too sacred a thing to be bartered at a moment's notice. Is that so?"

"You have read my motives, Madame," Tom replied. "I must now return to my native land alone, as I came from it. For me the world is very lonely."

"I, too, must be a wanderer," she said. "But before we part I must give you a keepsake." She tried to remove a ring from her finger, but it would not come off. "Give it to me where it is," cried Tom. "Yes, Marie, the devotion of a heart wholly yours should not go unrewarded." When Tom's rapid and almost incoherent declaration was over Marie replied with a smile, placing her hand in his, "It is yours."

for Tom. Next morning as Marie was standing before him. As their eyes met she [illegible] and blushed. She was dressed in deep mourning, for General d'Auvergne had been killed in one of the last battles of the Empire.

"I was about to leave France, Colonel," she said, "when I heard that you were here, and delayed my departure to have an opportunity of seeing you. His Royal Highness has offered you a command, I hear."

"True, Madame," replied Tom, "and I have refused it."

"You loved the Emperor," she exclaimed, with a most passionate earnestness, "even as I loved my dear, dead mistress, the Empress. And you feel that allegiance is too sacred a thing to be bartered at a moment's notice. Is that so?"

"You have read my motives, Madame," Tom replied. "I [illegible] my return to my native land alone, as France [illegible] from it. For me the world is very lonely."

"I, too, must be a wanderer," she said. "But before we part I must give you a keepsake." She tried to remove a ring from her finger, but it would not loosen. "Give it to me where it is!" cried Tom. "Yes, Marie, the devotion of a heart wholly yours should not go unrewarded." When Tom's rapid and almost incoherent declaration was over Marie replied with a smile, placing her hand in his, "It is yours!"